MURDEROUS CONTAGION

A Human History of Disease

Mary Dobson

First published in hardback in 2007 by Quercus Editions Ltd
under the title *Disease*

This revised and updated paperback edition published in 2015 by
Quercus Editions Ltd
55 Baker Street
Seventh Floor, South Block
London
W1U 8EW

A CIP catalogue record for this book is available
from the British Library

PB ISBN 978 1 78206 943 0
Ebook ISBN 978 1 84916 668 3

10 9 8 7 6 5 4 3 2 1

Text designed and typeset by Hewer Text UK Ltd, Edinburgh

Plates designed by Rich Carr

Printed and bound in Great Britain by Clays Ltd, St Ives plc

Contents

Preface

'I hope that Lord Grey and you are well; no easy thing seeing that there are about fifteen hundred diseases to which man is subject.' Sydney Smith to Lady Grey, February 1836

The diseases described within this book have affected human history in a multitude of ways over the past few millennia. Choosing a selection of diseases out of the 'fifteen hundred' or so suggested by the English clergyman Sydney Smith (1771–1845) has been both stimulating and challenging. The final decision was based on the idea of including a varied range of some of history's classic plagues and pandemics (amongst which typhus in the early nineteenth century was called a 'murderous contagion') and to cover those diseases that have had, and continue to have, a major impact in many parts of the world today. I have also chosen a number of less-well publicized diseases (often known as 'Neglected Tropical Diseases') that still seriously affect some of the poorest countries (where, in the twenty-first century, average life expectancy at birth can be less than fifty or sixty years compared to over seventy or even eighty years in the wealthiest nations), as well as including some of the better-known major non-communicable diseases of the modern era such as heart disease, cancer and dementia, along with a selection of the more unusual and mysterious pestilences which have afflicted humans over the years.

Some of the diseases covered in this book, for example, malaria and schistosomiasis, are 'ancient' diseases – possibly first emerging as human diseases some 10,000 years ago when people and domestic animals began to live in close proximity. Infections, like smallpox and measles, which are easily transmitted from person to person, and are often known as 'crowd diseases', may have accompanied the rise of early urban settlements from around the third millennium BC. The opening up of overland and ocean trade routes, including circumnavigations of the globe from the late fifteenth century onwards, accelerated the spread of many diseases from place to place and continent to continent, and now, with rapid air travel, we are living in a highly interconnected 'microbial' world. Some diseases, notably HIV/AIDS, are relatively 'new' to human society, emerging and spreading rapidly only in the past fifty or so years. Cardiovascular disease and cancer, the two leading causes of deaths worldwide today, together with dementia and type 2 diabetes, are now increasingly prominent in the modern world and are also becoming common in low- and middle-income countries. A few diseases have seemingly come and gone. SARS – the first serious and easily transmissible new disease to emerge in the twenty-first century – spread around the globe over a short period of time in 2003, was contained, and has, so far, not reappeared, though a recent related viral disease, named MERS-CoV (Middle East respiratory syndrome – coronavirus), is of current concern.

Some of the diseases in this book, such as kuru in Papua New Guinea, have had a serious but largely local impact. Several,

2

especially those like malaria, dengue fever and African trypano-somiasis (sleeping sickness), which are transmitted by insect vectors, have had, and continue to have, a devastating effect on tropical and subtropical regions. Others, such as the Black Death (bubonic plague) of the mid-fourteenth century; smallpox, measles, typhus and syphilis from the early sixteenth century; the cholera pandemics beginning in the nineteenth century; the Spanish influenza pandemic of 1918–19; and the current HIV/AIDS pandemic have been tragedies on a global scale with far-reaching consequences for societies and individuals the world over. Tuberculosis – also known historically as the 'White Plague' – although thought to have been controlled with antibiotics and vaccines, has resurged in the past few decades, especially as a 'co-endemic' infection with HIV/AIDS in some of the poorest parts of the world. Multi-drug resistant TB is a serious concern and, indeed, antibiotic resistance more generally is now one of the world's most pressing medical issues. The recent outbreaks of bird flu (H5N1) and swine flu (H1N1) have presented global threats that, fortunately, have not been on the same scale as the 1918–19 Spanish flu as had been initially feared. Ebola virus – a 'newly emerging' disease – has attracted worldwide media attention both during its earlier outbreaks in Central Africa in the mid-1970s and, again, in the recent tragic outbreak of this highly contagious and frequently fatal disease in West Africa in 2014 – a situation that, as this book goes to press, has escalated to crisis levels. Some two-thirds of human pathogens, which include the Ebola, influenza and HIV/AIDS viruses, are thought to have a 'zoonotic' origin, when infections cross the species barrier and 'jump' or 'spillover' from bats, birds, wild and domestic animals to humans, often adapting in the human host to spread efficiently from person to person.

3

One disease covered in this book has been effectively eliminated by human intervention. In 1979, the World Health Organization (WHO) announced that smallpox, one of the worst scourges of humanity, had been eradicated from the globe by a vaccine developed nearly 200 years before. This is one of the most outstanding achievements in the history of medicine. Polio is now so close to elimination that we await the 'final push'. More than a decade after world leaders adopted the United Nations Millennium Development Goals (MDGs), 2000–2015, there have also been some substantial reductions in early childhood mortality with corresponding increases in life expectancy, even in some of the poorest countries. We can only hope that there will be further success stories and that the global burden of disease will be reduced significantly in the coming years.

The diseases chosen have been grouped into four categories and arranged, at least very approximately, according to the first recorded serious impact of each disease on the world, with some of the oldest first and the most recent last. The first three groups comprise infectious diseases: bacterial diseases (from plague to encephalitis lethargica); parasitic diseases (from malaria to onchocerciasis); and viral diseases (from smallpox to SARS and MERS CoV). The fourth group of diseases (scurvy, kuru, CJD, dementia, cancer and heart disease) do not conform to the models of bacterial, parasitic and viral maladies and are loosely labelled 'lifestyle diseases', since factors such as diet, smoking, physical exercise, occupation and ageing play a key (though not the only) role in their causation. Indeed, for each of the diseases selected – whether primarily infectious or non-infectious – there is always a complex set of interrelated biological, genetic, environmental and social factors that mean some people succumb, while others survive or remain untouched by the circulating pathogen or potentially fatal disorder.

In each of the chapters the aim has been to give a broad overview and chronology of the history of each disease, its impact on human societies, and estimates of numbers affected, both past and present. I have also tried to include some of the early and more recent ideas about the causes of the different diseases (from 'contagion' to 'miasmas' and from 'germs' to 'genes'); to describe public health interventions as well as key scientific and medical discoveries associated with each disease; and to highlight the often remarkable human endeavours and some extraordinary achievements in identifying, preventing or treating each disease. The accompanying quotes aim to convey something of the suffering, pain, misery and bewilderment experienced by people in times of sickness over the centuries, as well as the commitment and determination of men and women in their search for solutions. I have, in some chapters, touched on a few of the many mysteries that, throughout the ages, have perplexed scholars, scientists, physicians and patients in their quest to understand the origins, nature and cause of disease and its effect on human societies and individuals across the globe.

The history of medicine is a rich and expanding field of wide interest. Each new scholarly or scientific study brings with it further facts, findings and figures, and I have updated the chapters since the original 2007 publication according to our current knowledge. I have also included 'new' outbreaks of disease which have occurred over the past few years and added a section on dementia which has recently been described as a 'twenty-first century plague' and which, with conditions such as Alzheimer's disease now becoming more prominent and of huge concern in our ageing populations, warrants global attention.

Novel techniques for recovering and analyzing ancient DNA are making it easier to identify some of the puzzling pathogens of the past and helping to solve a number of historical debates. With the sequencing of the human genome and many microbial genomes, together with advances in such fields as molecular medicine, we are also now in a stronger position than ever before to understand better human predisposition and susceptibility to disease, to discover the mysterious ways of microbes and animal and insect vectors, and to bring to the seven billion people that currently inhabit the Earth the promise of new diagnostics, vaccines and therapies.

We are increasingly living in a complex and highly interconnected world. As French physician Charles Nicolle (1866–1936), discoverer of the body louse that transmits typhus and a Nobel Prize winner, noted with great insight in his 1932 book, *The Destiny of Infectious Diseases*: 'If human civilization lasts, if it continues to spread, infectious diseases will increase in number in every region of the globe. Exchanges and migrations will bring the human and animal diseases of all regions to every country. The work is already well advanced; its future is assured.'

Since Nicolle wrote his book we have gone through periods of determination, optimism and confidence that infectious diseases could be 'conquered' to more recent awareness that re-emerging and newly emerging diseases are still current and worrying threats to modern societies. Surveillance and international vigilance remain of utmost importance in the field of infectious diseases in order to detect potential outbreaks at their very earliest stages of development and to stop their global spread, while reducing poverty and hunger, and improving sanitation, hygiene, education and health services are, also, fundamental for many countries still severely affected by infectious diseases. At the same time as we endeavour to control infections and increase life expectancy, we need to be active in tackling a range at non-communicable diseases. I hope that this book will raise awareness of the history of human diseases as well as many facets of present-day medicine and offer, too, some hope for ensuring the future health and happiness of people in many parts of the world.

My sincerest thanks go to all those who have made this book possible – my acknowledgments and suggestions for further reading are given on pp. 565–69.

Mary Dobson
St John's College
Cambridge

October 2014

Bacterial Diseases

PLAGUE

The very mention of plague induces shudders of horror in adults and schoolchildren alike. Plague has been responsible for some of the worst catastrophes in the story of humankind, and more than once has changed the course of history. Bubonic plague is caused by a bacterium, *Yersinia pestis*, mainly transmitted to humans by fleas from infected rodents, notably the black rat, *Rattus rattus*. Although most historians confidently assume that this was the prime mode of transmission of most plague epidemics, some 'plague deniers' have questioned whether the so-called plagues of the past really were 'true' bubonic plague. Recent DNA analysis of skeletal remains from the Plague of Justinian in the mid-sixth century and the Black Death in the mid-fourteenth century, however, has confirmed that *Yersinia pestis* was, indeed, the causative pathogen. The story of plague is at once the most gruesome and the most fascinating of medical mysteries.

∾

In the novel *La Peste* ('The Plague'), first published by the French philosopher Albert Camus (1913–60) in 1947, the story begins with an unsettling moment:

> When leaving his surgery on the morning of April 16, Dr Bernard Rieux felt something soft under his foot. It was a

dead rat lying in the middle of the landing. On the spur of the moment he kicked it to one side and, without giving it a further thought, continued on his way downstairs. Only when he was stepping out into the street did it occur to him that a dead rat had no business to be on his landing, and he turned back to ask the concierge of the building to see to its removal.

This unsettling moment comes near the beginning of *La Peste*.

Thus a dead rat, a doctor and a concierge become bound up in one of the most compelling fictional accounts of plague, set in the late 1940s in the Algerian port city of Oran. An allegory of the Nazi occupation of France, and a metaphor of the meaning of life and suffering, the story also contains all the classic plague scenarios. A few days after Dr Rieux comes across his first dead rat, the city is overwhelmed by the creatures. From basements, cellars and sewers the rats 'emerged in long wavering files into the light of day, swayed helplessly, then did a sort of pirouette and fell dead at the feet of horrified onlookers'. Some die with blood spurting from their mouths, others are bloated and already beginning to rot. Everywhere people feel underfoot the squelchy roundness of dead – or still squealing but dying – rats. On 30 April the concierge, M. Michel, dies of bubonic plague. His last words are: 'Them rats! Them damned rats!'

As plague sweeps through the city, the doctor describes the panic, the horrors, the pain of death and broken hearts, the attempts to clean up and cordon off the city, separating loved ones and fuelling despair, frustration, compassion and anguish. When the plague recedes and the gates of the city once more open, there is rejoicing and relief. But Dr Rieux knows that 'the plague bacillus never dies or disappears for good . . . and that perhaps the day would come when . . . it would rouse up its rats again and send them forth to die in a happy city'.

Dead rats, fleas and buboes

Rats and rat fleas invariably feature together in our imaginations as the harbingers of the terrible plagues of the past. Although much remains to be understood about the three great historical plague pandemics (c.AD 540 to the mid-eighth century; c.1330s to the eighteenth century; and c.1890s to 1950s), recent evidence suggests that plague is a classic example of a zoonotic disease – when a pathogenic agent (in this case the plague bacillus, *Yersinia pestis*) jumps from an animal reservoir into the human population. Plague is essentially a disease of wild rodents and can be spread by fleas from one rodent to another including to rodents which live in close proximity to humans, such as the black rat, *Rattus rattus*. The black rat, often known as the 'ship rat' because of its ability to stow away on ships and other forms of transportation, is the most maligned creature in history. But the rats, once infected, also suffer and die from the plague. At the start of a typical epidemic, large numbers of rats are suddenly afflicted. As in Camus' story, when the rats begin to 'die off', their infected rat fleas, frantic with hunger, search for new sources of blood, and thus turn to humans. Engorged with plague bacilli, the flea acts like a hypodermic needle, injecting the bacilli into the lymphatic system of humans.

The early signs of the disease are the hard, swollen buboes (from the Greek *boubōn*, 'swollen groin') in the groin, armpit or neck, close to the site of the flea bite. Plague can also become pneumonic when the bacilli enter the lungs, and when this happens the disease can be transmitted directly from person to person through respiratory droplets expelled by sneezing and coughing. Septicaemic plague is the most lethal form of all, occurring when the bacilli go straight into the bloodstream, and resulting in the haemorrhaging body being covered with ominous black 'tokens'. Untreated, bubonic plague kills up to 60 per cent of its victims, pneumonic plague some 90 per cent, and septicaemic plague virtually 100 per cent. The most efficient flea vector is the biting rat flea, *Xenopsylla cheopis*. The human flea, *Pulex irritans*, may also play a role in the subsequent inter-human dissemination of the plague – this remains a plausible but contentious theory.

The first great plague

'But for this calamity, it is quite impossible either to express in words or to conceive in thought any explanation, except indeed to refer it to God.' Procopius of Caesarea (*c.*AD 500–565)

The word 'plague' derives from the Greek word *plēgē*, and the Latin word *plaga*, meaning 'blow' or 'stroke'. Like the words 'pest', 'pestilence' and 'pox', it was often used to cover a multitude of devastating epidemic diseases. The various biblical 'plagues' and some of the ancient 'plagues', such as the Plague of Athens (*c.*430–426 BC), the Plague of Orosius (AD 125), the Antonine Plague (*c.*AD 166–90) and the Plague of Cyprian (*c.*AD 250–70), were lethal epidemics but, while their identity remains uncertain, they were probably not bubonic plague.

The first great plague to bear the characteristic swollen

14

buboes was the Plague of Justinian in AD 541–4. It is thought to have originated in Asia, and may have been triggered by an extreme sequence of climatic or environmental events which, perhaps, led to crop failure, famine and mass movements of people and plague-carrying rodents. Spreading to North Africa, the Middle East and Europe, the Plague of Justinian is said to have played a role in weakening, if not causing, the eventual collapse of the Eastern Roman Byzantine empire.

In the fourth century, the Roman empire had split in half with two capitals – Rome in the west and Constantinople in the east. By the sixth century, the western Roman empire, invaded by Goths and Vandals, had already fallen apart; in the east the Emperor Justinian (r.527–65) was determined to reconquer and unite the western and eastern realms. But his ambitions may have been thwarted by the plague that bears his name. The Plague of Justinian killed, at its peak, according to one eyewitness, as many as 10,000 people a day in Constantinople (now Istanbul), and although this may be an exaggeration, it spread like wildfire through coastal ports and inland towns. It is estimated that perhaps one-quarter of the population of Mediterranean Europe died over the following years, and while the true number of deaths will never be known, the overall mortality was certainly very high.

The Byzantine chronicler Procopius of Caesarea vividly described the horrors of this 'pestilence', 'by which the whole human race came near to being annihilated'. Victims, he reported, writhed in fever, suffering agonies from grossly swollen buboes. Some became delirious and hallucinated, others died vomiting and choking on blood – possibly suggesting that both the bubonic and pneumonic forms of the disease were involved. There were too many corpses to bury. Roofs were removed from the fortified towers of Constantinople so that the dead bodies could be piled high. Some of the corpses were tossed onto rafts and allowed to drift out to sea. Panic, disorder and madness reigned. Thus began the first cycle of bubonic plague.

Further and frequent waves of plague continued to strike throughout the sixth, seventh and eighth centuries A D, often more localized and less virulent. After the last recurrence in A D 750, bubonic plague would not appear again in Europe until the Black Death of the fourteenth century, for reasons which, like many uncertainties of the plagues of the past, are still debated.

The origins of the Black Death

'How many valiant men, how many fair ladies, breakfasted with their kinsfolk and that same night supped with their ancestors in the other world.' Giovanni Boccaccio (*c*.1313–75)

The eruption of the second cycle of plague – the catastrophic Black Death, which spread from Asia to the Middle East, North Africa and Europe in the mid-fourteenth century – is firmly imprinted on many people's imaginations. Descriptions of buboes the size of an egg or even an apple, plus blotches, boils, bruises, black pustules and the coughing up of blood, vomit and sputum suggest that the Black Death may have been a combination of bubonic, septicaemic and pneumonic plague. While there are still many unsolved riddles about the Black Death, most historians agree that in Europe alone, in the space of a few years, from 1347–53, somewhere between 25 and 50 million people died, and possibly more than one-third to one-half of the population of Europe, Asia and the Middle East was wiped out by the disease. It was the greatest demographic crisis of the medieval period, and in terms of the proportion killed, the single most calamitous epidemiological event in all of history.

How, where and why the Black Death started is less certain. It is possible that it erupted somewhere in the steppes of Central Asia in the 1330s. Climatic and environmental changes may have disturbed the ecosystem, triggering the initial transfer of the *Yersinia pestis* bacterium from its natural reservoir in sylvatic-rodents (for example, plague-carrying marmots and gerbils) to commensal-rodent hosts, such as rats, and thence, via their fleas, to humans. Transformed from an epizootic disease of animals into a deadly human pandemic, the disease and its vectors moved along a number of major land and maritime trajectories with profound demographic, social and economic repercussions for a vast swathe of the known world.

The most gripping contemporary (but not necessarily the most plausible) account of its introduction to Europe begins on the Crimean coast of the Black Sea at the trading post of Kaffa (now known as Feodosia), where a group of Genoese merchants were trapped by besieging 'Tartars' (Mongols). When the attackers were struck by the plague, they were forced to retreat, leaving behind hundreds of unburied corpses. According to Gabriele de' Mussis (d.1356), as a passing shot the Mongol leader Kipchak Khan Jani Beg (d.1357), 'stunned and stupefied' by the immensity of the disaster, 'ordered corpses to be placed in catapults and lobbed into the city in the hope that the intolerable stench would kill everyone inside'.

The 'intolerable stench' did not, apparently, kill all the Genoese. Some escaped, unwittingly carrying the plague with them back to the shores of the Mediterranean. When they arrived at Messina in Sicily in the autumn of 1347 they tumbled off the ships with 'sickness clinging to their bones'. The Black Death had reached Europe.

The sorrow and the pity

The term 'Black Death' was coined only much later, the word 'black' referring possibly to the sheer horror of the pestilence (from the Latin, *atra mors*, which can mean 'terrible' or 'dreadful' death, the connotation of which was 'black death') or, as some have suggested, to the blackened bodies of its victims. Contemporaries called the epidemic the 'Great Pestilence', the 'Great Mortality' or the 'Big Sickness'.

The Italian author Giovanni Boccaccio described the route and symptoms of this devastating disease:

> Whatever its cause, it had originated some years earlier in the East, where it had claimed countless lives before it unhappily spread westward, growing in strength as it swept relentlessly on from one place to the next . . . its earliest symptom . . . was the appearance of certain swellings in the groin or the armpit, some of which were egg-shaped whilst others were roughly the size of the common apple . . . and it seemed that all the advice of physicians and all the power of medicine were profitless and unavailing.

The poignant accounts contemporaries left behind ring with the terrible sorrows it brought in its wake. The Italian poet, Petrarch (1304–74), expressed the perplexity and loneliness that must have haunted those who survived: 'Where are our dear friends now? Where are the beloved faces? Where are the affectionate words, the relaxed and enjoyable conversations? What lightning bolt devoured them? What earthquake toppled them? What tempest drowned them? What abyss swallowed them? There was a crowd of us, now we are almost alone.' A tax collector and shoemaker in Siena, Italy, called Agnolo di Tura believed, like many others, that 'This is the end of the world.' His whole family died: 'And I, Agnolo di Tura, called the Fat, buried my five children with my own hands.'

Jeuan Getting (d.1349), a Welsh poet, before his own death, recalled:

> We see death coming into our midst like black smoke, a plague that cuts off the young, a rootless phantom that has no mercy for fair countenance. Woe is me of the shilling [bubo] in the armpit; it is seething, terrible, where ever it may come, a head that gives pain and causes a loud cry, a burden carried under the arms, a painful angry knob, a white lump.

Everywhere – from the China Sea to the Mediterranean, across vast swathes of continental Europe and the British Isles, to the northern reaches of Scandinavia and Russia – countless bodies were buried by surviving family and friends, tossed onto rattling dead carts, buried in pest pits, or left to rot in the midday sun, to be devoured by wolves, pigs and dogs. As a vivid analogy of how the mass graves were 'stacked high with putrefying corpses' and separated with 'sprinklings of dirt', one observer, Marchione di Coppo Stefani, a Florentine, grimly reminded readers that it was 'just as one makes lasagna with layers of pasta and cheese.' In Venice the dead were dropped into gondolas and rowed out to sea with cries of '*Corpi morti, Corpi morti*'.

Rotting corpses and silent bells

The smell of death was all-pervading – in the foetid breath and buboes of the afflicted, in the filthy alleys of crowded towns and villages, in the ghost ships crewed by dying sailors, in the hastily dug plague pits. Boccaccio, describing Florence in *The Decameron* (1350–53), wrote:

> Many dropped dead in the open streets, both by day and by night, whilst a great many others, though dying in their own houses, drew their neighbours' attention to the fact more by the smell of their rotting corpses than by any other means. And what with these, and the others who were dying all over the city, bodies were here, there and everywhere.

With the sadness and the stenches came a dreadful silence. In some places even the funeral bells and weeping ceased – for 'all expected to die'. Petrarch, who had lost his beloved Laura to the plague in Avignon in 1348, noted the vast and dreadful silence hovering over the whole world. 'Is it possible,' he wondered, 'that posterity can believe these things? For we, who have seen them, can hardly believe them.'

Trying to make sense of this terrible calamity was hard. Boccaccio, like others, believed that the 'deadly pestilence' came 'either because of the operations of the heavenly bodies, or because of the just wrath of God mandating punishment for our iniquitous ways.' The fearful undertook penance and prayed for forgiveness in the hope of avoiding infection. Some people in the Christian world, known as flagellants, took penitence to extremes, flogging themselves or one another with knotted strips of leather or iron spikes, in the hope of expiating the sins of humanity. Yet more horrific was the violent and vicious abuse of 'scapegoats', who included social outcasts and religious minorities – especially Jews. Thousands of Jews were tortured and murdered in some European cities, accused by their attackers of poisoning wells and spreading the disease. These pogroms cast one of the darkest shadows over the era of the Black Death.

As the Black Death spread along trade routes – devastating many overcrowded and squalid settlements – attempts were made to restrict entry of ships into ports, along with their crews and cargoes, if they had come from 'infected' places. Cleaning up the filth of cities was also a reaction to the idea that foul smells and stenches might be part of the reason for the spread of plague. In Cambridge, the most insanitary parts of the university town were almost completed depopulated, and probably half the population died during the Black Death. In 1351, in a petition to the king in Parliament, the chancellor and the scholars of the university prayed 'that the townsmen should be compelled to clean the streets, then very noxious to all persons.' The idea that plague was 'contagious' or spread by noxious 'miasmas' (from the Greek, *miainein*, meaning 'to pollute') gained further credence in later centuries, leading to more stringent measures of control.

The impact of the Black Death

Perhaps no other single calamity has so changed the world. The sheer scale of the Black Death in terms of the numbers killed over just seven or so years must have resulted in huge demographic, social and economic upheavals. A wealth of historical material has been studied by researchers to document both its short- and long-term impact. In the immediate aftermath, accounts by survivors are chilling recollections of the cruelty and poignancy of the plague epidemic. As the 'Great Mortality' slowly retreated, there was also an outpouring of macabre art and literature across Europe. The artistic genre of *memento mori* or 'remembrance of death', although predating the Black Death, was thought to remind viewers of impending death. The Dance of Death, King Death, the Grim Reaper, fearsome visions of Hell, the Devil, and the Four Horsemen of the Apocalypse, the symbol of the skull and crossbones – all capture the sense of doom that seemingly descended on the world. *The Triumph of Death* by the Flemish artist, Pieter Brueghel the Elder, *c.*1562, shows an army of skeletons wreaking havoc across a desolate landscape, perhaps reflecting the ever-present threat of death in medieval and post-medieval Europe. But was it all doom and gloom for the survivors and later generations? Some historians would say not.

They point to beneficial changes for societies and economies – at least, in the longer run – albeit with wide variations across Europe, China and the Middle East. In England, for example, depopulation worked in favour of the peasants. With a severe shortage of labour and a surplus of agricultural land, wages for the landless classes rose and rents declined for rural tenants. Prices for agricultural products and other necessities fell, ensuring a more ready supply of nutritious food and growing prosperity for people at many social levels. Women filled vacancies in the job market. As the balance of power between lords and peasants altered, late medieval society witnessed the end of the old feudal system, allowing capitalism to flourish. A recent study of skeletons in London burial grounds suggests that, following the Black Death, subsequent generations were healthier, better fed and lived longer than ever before.

Several colleges in the universities of Cambridge and Oxford were founded or enlarged shortly after the Black Death, both to pray for the souls of those who had perished of the plague and to train new priests to replace those who had died. Such initiatives point to a remarkable sense of resilience, endurance and optimism in the aftermath of the calamity. A new spirit of enquiry and learning paved the way for the Renaissance and Reformation. The English anchoress and Christian mystic, Julian of Norwich, who lived though no fewer than eight outbreaks of plague including the Black Death, was yet able to declare that 'alle shalle be wele' with the world.

Historian John Hatcher reminds us in his 2008 book, *The Black Death: the Intimate Story of a Village in Crisis, 1345–1350*, of the complexities of the outcome of this calamitous event for England:

But it should always be remembered that the rising living standards and improved status that the ordinary folk came to enjoy were brought at the huge cost of a terribly high and unpredictable mortality . . . Such momentous mortality naturally had the potential to create confusion and disorder, but equally striking is the speed and power with which forces within society and economy moved to restore stability . . . Whereas the historian is struck by the continuities, contemporaries would have been overwhelmed by the scale of changes.

Economic recovery, improved standards of living and a reduction of social inequities in the Middle East, by contrast to England, are much less certain. In Egypt, for instance, downward population pressures did not give rise to the liberation of the *fellaheen* peasant labourers. Wages fell, grain prices rose and rents increased. A combination of circumstances, including many further episodes of disease and famine, led to the decay of Egypt's agriculture throughout the late medieval period in response to the Black Death. As historians continue to study and debate the global outcome of this catastrophe, differences between societies, cultures and religions will, undoubtedly, shed new light on its varied impact.

Plague continues to take its toll

After the ravages of the Black Death, plague did not disappear. It continued to reap its grim harvests, killing rapidly, and, seemingly, indiscriminately. Between the fourteenth and eighteenth centuries, some 50 million Europeans are believed to have died as the plague periodically swept from east to west, following the paths of sailors, soldiers, merchants and explorers.

The Great Plague of London in 1665–6 – so vividly described by Samuel Pepys (1633–1703) in his *Diary* and by Daniel Defoe (*c.*1660–1731) in his semi-fictional account, *A Journal of the Plague Year* (1722) – killed 70,000–100,000 people, or one-fifth to one-quarter of the population of London, causing panic and terror. 'Searchers' – often illiterate 'elderly matrons' – sought out the dead to ascertain the cause of death. Bills of Mortality recorded the numbers who had died of the plague and other diseases. 'Dead' carts travelled the streets at night calling 'Bring out your dead'; they carried away the corpses, filling up mass graves to the brim. Families and households in contact with suspected plague victims were incarcerated in their homes, their doors marked with a red cross and the words 'Lord have mercy upon us'. Watchmen stood guard outside to prevent their escape and provide them with provisions. The churches were crammed with the grieving, the penitent and the sickly. Following traditional advice during times of epidemics – *Cito, longe, tarde* ('Flee early, flee far, return slowly'), many who could afford to do so left the city, including not only King Charles II (r. 1630–85) and his court, but also priests and physicians. 'But Lord,' wrote Pepys on 16 October 1665, 'how empty the streets are, and melancholy, so many poor sick people in the streets, full of sores, and so many sad stories overheard as I walk, everyone talking of this dead, and that man sick, and so many in this place, and so many in that.'

Other writers, including the English Puritan minister Thomas Vincent (1634–78), also commented on the deathly hush that hung over London:

> Now, there is a dismal solitude … shops are shut … people rare, very few walk about … and there is a deep silence in almost every place. If any voice can be heard, it is the groans of the dying, and the funeral knell of them that are ready to be carried to their graves.

Pepys himself survived, and even at times enjoyed the occasional merrymaking. His wife, whom he sent to Woolwich, was much 'afeared' about her pet dog, as the authorities rounded up and killed all stray dogs and cats. She also washed her hair in vinegar while Pepys worried about wearing his latest wig, noting in his *Diary*: 'It is a wonder what will be the fashion after the plague is done, as to periwigs, for nobody will dare to buy any hair for fear of the infection, that it had been cut off people dead of the plague.' He took a number of precautions when he was 'put into an ill conception of myself and my smell' and felt 'forced to buy some roll tobacco to smell and chaw – which took away the apprehension.' During the Great Plague of 1665–6 a schoolboy at Eton College is recorded as being 'never whipped so much in his life as he was one morning for not smoking' – tobacco being regarded as a way of preventing infection!

Individuals also sought to save themselves by contrasting means – such as either sitting under a foul-smelling latrine or sniffing fragrant roses. Incense was a popular means of camouflaging the stench of the body, and perfumes, along with prayers, wafted through the churches. Defoe described the churches of London as 'like a smelling bottle; in one corner it was all perfumes; in another aromatics, balsamics, and a variety of drugs and herbs.' Piercing the bubo with a lancet or strapping a live chicken on the bubo was said to help. Bloodletting, sweating and forced vomiting were tried as ways of purging all corruptions from the blood and rebalancing the 'humours' (based on the ancient Greek and Roman idea that the body was made up of four 'humours': black bile, yellow bile, phlegm and blood).

Vipers' fat, spiders' webs, toad poison, woodlice and crabs' eyes were amongst the plethora of antidotes offered for sale. Theriac or Venice treacle, made from sixty-four ingredients including serpents' flesh and opium, was the most expensive remedy money could buy. Quack doctors took advantage of citizens' fears and saw a ready market for their wares, as Defoe conjured up the scene:

it is incredible and scarce to be imagined, how the posts of houses and corners of streets were plastered over with doctors' bills and papers of ignorant fellows, quacking and tampering in physic, and inviting people to come to them for remedies, which was generally set off with such flourishes as these, viz. 'Infallible preventive pills against the plague' ... 'Sovereign cordials against the corruption of the air' ... 'The only true plague water.'

Indeed, Defoe said there were so many claims for these pills, potions and preservatives that 'I could fill a book' of them. Most, he believed, poisoned the unfortunate bodies with their 'odious and fatal preparations'.

But a desperate situation in the face of the unknown meant desperate remedies. When the plague threatened London, someone even suggested filling a ship with peeled onions and letting it float down the Thames, in the hope that its absorbent powers would protect the city!

The plague spread to many other towns and villages across Europe during this ongoing second cycle. Spectacular eruptions occurred, such as the Plague of Naples in 1656–7, which killed half of the city's roughly 300,000 inhabitants. Even small villages were not immune. When the little community of Eyam in the Peak District of Derbyshire was hit, the rector, William Mompesson (1639–1709), cordoned off the village with a circle of stones in an attempt to prevent the plague spreading to the surrounding countryside. The villagers left 'disinfected' coins in vinegar-filled holes in gateposts along the bounds of the village to pay for food left for them by neighbours. By the autumn of 1666, over 250 of Mompesson's flock had died, possibly one-third or more of the population of Eyam. As one chronicler described it, 'shut up in their narrow valley, the villagers perished helplessly like a stricken flock of sheep.' The rector's own wife was one of the victims. Mompesson survived and, reflecting on the tragedy, wrote: 'The condition of this place hath been so dreadful that I persuade myself it exceedeth all history and example. I may truly say our Town has become a Golgotha, a place of skulls ... My ears never heard such doleful lamentations. My nose never smelt such noisome smells and my eyes never beheld such ghastly spectacles.'

Why me? Why here? Why now?

Written accounts of plague epidemics dating from the medieval and early modern periods remind us of the many ways in which people at the time wrestled to make sense of the origin, cause and spread of the plague. At one level were the divine and celestial explanations – God's reaction to the sins of humanity, or some ominous configuration of stars and planets. There were also the 'down-to-earth' explanations (the natural or terrestrial causes): earthquakes, unusual weather, and, above all, the rot and decay of rubbish accumulating in streets and dung heaps, emitting foul miasmas that poisoned the air. And then there were the people themselves: whether sinful, smelly or sickly, humans were somehow bound up with the pestilential corruption of humankind, and also capable of spreading sickness by contagious vapours from breath, buboes or clothes.

The many different ideas of the cause of plague inevitably led to a range of religious and secular responses. In Europe the Christian saints Cosmas, Damian, Sebastian and Roch were traditionally invoked for protection against the plague. As plague continued to rage in the centuries following the Black Death, citizens and the clergy even built churches in the hope of appeasing the Almighty's wrath. In Venice, the Redentore Church, designed by the architect Andrea Palladio (1508–80), was built as a votive church following the 1575–6 plague, when up to a third of the population of Venice died. The *Festa del Redentore*, on the third Sunday of July each year, still celebrates Venice's deliverance from the plague. The Passion Play, held every ten years at Oberammergau, Bavaria, also owes its origins to plague. The village's residents vowed that if God protected them from the effects of the plague ravaging the region they would produce a play every ten years thereafter depicting the life of Jesus. They believed they were spared after they kept their part of the vow when the play was first performed in 1634.

Alongside religious appeals for mercy from God, civic authorities attempted to control plague by introducing a number of measures to counteract the 'evil' stenches and poisonous miasmas thought to be associated with the spread of plague or to restrict the movements of people and goods deemed to be 'contagious'. Many of these responses dated back to the Black Death and even earlier, but they gained added impetus during the fifteenth to the eighteenth centuries. 'Orders of the Plague' instructed towns and cities as to how best to deal with the epidemics. Anything from installing large bonfires in the streets and fumigating the air with strong-smelling essences to killing all the cats and dogs and ridding the streets of noxious rubbish and rotting matter were imposed on plague-threatened localities, with varying degrees of legislation and success. In 1580, Nicholas Woodroffe, Lord Mayor of London, ordered that the streets and the kennels (street gutters) be cleansed 'for the avoydinge of the infection of the plague and the loathsome stinkes and savours that are in the severall streets of this cyttie.'

In Europe, Italy led the way in setting up health boards to enforce sanitary laws and impose 'cordons sanitaires' around towns and ports to control the spread of infection. Two of the most notable public health measures were the isolation of the sick and infected – either in their homes or in pest-houses – to 'segregate' them from the healthy, and quarantine to 'contain' those believed to have come into contact with plague to prevent the risk of possible infection spreading to the wider population. While isolation and quarantine played slightly different roles, they overlapped in their general belief that plague was contagious (although the concept of contagion was contested in the Islamic world).

Pest-houses and plague doctors

Pest-houses for plague were set up during the many outbreaks of plague, often taking over the old medieval leper hospitals. Temporary shacks were also erected in areas downwind of the 'pestilential vapours'. We can only imagine the horrors of these pest-houses where the dangerously ill and 'contagious' were crammed four or five in one bed. A cardinal in 1630 described the alarming conditions of the pest-houses of Bologna, Italy, where he saw people 'strip themselves to the skin, others lose their minds', adding, 'here you are overwhelmed by intolerable smells. Here you cannot walk but among corpses. Here you feel naught but the constant horror of death. This is a replica of hell.'

While many professionally trained physicians did their best to avoid the infection, some brave souls (possibly lured by the lucrative pay offered to volunteers, given the risk of death involved) were specifically hired as 'plague doctors'. The iconic image of the plague doctor (see plate section) shows him fully garbed in a head-to-toe protective costume, with the long, beak-like nosepiece stuffed with aromatic substances to combat the stench associated with plague. This popular seventeenth-century poem describes the plague doctor's costume:

> *In Rome the doctors do appear,*
> *When to their patients they are called,*
> *In places by the plague appalled,*
> *Their hats and cloaks of fashion new,*
> *Are made of oilcloth, dark of hue,*
> *Their caps with glasses are designed,*
> *Their bills with antidotes all lined,*
> *That foulsome air may do no harm,*
> *Nor cause the doctor man alarm,*
> *The staff in hand must serve to show*
> *Their noble trade where'er they go.*

Although the connection between rats, fleas and plague transmission was unknown at the time, the long waxed robes, gloves and mask may have helped to give the wearer protection from flea bites. Indeed, in Genoa in 1657, Father Antero Maria da San Bonaventura noted that while his local pest-house was infested with fleas, the protective garment was a good way to avoid being bitten.

Breaking the cycle – the role of quarantine?

The last devastating outbreak of plague in western Europe was in Marseilles in 1720–22, when around 50,000 died. Although rats had not been associated with many of the earlier plague epidemics, on this occasion dead rats were noted: apparently 10,000 of them were gathered up by fishermen and dumped out at sea. Thereafter, plague 'disappeared' from western Europe – or at least never reappeared again, except for a few brief flurries.

Historians have long debated all sorts of theories about the disappearance of plague from western Europe. For England, the Great Fire of London in September 1666, the cleansing of urban environments, the development of resistance to plague amongst the black rats, the ousting of the black rat (*Rattus rattus*) by the brown or sewer rat (*Rattus norvegicus*), and changes in climate are just a few of the ideas that have been mooted, but which have generally been questioned.

Quite a number of historians have highlighted the effectiveness of quarantine measures. The use of quarantine to prevent contagious epidemics from entering ports arose in the wake of the Black Death. A number of ports on the Mediterranean and Adriatic Sea were among the first to deny entry to ships coming from pestilential areas. The official legal use of the word 'quarantine' is believed to have been introduced in the late 1370s and early 1380s. In 1377 the Republic of Ragusa (now Dubrovnik in Croatia) – with a trading port on the Adriatic Sea – detained travellers from infected places on a nearby island for thirty days – *trentini giorni*. When this proved ineffective, the period was raised to forty days – *quaranta giorni* – from which we derive the word 'quarantine'.

The Italian states, thereafter, began to impose stringent quarantine regulations during times of plague and pestilence. In the Venetian lagoon, archaeologists have recently uncovered more than 1,500 'plague' skeletons dating back to the end of the fifteenth century on an 'old' quarantine island known as Lazaretto Vecchio. Another quarantine island in the lagoon, Lazaretto

Nuovo, can still be visited – a harrowing reminder of those who were detained there along with their merchandise. Elaborate methods of fumigating goods were used to prevent the spread of 'contagious' particles. It seems likely that those who showed signs of plague were quickly shipped off to Lazaretto Vecchio where they died a horrible and painful death. Similar quarantines were also used by land-locked cities as travellers and their goods were required to remain outside the gates for up to forty days until it was clear they were not carrying the plague. The Italian system of quarantine became the model for other European ports and cities in the following centuries.

The most impressive example of quarantine on the European continent was the Habsburg *cordon sanitaire*, which from the early eighteenth century ran from north of the Danube to the Balkans. It was lined with watchtowers and patrolled by soldiers with checkpoints and quarantine stations to prevent the movement of contagious people coming into Europe from the adjacent Ottoman empire. Soldiers could shoot anyone who tried to break through the border without observing quarantine.

But why the second cycle of plague was eventually broken still remains something of a puzzle (and, indeed, even the strictest of maritime or land quarantines might not have prevented the movement of rats and fleas). Although plague receded from western Europe, it continued to flare up in eastern Europe, and by the late nineteenth century was once more circling the globe. This third great plague pandemic probably originated in China in the mid-nineteenth century, and by the 1890s was causing massive mortality in many parts of South-east Asia. With plague raging in Canton (Guangzhou) and Hong Kong in 1894, two leading scientists were sent to find its cause.

The rat race

Alexandre Yersin (1863–1943), a Swiss-born bacteriologist, who had trained in Louis Pasteur's laboratory in Paris and Kitasato Shibasaburō (1853–1931), a Japanese bacteriologist who had worked with Robert Koch (1843–1910) in Berlin, were in a race to come up with an answer. This was the 'golden age' of bacteriology when the 'germ theory' – the recognition that diseases were caused by specific bacteria – was gaining acceptance. Kitasato had the backing of the British authorities in Hong Kong and access to a large number of autopsies in Kennedy Town Hospital. Yersin made do with a straw hut and a few basic medical tools. He procured cadavers of plague victims to study by bribing English sailors who had the job of disposing of bodies. Both scientists thought they had found the plague bacillus in the summer of 1894. It was, however, Yersin's bacillus – a gram-negative bacterium – that was identified as the correct one. He named it *Pasteurella pestis* in honour of his French patron, Louis Pasteur (1822–95). It was later renamed *Yersinia pestis* in recognition of Yersin's discovery.

Yersin also developed an anti-plague serum (from the blood of horses, to boost the immune system) that became the first 'cure' for plague. And in 1896–7 the Russian-born bacteriologist, Waldemar Haffkine (1860–1930), developed a partially effective plague vaccine while working in Bombay (Mumbai), India. But there was still one critical piece of the puzzle to solve – how was plague spread? Yersin had noticed large numbers of dead rats lying on the road in infected areas of Hong Kong and had speculated that plague might be rat-borne after dissecting dead rats whose bodies revealed vast quantities of microbes. But the final connections were identified by others.

Japanese scientist Ogata Masanori (c.1853–1919), working in Formosa (now Taiwan), suggested that blood-sucking rat fleas were the likely vectors of plague. And in 1898 Paul-Louis Simond (1858–1947), a French scientist and protégé of Pasteur based in India, confirmed that plague was transmitted from rats to rats and rats to humans by the bite of the Oriental flea (*Xenopsylla cheopis*). Elated at his discovery, Simond could not resist remarking that he 'had uncovered a secret that had tortured man since the appearance of plague in the world.' His idea was initially ridiculed, and it took nearly a decade before it was finally accepted by the scientific community, although an enlightened public health officer, John Ashburton Thompson (1846–1915), in Sydney, Australia, was one of the first to attempt to apply this new finding to practical use. When the city was struck by plague in 1900, he insisted that rat-control measures were a priority.

A global pandemic

In spite of the impressive scientific discoveries about the cause of plague and its mode of transmission, the third pandemic of plague – lasting through to the mid-twentieth century – still had the power to cause vast disruption and painful consequences. Millions died from plague in Asia, with an estimated 12.6 million deaths from the disease between 1898 and 1948 in India alone. Moreover, this was a truly 'global' pandemic (the word 'pandemic' comes from the Greek, *pan*, 'all, the whole of' + *dēmos*, 'people'). Plague reached every continent in the world (excepting Antarctica) including for the first time (as far as we know) sub-Saharan Africa, Australia and the Americas as well as touching some of its old haunts in Europe such as Glasgow,

Cardiff and Liverpool. Increasingly rapid systems of transportation via steamships and railways in an interconnected world meant that nowhere was safe from the spread or importation of plague.

As Myron Echenberg in his 2007 book, *Plague Ports: The Global Impact of Bubonic Plague, 1894–1901*, notes, the third pandemic has received less attention from historians than the Black Death. Yet, across the world, ports and cities struggled to contain the disease and the situation was, in many ways, reminiscent of older outbreaks, while also linked to newer issues of imperialism and race. People panicked and fled. Blame was attached to certain groups – often, in this case, to immigrants, such as the Chinese, or to the marginalized poor, who inhabited squalid slums. The authorities used whatever measures they could to stop its spread and, although the death toll and response to the epidemic varied in different places, control strategies included: fumigating affected houses, flushing gallons of carbolic acid through the drains and sewers, searching for the sick and forcibly isolating them in hospitals, and restricting travel, as well as other drastic 'solutions' such as demolishing 'plague' neighbourhoods.

Following bitter opposition to intrusive policies by British colonial authorities in, for example, India, there was a willingness to accommodate indigenous ethnic and religious traditions, and, in time, control measures focused on trapping and killing rats and their fleas rather than quarantining the human population. The contrast between the 'old', unpopular public health model, based on 'miasmas' and 'contagion', and the 'new' bacteriological approach, based on the rat-flea mode of transmission, is illustrated by the first two epidemics in North America.

Plague arrives in North America

In 1900, following an outbreak of plague in the newly acquired US territory of Hawaii, plague arrived at San Francisco and, although some ships had been quarantined in the harbour or given a 'clean bill of health', the disease somehow reached the cramped Chinese community. A Chinese American, Wing Chung Ging (also known as Chick Gin), was the first victim. He was found dead in a filthy, overcrowded 'flophouse' called the Globe Hotel, with foaming, bloody spittle over his face, ashen-grey skin and huge swellings around his groin and armpits. Initially, the authorities tried to deny that this was bubonic plague. But once made public, his death was quickly followed by draconian measures to quarantine, experimentally vaccinate and 'cleanse' Chinatown. The Chinese responded by organizing and successfully opposing government quarantines and evacuation plans in the federal court.

When plague struck San Francisco again after the terrible earthquake in 1906, there was, by this time, a better understanding of the role of the rat and its flea in the transmission of plague. The authorities set out to wage 'a war on the rats': posters encouraged people to trap and poison them, but they also warned against picking up dead rats, or squashing fleas with fingers or teeth. There were, however, several hundred cases and deaths in each of the two outbreaks, with high case-fatality rates.

Los Angeles was hit in 1924–5, but even recently there have been curious cases of plague in isolated rural settings in the USA – some of which have been traced not to rats but to prairie dogs. Indeed, it would seem that the outcome of the third pandemic was not simply the global dissemination of

Yersinia pestis carried by rats to humans but also the establishment of 'new' endemic rodent reservoirs in the wild.

Pockets of pestilence

A number of small mammals are now known to harbour the plague bacillus, and besides prairie dogs, these include ground squirrels, marmots, chipmunks, gerbils and rabbits. An epidemic of pneumonic plague in Manchuria in 1910–11 was traced to infected tarabagans (Russian marmots) after hunters, in a quest to cash in on the booming trade for their fur, handled and ate the meat. The epidemic spread along newly constructed railway lines, killing 60,000 people.

The last great plague pandemic, accounting for some 15 million deaths worldwide, had fizzled out by the mid-twentieth century. Today, there are antibiotics to treat plague and a vaccine that confers some protection for people at high risk of exposure, but there are still about 1,000 to 2,000 reported cases a year, mostly in Africa (though this is probably an underestimate). When in 1994 pneumonic plague broke out in Surat, a teeming industrial city in the Indian state of Gujarat, there were, again, scenes reminiscent of the Black Death: panic, people fleeing, scientists in plague-protective garb, and, above all, confusion. And while this outbreak was dealt with quickly by an effective public health response and the mass production of antibiotics, it reminded the world that plague is still a disease that can terrify and perplex us.

'Pockets of pestilence' in rodent foci remain in many parts of the world and outbreaks in the twenty-first century, including Algeria in 2003 – the setting for *La Peste* – and Madagascar in 2013–14, have shown that plague is capable of emerging and igniting epidemics in human beings. The WHO has now reclassified plague as a 're-emerging' rather than a 'dormant' disease. As Camus' Dr Rieux foresaw, 'the plague bacillus never dies or disappears for good.'

Plague puzzles – digging up the evidence

The story of plague – the most 'murderous contagion' of all time – has featured in history books, novels, children's stories, films, popular culture and museum exhibitions. The traditional view has been that all past 'plague' epidemics, which have been characterized by the classic buboes, have been caused by the plague bacillus, *Yersinia pestis*, and carried by rats and their fleas. However, in the late twentieth century, a number of prominent historians began to question this interpretation of the first two pandemics, including asserting that the infamous 'Black Death' was not bubonic plague at all. The arguments of the 'plague deniers' have been many and varied. In contrast to the third pandemic of plague, it has been suggested that the fateful disease in its first two cycles may have been anthrax, typhus or even some highly contagious haemorrhagic fever, rather like the Ebola virus.

Some of their arguments have seemed persuasive. Why, for example, are there almost no contemporary European descriptions of rat 'die-offs' preceding the plague? How could plague have spread so rapidly from Asia to Europe in the mid-fourteenth century prior to modern forms of transport? Why were the mortality rates so shockingly high compared to recent plague outbreaks? For those who have challenged the plague deniers, lack of firm evidence about the exact pathogen in the historic past has, nevertheless, remained frustrating.

Now exciting new techniques based on ancient pathogen genome sequencing are swinging the debate back to the side of the 'plague believers'. From skeletal remains in a widely dispersed number of cemeteries, dating back to the Plague of Justinian and the Black Death, *Yersinia pestis* has been extracted from dental pulp and identified as the causative agent. The evidence is increasingly strong. It would also seem that the strain that caused the first pandemic of the sixth to the eighth century AD is now extinct, while that which caused the Black Death is the ancestor to modern strains of *Yersinia pestis*.

There are still mysteries to uncover – digging up the black rats (*Rattus rattus*) to see if they carried *Yersinia pestis* is the next part of the puzzle. And if they were implicated, we must remember that rats, like humans, were also victims in this complex zoonotic disease. It is also quite likely that some of the devastating medieval and early modern outbreaks were a combination of bubonic and pneumonic plague. Once circulating in the human population (which was, undoubtedly, malnourished as well as host to and susceptible to a multitude of infections), transmission via airborne droplets in the form of pneumonic plague could explain its rapid spread and high mortality.

Although the origin of the traditional nursery rhyme, 'Ring-a-ring o' roses', is much debated, its evocative chant conjures up a poignant reminder of the horrors and history of plague:

> *Ring-a-ring o' roses,*
> *A pocket full of posies,*
> *Atishoo, atishoo*
> *We all fall down.*

LEPROSY

Leprosy, or Hansen's disease, is a chronic bacterial infection caused by the bacillus *Mycobacterium leprae*. In serious cases it can eventually (after a long incubation period) lead to nerve, skin and bone damage. Contrary to popular belief, leprosy is the least contagious of all major communicable diseases, and there are still many puzzles about its mode of transmission. Leprosy hospitals (known as *leprosaria*) in the medieval period provided both physical and spiritual care for those suffering from this disfiguring disease. In the nineteenth and twentieth centuries leprosy colonies were set up to isolate the infected in many parts of the world. There are now more appropriate ways to treat the disease, including effective antibiotics, and there has been an encouraging reduction in the global prevalence of leprosy over the past two decades. Cases of the disease do, however, still occur in Africa, Latin America and Asia, and continued efforts, with early detection, diagnosis and treatment, are needed to eliminate leprosy and overcome its stigma.

∽

Gerhard Henrik Armauer Hansen (1841–1912), the Norwegian physician who in 1873 discovered the causative agent of leprosy, later recalled his early experience working in the National

41

Leprosarium No. 1 in Bergen in 1868: 'I suffered terribly. I had never seen so much misery concentrated in one place. Gradually, though, as I commenced handling the patients, my aversion disappeared and was replaced by a great desire to learn the illness in detail ... the result was that after a few months I eagerly looked forward to dealing with my ravaged patients.' With a generous grant from the Norwegian government, Hansen conducted a comprehensive epidemiological study of leprosy in Norway. He travelled along the fjords visiting affected families, until he was finally convinced that leprosy was a communicable disease. After further clinical and experimental studies, Hansen and others were able to show that leprosy was a bacterial infection.

The clinical manifestations of leprosy (which can take many years to appear) vary in a continuous spectrum between two polar forms. One (known as lepromatous or multibacillary leprosy) is characterized by nodular tubercles that ultimately, if left untreated, destroy the facial features and cause permanent damage to the skin, nerves, limbs and eyes. The other form (known as tuberculoid or paucibacillary leprosy), which progresses more slowly, is a milder form, and more typically leads to patchy areas on the skin with loss of sensation.

In the late 1940s, leprosy became officially known as Hansen's disease, both in honour of the Norwegian pioneer and in order to reduce the stigma so often associated with the pejorative terms 'leprosy' and 'leper' – though the name 'leprosy' still remains in common use in historical and medical accounts (and for historical veracity is used here).

Leprosy in the medieval period

Prior to Hansen's discovery, the history of leprosy is shrouded in myths, misconceptions and mystery. It is generally thought that leprosy is an old disease, probably dating back to the ancient civilizations of the Near East, Egypt, China and India. It has been speculated that one of the earliest accounts of possible leprosy appears in an Egyptian papyrus (c.1550 BC) and there is written mention of what may have been leprosy in historical documents from India around 600 BC. Ancient Greek physicians compared the effects on the human skin of a disease called *lepra* ('the scaly disease') to the hide of elephants.

In Europe the disease does, however, appear to have become a serious problem in the medieval period although historians debate what role the Crusaders played in spreading leprosy. While it is unlikely that all 'leprosy' (*lepra*) cases were, in fact, suffering from Hansen's disease (rather than any of the other disfiguring skin diseases prevalent at the time), recent bio-archaeological evidence from skeletons found at burial sites shows that some reveal the unmistakable skeletal evidence of the ravages of the disease. DNA analysis further indicates that medieval strains of leprosy are similar to modern strains, and scientists are continuing to examine ancient and medieval skeletal remains to understand how leprosy evolved and adapted to humans.

Between the early eleventh century and the Dissolution of the Monasteries in the 1530s, at least 320 'leper' hospitals (or *leprosaria*) were founded in England by lay and religious benefactors, and usually run either by the Church or towns and cities. One of the first known early eleventh-century leprosy hospitals in England was at Harbledown, near Canterbury, Kent. Sites and buildings of some of the 'leper' hospitals and their chapels can still be seen. On the east side of Cambridge the 'Leper' Chapel of St Mary Magdalene, once part of the hospital, still stands and continues to commemorate its annual Stourbridge Fair. In the medieval period this was the largest fair in Europe and took place on Stourbridge Common. By attracting a large number of visitors, it would have provided a much-needed source of income for the hospital. In east Oxford, Bartlemas Chapel, built as part of the leprosy hospital in the early fourteenth century, continues to hold regular services. London's earliest leprosy hospital was the Priory Hospital of St James, which stood on the site of what is now St James' Palace. From the eleventh century, an order of Augustinian nuns cared for several dozen young female 'lepers', who were allowed to keep pigs on marshland adjacent to the hospital – now St James' Park and Green Park.

Many leprosaria were also established during this period in continental Europe as charitable institutions to care for the rapidly expanding number of victims. And even further back in time, the eastern Roman empire first opened leprosaria during the fourth century AD when Church leaders perceived a rise in those with the disease. From 400 to 1300, specialized institutions continued to care for 'lepers' within Byzantine territory.

There were, undoubtedly, wide variations in the way that leprosy sufferers were identified (or misidentified) and treated in different parts of the medieval world. The disease has left behind a terrifying image in history and human memory of rejection and exclusion from society. A commonly held perception of medieval England involves 'lepers', as outcasts from society, carrying a clapper or bell to warn people of their presence and being forcibly isolated in 'leper' hospitals for fear of spreading contagion. Recently, however, it has been suggested that this view was introduced into nineteenth-century accounts of English medieval history by those who were arguing at the time for the compulsory isolation of 'lepers'. Skeletal evidence has, moreover, shown that most of those with distinctive signs of leprosy were buried not in the graveyards attached to 'leper' hospitals but in a number of church cemeteries, again suggesting that society was more accepting of the disease than has commonly been assumed.

Care of those sufferers who were looked after by monks, nuns and others in the medieval hospitals was also probably more compassionate than popular opinion would suggest. Responses to the disease were often dictated by theology rather than medicine. In Christian societies, the concept of *Christus quasi leprous*, for example, was a reminder that Christ was like a 'leper' in his suffering. Cures and preventatives to heal both soul and body ranged from prayer and confession to the adoption of a healthy diet, herbal baths, bloodletting and ointments (either soothing or caustic) for the skin. Historian Carole Rawcliffe in her book, *Leprosy in Medieval England* (2006), quotes from a fourteenth-century English sermon, highlighting the role of the priest in providing a spiritual and physical regimen for 'lepers': 'He gives us relief from our pain through contrition, and through confession we receive a purgative; he recommends a healthful diet through our keeping of fasts; he orders therapeutic baths through our outpouring of tears; he prescribes bloodletting through our recollection of Christ's passion'. Reflecting a similar perspective, Timothy Miller and John Nesbitt in their recent book, *Walking Corpses: Leprosy in Byzantium and the Medieval West* (2014), argue that in the Byzantine world and Catholic Europe theologians saw the disease as 'a mark of God's favour on those chosen for heaven'. They describe leprosaria, not as prisons to punish lepers, but as centres of care to offer them support. Some of these leprosaria, their researches show, provided both male and female residents the opportunities to govern their own communities. Leprosy even came to be called 'the Holy Disease' by Byzantine writers.

Nevertheless, the fear of 'contagion', at a time when there was little understanding of the causes of disease and difficulties in making a diagnosis, played a role, too. Unlike many of the 'plagues' of the past, leprosy did not kill rapidly but left its victims with distinctive and disfiguring marks. As in the title of the book by Miller and Nesbitt, sufferers were described by one Byzantine chronicler as 'walking corpses'. An ambivalent conundrum faced medieval society – if the disease was contagious there was, for the sake of public health, a need for isolation, and yet there was also the need to alleviate suffering and to care for and support people with leprosy. Indeed, to balance these conflicting issues, many leprosaria were generally located outside city walls – to separate lepers from society at large – but their location, close to cities, enabled lepers to live together as a community, and to engage in trade, receive alms and visits from relatives, friends and patrons. However, the trauma for those afflicted – whether living in the leprosaria or in the community – must have been as hard as it still is in the modern era.

Between the eleventh and fourteenth centuries leprosy appears to have been at its peak in Europe, but over the next few centuries, for reasons that are still not understood, it slowly retreated. In England, few new leprosaria were built after the fourteenth century, and by 1400 a number of hospitals had been abandoned, while some were later used to house the elderly or those suffering from other diseases, such as plague or the pox.

How and why the disease petered out and why leprosaria fell into disuse for leprosy patients may be accounted for by a combination of epidemiological, religious and socio-economic changes. Like many puzzles in the history of disease, the reasons for the rise and decline of leprosy will continue to generate lively scholarly debates.

Leprosy rumbles on in Europe: hereditary or contagious?

'Leprosy is, perhaps, the most terrible disease that afflicts the human race. It is hideously disfiguring, destructive to the tissues and organs in an unusual degree, and is hopelessly incurable, the fate of its victims being, indeed, the most deplorable that the strongest imagination can conceive, and many years often passing before death rids the unhappy sufferer from a life of misery to which there is scarcely any alleviation.' *British Medical Journal*, 1887

Leprosy was still endemic in Scandinavia in the mid-nineteenth century, with around 3,000 people known to have the disease in Norway, when Hansen made his discovery of its causative agent. The first scientific study of leprosy was undertaken by the Norwegian dermatologist Daniel Danielssen (1815–94) – sometimes referred to as the 'father of leprology' – with his friend Carl Boeck (1808–75), working in the St Jørgens Hospital in Bergen. In 1847 they produced a remarkable book entitled *Om Spedalskhed* ('On Leprosy').

They differentiated between the two main forms of leprosy and drew a distinction between leprosy and a range of other diseases with similar symptoms such as syphilis, scurvy, psoriasis and scabies. Danielssen was, however, convinced that the disease was an inherited disorder. In order to prove his point, in 1856 he injected himself and some of his assistants repeatedly with 'leprous material' that he had extracted from the nodules of patients. They did not contract leprosy, and so Danielssen stuck to his theory that the disease was not a contagious one.

In 1873 Hansen (Danielssen's son-in-law) took two biopsies from the skin of the nose of one of his patients, and examined them under the microscope. There he saw large numbers of rod-shaped bodies. Convinced that he had found the causative agent of leprosy, Hansen tried a number of experiments with animals to confirm its infectious nature and to determine whether the rod-shaped bacilli (later called *Mycobacterium leprae*, or Hansen's bacillus) caused leprosy – though without success.

One experiment, however, was to cost Hansen his job. Frustrated at his inability to use an animal model to confirm the infectious nature of the disease, in 1879 he inoculated leprous material from a patient with lepromatous (multibacillary) leprosy, the most aggressive chronic form, into the cornea of a 33-year-old female patient, Kari Nielsdatter, who was suffering from the tuberculoid (paucibacillary) or milder form – without harm, but without her consent. The case ended in court, and Hansen was banned from ever practising medicine again. He continued as medical officer for leprosy in Norway, but his days of clinical research were over. The bacillus that Hansen had first observed under the microscope continued to frustrate scientists for another five generations as they unsuccessfully attempted to grow it in a test tube or to infect experimental animals and fulfil what had become widely known as Koch's Postulates, after the German scientist and bacteriologist, Robert Koch.

The 'separating sickness'

'It seems impossible ever to calculate the hundreds of thousands of hearts this merciless disease has broken, the agonizing loneliness and misery left in its wake.' Peter Greave, a patient at the St Giles' leprosy hospital in Essex founded in 1914, in his book, *The Seventh Gate*, 1976

Although leprosy persisted in only a few areas of Europe in the nineteenth and early twentieth centuries, the question of segregation of the infected raised many sensitive and conflicting issues. Because of the fear among a growing number of people that the disease was highly contagious and might become a global epidemic, leprosy colonies for the infected began to proliferate throughout the world, most commonly on offshore islands, including Robben Island off the coast of South Africa (later the prison of Nelson Mandela and now a UNESCO World Heritage Site).

One remarkable story is that of Jozef De Veuster (1840–89) – more widely known as Father Damien. In 1873, Father Damien, a Belgian priest and missionary, went to the island of Molokai, Hawaii, to help in the leprosy colony at Kalawao. The first patients had been shipped there in 1866 when King Kamehameha V instituted an 'Act to Prevent the Spread of Leprosy' and forced all those with the disease to be secluded on the island. The local name for the disease had become *mai ho'okawale*, the 'separating sickness'.

What Father Damien found, on arrival, was heartbreaking. There were some 800 leprosy sufferers housed in the most degrading conditions:

Nearly all the lepers were prostrated on their beds, in damp grass huts, their constitutions badly broken down. The smell of their bodies, mixed with the exhalation from their sores, was simply disgusting and unbearable for a newcomer. Many times in fulfilling my priestly duties in their huts, I have had to close my nostrils and run outside for fresh air . . . At that time the progress of the disease was fearful, the rate of mortality high.

Father Damien did what he could to help the people in the colony, serving as both priest and physician, and in a short time he had transformed their lives. Sadly, Father Damien himself eventually contracted leprosy and died on the island.

From the mid-nineteenth to the mid-twentieth century, efforts to contain, control or treat leprosy across the world, however, varied widely, often with tensions between religious and medical approaches, indigenous practices and 'colonial' or 'state' interventions, and with arguments for and against enforced isolation, depending on whether the disease was viewed as highly contagious or completely non-contagious. For example, in 1867 the Royal College of Physicians in London reported on the basis of an empire-wide survey (and acknowledging Danielssen's experiments) that leprosy was not contagious and was best tackled by improvements in health, diet and living conditions. The Mission to Lepers in India (now more sensitively called the Leprosy Mission) was founded in 1873, the year of Hansen's discovery of the leprosy bacillus, with the aim of investigating the disease in British India, establishing a number of leprosaria, and bringing physical and spiritual relief to sufferers who had been shunned by society. The First

International Congress on Leprosy, held in Berlin in 1897, recommended isolation as the appropriate response to leprosy.

'Don't fence me in': the story of Carville in the United States

In the United States there has only ever been one leprosarium on the mainland, at Carville in Louisiana. Leprosy probably reached the Americas during the early modern period via European settlers and enslaved Africans. In Louisiana in the nineteenth century, leprosy was known as *la maladie que tu nommes pas* – 'the disease you do not name'. In 1894 five male and two female leprosy sufferers were taken by barge to an abandoned sugar plantation on a bend of the Mississippi River, establishing the Louisiana Leper Home at Carville.

Carville was slowly transformed from a 'swampy hell-hole' into a beautiful estate. The history of its patients and carers, the Daughters of Charity of St Vincent de Paul, are especially moving – there are many stories of sadness and separation, rejection and despair, tolerance and understanding, love and determination. Although in principle it was designated 'a place of refuge, not reproach; a place of treatment and research, not detention', Carville, like many leprosaria of the nineteenth and first half of the twentieth century, imposed strict segregation and isolation. Carville encapsulates all that is both sad and good in the history of leprosy.

In 1921 the US Public Health Service took over its operational control, at which time it was known as the American National Leprosarium at Carville. A number of new therapies were pioneered at Carville, and it also became the focus of a transformation of attitudes towards the disease. Up until 1952 patients were not allowed to marry, and those already married were not permitted to live with their non-patient spouses. Patients could not vote in either state or national elections, and outgoing post was sterilized. When patients were discharged they were handed a certificate that labelled them 'Public Health Service Leper', with, under reason for discharge, the comment: 'No longer a menace to public health'.

Beginning in the 1930s, one patient, Stanley Stein, known as the 'Carville Crusader', did much to campaign for change and to raise international awareness of the plight of leprosy sufferers. He began a newspaper later called *The STAR* 'to cast the light of information on a disease that has been thrust into the shadows' and help change perceptions of the disease. Initially an in-house newspaper, it attracted the attention of campaigners elsewhere. It was through the insistence of patients and staff at Carville that in 1948 the name 'Hansen's disease' officially replaced the name 'leprosy'.

After patients at Carville began to be successfully treated with the new drug dapsone in 1945, they started to envisage a life beyond the barbed wire fence that separated them from family and friends, adopting as their theme tune one of the hit songs of the time – 'Don't Fence Me In'. In 1948 the barbed wire fence was removed. For those cured of the disease and trying to find a life elsewhere, the stigma of leprosy was, however, ever present. *No One Must Ever Know*, the title of a memoir published in 1959 by a former patient, Betty Martin, reflects the difficulty she and her fellow sufferers had in shaking off the past.

In 1986 the hospital at Carville was renamed the Gillis W. Long Hansen's Disease Center, after the distinguished US congressman, Gillis W. Long (1923–85), who was an advocate for people living and working with Hansen's disease. It is now, from its new base in Baton Rouge, Louisiana, at the forefront of research into Hansen's disease. Patients who were still at Carville in the 1990s were given the opportunity and money to move away, but if they chose to remain, care and support continued to be offered.

Pioneering treatments

In 1915 Leonard Rogers (1868–1962), a British doctor working in India and one of the founders in 1924 of the British Empire Leprosy Relief Association (BELRA) to 'rid the Empire of leprosy' (later known as the British Leprosy Relief Association, or LEPRA), pioneered a preparation for intravenous injection based on the active agents of chaulmoogra oil. This plant-based remedy had been used as a traditional natural treatment for centuries in Asia but had produced nauseating side effects when taken by mouth.

In 1941 a new drug called Promin (a sulphone drug) was developed and tested on twenty-two patients at the leprosy hospital at Carville, Louisiana, with impressive results – described by one patient as a 'miracle'. This was followed by dapsone which could be administered orally rather than by injections. Carville was also one of the centres to pioneer new techniques of reconstructive surgery. By the second half of the twentieth century other drugs were available, and in the 1960s the WHO recommended the abolition of compulsory isolation of those suffering from leprosy – based on the scientific knowledge that the disease is not highly contagious and drug treatment was available. However, compulsory isolation continued in some countries, such as Japan, until the mid-1990s.

Leprosy today: a disease not to be forgotten

'Stigma shouldn't be seen as residing in an individual with a disease, but it resides in the society that has not found a way to be inclusive. We have a duty to diagnose and treat this stigma.' *The International Leprosy Association Global Project on the History of Leprosy*, 2007

Scientists continue to try to unravel the immunology of leprosy and its mode of transmission – possibly, but not always, involving inhalation of airborne droplets through the nose or mouth during close and frequent contacts with untreated cases. They are also trying to understand the reasons for its exceptionally low level of infectivity, and its long latency period. The disease is, as Hansen suspected, contagious, but of all the infectious diseases it is one of the hardest to catch. It would seem that 95 per cent of the population is naturally immune.

Armadillos have started to play an interesting role in the story. In the early 1970s scientists succeeded in growing large quantities of *Mycobacterium leprae* in the nine-banded armadillo – one of the first real opportunities for studying the micro-organism since its discovery in 1873 by Hansen. The bacterium still cannot be grown in cell culture but it can also be grown in the footpads of mice (but not in the rest of the mouse). More recently, moreover, it has been discovered that armadillos are, themselves, a source of leprosy infections in humans, raising interesting speculations about its transmission as well as the animal or human origins of the disease.

In the last few decades the WHO has been optimistic that there are sufficient drugs to eliminate leprosy. When cases of resistance to dapsone appeared in the 1960s, the WHO pushed for a multi-drug therapy (MTD) combining dapsone with clofazimine and rifampicin. Since 1995 the WHO, with donations from the pharmaceutical company, Novartis, has provided the drugs free of charge to all patients worldwide. In 1999, in collaboration with other agencies, the WHO launched the Global Alliance for the Elimination of Leprosy (GAEL) followed in 2006 by the Global Strategy for Further Reducing the Leprosy Burden and Sustaining Leprosy Control Activities, and in 2009 the Enhanced Global Strategy for Further Reducing the Disease Burden due to Leprosy (2011–15). International and national campaigns continue to emphasize early case detection, treatment with MTD, contact tracing and the integration of primary leprosy services into existing general health services, as well as overcoming the stigma and ameliorating the social and psychological consequences of leprosy.

There is as yet no vaccine for leprosy, but the widespread use of MTD – a highly effective cure for all types of leprosy – has dramatically reduced the burden of the disease. There is also a new cheap rapid diagnostic test so that cases of the disease can be detected and treated before the debilitating symptoms permanently damage the patient. It is estimated that some 16 million patients have been cured over the past few decades, and leprosy has now been eliminated from 119 out of 122 countries where the disease was considered a major public health problem in the mid-1980s. Leprosy is at present mostly concentrated in a small number of countries in Africa, Asia and Latin America, and is included in a group of diseases now known as Neglected Tropical Diseases with the aim of attracting more attention and funding for diseases of the poorest, under-served and marginalized communities.

Although there has been a decline in the global prevalence of leprosy, there are still over 200,000 new cases detected every year, as well as many more sufferers who have already been disabled by the disease and who are now beyond the hope of early treatment. Some continue to feel the stigma of leprosy and do not come forward for treatment. The disease is retreating, but it is far from being eradicated. It must not be forgotten.

SYPHILIS

Syphilis – the 'great pox' – struck Europe in the late fifteenth century, and the impact was devastating. Many people in Italy, France, Spain, England and elsewhere became infected, primarily through sexual contact. The hideous symptoms induced horror and loathing, and in very many cases resulted in death. Over the next few centuries, syphilis became less lethal, but nevertheless remained a major cause of sickness and death for many people across the globe. Its causative organism, a bacterium called *Treponema pallidum*, was identified in the early twentieth century, and since the mid-twentieth century antibiotics have proved highly effective against what was, until the advent of HIV/AIDS, the most dreaded of all sexually transmitted diseases.

∽

In 1530 an Italian physician, Girolamo Fracastoro (*c.*1476/8–1553), published a poem entitled '*Syphilis sive morbus Gallicus*' ('Syphilis, or the French Disease'). The poem tells the story of a swineherd named Syphilus [*sic*] who, for insulting the sun god Apollo, is punished with a horrible pestilence that brings out 'foul sores' on his body. The swineherd's name may be a combination of the Greek words for 'pigsty' and 'love' or it is possible that Fracastoro borrowed the word from Sipylus, a character in

Ovid's *Metamorphoses*, who lived not far from Mount Sipylon in Asia Minor. Whatever its derivation, this was the first appearance of the word 'syphilis', although the disease had already been called by any number of different names since its eruption in Europe a few decades earlier.

Naming the disease

'In recent times I have seen scourges, horrible sicknesses and many infirmities affect mankind from all corners of the earth. Amongst them has crept in, from the western shores of Gaul, a disease which is so cruel, so distressing, so appalling that until now nothing so horrifying, nothing more terrible or disgusting, has ever been known on this earth.' Joseph Grüenpeck (*c*.1473–*c*.1532)

An epidemic that hit the warring nations of Europe in the mid- to late 1490s seemed to contemporaries to be a completely new and appalling affliction, one that caused gross pustules to erupt over the entire body, abscesses to eat into the bones, and the flesh to fall off the face. Death was the outcome more often than not. It was said that the disease first appeared in 1495, after King Charles VIII of France (r. 1483–98) laid siege to Naples. When the city fell, the French army was struck by an unfamiliar and foul disease, forcing Charles to end his campaign. The French blamed the pestilence on the Neapolitans. But once the pox-ridden French army of soldiers, from various countries, and their female camp followers, disbanded and retreated to their homelands, they took the terrible scourge with them. Within five years of the first reported cases, this seemingly 'new' disease was all over Europe and reaching into North Africa. 'What other contagion has ever spread so quickly to all countries of Europe, Asia and Africa?' asked Desiderius Erasmus ('of Rotterdam') (1466–1536) in 1520.

No one wanted to be held responsible for this vile disease. The English, Germans and Italians called it the *morbus gallicus* or the 'French disease'; the French preferred the 'disease of Naples' or the 'Spanish pox'; while the Russians called it the 'Polish disease'. Despite being the most disowned affliction in history, two names stuck: *morbus gallicus*, the French disease, became the most common term in most of Europe, while to the French, it became known simply as *la grande vérole* – the 'great pox' – perhaps because its pock marks were larger than those of smallpox or perhaps because at the time it seemed infinitely worse as a disease.

The mystery of the origin of the 'great pox'

In the late fifteenth century the Italian physician Niccolò Leoniceno (1428–1524) wrote one of the first treatises on this mysterious sickness, *De epidemia quam vulgo morbum gallicum vocant* ('On the epidemic vulgarly called the French disease'). The name 'syphilis', coined by Fracastoro in 1530, was not widely adopted until the early nineteenth century, although his published Latin verse on the *morbus gallicus* was read by many and translated into several languages. But while each nation blamed somebody else for the terrible disease, physicians throughout Europe were anxious to discover why and from where this 'great pox' had actually arisen. Had it just struck the French army in Naples out of the blue – a thunderbolt from the Almighty, perhaps, to punish people for their sins (as Fracastoro's Apollo had cursed the swineherd)? Or, as many contemporaries began to suspect, had the disease been brought from overseas – for example, by the explorer Christopher Columbus (1451–1506) and his sailors returning from the New World shortly before the spectacular eruption of the 'great pox' in Europe?

It is a question that has engaged some great minds over the past five centuries. Two main hypotheses have been debated: was syphilis a 'new' disease imported to the Old World – the 'Columbian' hypothesis – or was syphilis already endemic in the Old World and perhaps overlooked and misdiagnosed amongst many other disfiguring illnesses, such as leprosy – the 'pre-Columbian' hypothesis? The pendulum of opinion has swung back and forth in these debates. But, now – as with speculations about the origins of plague – modern techniques are enabling bio-archaeologists studying skeletons in both the New and Old Worlds to resolve these debates. The latest findings suggest that syphilis was indeed already endemic in the Americas prior to Columbus' 'discovery' of the New World in 1492, and may well have been 'new' to Europe in the late fifteenth century. For some, this 'Columbian' thesis has a certain poetic justice, since many lethal diseases (such as measles, smallpox, malaria and influenza) were taken across the Atlantic from the Old World to the New, wreaking havoc amongst the Native American populations, who had no immunity to such diseases. It has, however, also been argued that other infections, closely related to syphilis, such as yaws, pinta and bejel, which are primarily childhood diseases spread by skin contact, were endemic in the Old World in pre-Columbian times – adding to the intrigue of this contested history.

'One night with Venus, and a lifetime with Mercury'

Whatever the origin, an association of the 'great pox' with loose women, prostitutes and 'general godlessness' was recognized from an early date. This gave rise to the use of yet a further term: *lues venerea* or 'venereal plague' (from Venus, the Roman goddess of love). This led to the later abbreviated term VD – for venereal disease. Another venereal disease, gonorrhoea (often known as 'the clap' or *la chaude pisse* – 'hot piss'), had possibly been around since ancient times (though, again, its origin remains uncertain) and, when syphilis struck Europe, some thought that the two diseases were one and the same. The alarming and more serious symptoms of syphilis were, it was mooted, just one added complication caused by the same venereal poison spreading more widely around the body.

The authorities in a number of countries were so appalled by the heightened escalation of venereal diseases that they attempted to control prostitution and casual sexual encounters. Henry VIII (r.1509–47) tried to close down the 'stews', or brothels, of London as well as communal bathhouses. (It has often been speculated that he himself suffered from syphilis, but this was probably not true.)

In the seventeenth century, condoms were recommended as a prevention against the 'great pox'. Folk etymology claims that the word 'condom' came from a certain Dr Condom who made the devices for Charles II (r.1660–85). It is more likely that the term originated from other derivations including the Latin *condere*, 'to hide, suppress or conceal'. Condoms or sheaths had, in fact, been used in ancient times (including for ritual purposes), and over the centuries were made from anything from sheep's gut to tortoiseshell, leather or silk. The 'great pox' gave an added impetus to their use as a protective barrier. It is said that the English gentry, eagerly awaiting their arrival in the post from France, called them 'French letters'. The French aristocracy returned the compliment, calling them *capotes anglaises* ('English overcoats'). A late eighteenth-century advert for a 'Mrs Phillips warehouse' in London stated that 'gentlemen of intrigue may be supplied with those Bladder Policies, or implements of safety, which infallibly secure the health of our customers', adding an extra snappy advertising slogan:

> *To guard yourself from shame or fear,*
> *Votaries to Venus, hasten here;*
> *None in our wares e'er found a flaw*
> *Self-preservation's nature's law.*

Although fifty to a hundred years after its initial spectacular appearance, the disease seemed to become less virulent and less lethal, it nevertheless caused agonizing long-term symptoms for its sufferers, as well as shameful sores, known as chancres. Once acquired, syphilis can pass through four distinct stages of the disease: primary, secondary, latent and tertiary, with each stage being characterized by different symptoms and levels of infectivity. The primary stage begins with genital sores, usually at the site of contact. In the secondary stage these lesions heal, and several weeks later a rash appears, often accompanied by fever, aches and tiredness. There is then a latent (hidden) period in which the patient has few symptoms. The tertiary stage might occur at any time between five to thirty years after the original infection. This last stage, however, is the worst: abscesses crop up all over the body, and the disease may eat away the face, bones and internal organs. In some cases the disease can also invade the cardiovascular or nervous systems, leading to paralysis, blindness, insanity and eventual death. Children born to syphilitic mothers can also be infected in the womb ('congenital syphilis'): these so-called 'innocents' may be afflicted with various deformities, including blindness, deafness and characteristic 'peg-shaped' teeth. Syphilis can also lead to infertility, and historians are currently examining the demographic impact of this in the past.

Any number of treatments were touted by doctors and quacks as cures for this notorious disease. The ancient custom of bloodletting was widely practised – to no avail. Rose's Balsamic Elixir offered, according to its vendors, to cure 'the English Frenchify'd' by removing 'all pains in three or four doses and making any man, tho' rotten as a Pear, to be as sound as a sucking lamb'. One of the most common treatments involved the use of mercury – hence the popular saying, 'One night with Venus and a lifetime with Mercury'.

Patients would be shut up in 'stew', a small steam room, often for twenty or thirty days at a time. Wrapped in blankets, they were left to sweat in a hot tub or by a fire and given mercury, either as a drink or as an ointment for their suppurating sores. One of the more curious methods was fumigation, in which the patient was placed in a closed box with his or her head sticking out. Mercury was placed in the box and a fire was started under the box that caused the mercury to vaporize – a gruelling process of breathing in the fumes for the patient. These methods induced sweating and salivation. It was said that the patient needed to produce at least three pints of saliva for the poison to be expelled from the body. In fact, the highly toxic mercury 'cure' caused as many complications as the disease itself. During the treatment disgusting secretions issued from the patients' mouths and noses; sores filled their throats and tongues; their jaws swelled and often their teeth fell out. The cure could be as fearsome as the disease.

There are many contemporary images depicting the medicinal rituals of the sweating and mercury treatments, with titles such as 'The Martyrdom of Mercury' or 'The Scourge of Venus and Mercury'. One early sixteenth-century woodcut shows the German scholar, Ulrich von Hutten (1488–1523), in bed, suffering from the 'great pox'. He described the horror of the disease:

> [The physician] cared not even to behold it . . . for truly when it first begun, it was so horrible to behold. They had boils that stood out like acorns, from whence issued such filthy stinking matter, that whosoever came within the scent, believed himself infected. The colour of these was a dark green, and the very aspect as shocking as the pain itself, which yet was as if the sick had lain upon a fire.

He also experienced the torture of mercury treatment. In fact, von Hutten was so appalled at the outcome of his years of mercury treatment that he advocated a far more gentle remedy called guaiacum or 'holy wood', a decoction made from a tree indigenous to the West Indies and South America. Since it was presumed by some that the disease itself came from the New World, a local plant seemed an attractive remedy. Large quantities of the wood were imported into Europe, and the syphilitic rich drank guaiac cocktails. Whether it worked or not is another matter, but it was certainly less dangerous than mercury.

Following the spread of syphilis, pox-houses were built, first in south-west Germany. Special hospitals were set up in Italy during the sixteenth century: the *incurabili* (incurables) hospitals. In Venice, the Ospedale degli Incurabili was built in 1522 in response to the spread of syphilis. There is a head with a sweetly sad expression over a door for those who did not recover, and a smiling head over a second door for the few who did. Some of the medieval leper hospitals had been known as 'Lock Hospitals', referring to the bandages or 'locks' that covered a patient's sores. The name lived on in hospitals for the treatment of venereal diseases such as the famous London Lock Hospital which opened in 1747 near Hyde Park Corner. The hospital treated nearly 300 patients during its first year. A separate female ward was established that offered care for 'females suffering from disorders contracted by a vicious course of life' – many of whom when admitted arrived 'almost naked, penniless and starving.' In some hospitals, 'Foul Wards' isolated those suffering from syphilis.

The link between prostitution, poverty and syphilis remained of huge concern over the centuries. Such a 'scenario' is depicted in six scenes by the English artist William Hogarth (1697–1764) in *A Harlot's Progress*. By the fifth scene, the 'innocent country girl', Moll Hackabout, who has turned to prostitution on the streets of London, is dying from venereal disease. She is pictured close to the fire with shroud-like 'sweating' blankets swathing her body as she nears death, while two doctors argue about the efficacy of their respective cures. In the final scene, Moll dies aged twenty-three. Skeletal remains of victims of syphilis from Victorian London, where it is estimated that 20 per cent of the population may have been infected, are reminders of the ravages of this tragic disease on the human body.

A 'magic bullet'

Confusion over the differences and similarities of syphilis and gonorrhoea had long vexed physicians. In the mid-eighteenth century, after conducting a gruesome experiment, the Scottish surgeon John Hunter (1728–93) claimed that they were the same disease. He inoculated an 'unknown individual' (possibly himself) with 'venereal matter' taken from a patient who had gonorrhoea. Hunter then watched to see the development of symptoms. During the following months, the signs of both 'the clap' and 'the pox', including the chancre of syphilis, were evident. It is quite likely that the 'donor' actually had both syphilis and gonorrhoea, deluding Hunter into thinking that the two were from the same 'poison'.

Over the course of the nineteenth and early twentieth centuries, much of the confusion about the cause of these two venereal diseases was cleared up. In 1879 the gonococcus germ causing gonorrhoea (later known as *Neisseria gonorrhoeae*) was described by the German bacteriologist Albert Neisser (1855–1916), and in 1905 the German researchers Fritz Schaudinn (1871–1906) and Erich Hoffmann (1868–1959) found spiralling, thread-like bacteria in syphilitic chancres. The causative organism of syphilis was originally called *Spirochaeta pallida* and subsequently given the name *Treponema pallidum* (meaning 'pale twisted thread').

In the following year a new blood test was developed by German scientist August von Wassermann (1866–1925) and his colleagues, known as the Wassermann reaction, which could easily identify those suffering from syphilis. When, in 1913, Japanese scientist Hideyo Noguchi (1876–1928) and his colleagues working at the Rockefeller Institute of Medical Research in the USA isolated the causative microbe from the brains of patients with insanity and paresis due to late-stage syphilis, it became clear that all of the stages of the disease were linked to one 'seed of contagion', *T. pallidum*.

The first sign of hope in the form of a treatment for syphilis came in 1910. Paul Ehrlich (1854–1915), a German medical scientist who had shared the 1908 Nobel Prize in Physiology or Medicine with the Russian scientist, Ilya Ilyich Mechinov (1845–1916), 'in recognition of their work on immunity', had been studying over 600 different arsenic-based compounds in the search for a 'magic bullet', a chemical agent that would target a specific micro-organism in the body without harming healthy cells. His colleague, the Japanese scientist Sahachiro Hata (1873–1938), found that the 606th in their series was effective against the spirochaete, *T. pallidum*, that causes syphilis. Its discovery was announced in 1910 and called arsphenamine. It was then marketed under the name 'Salvarsan' ('salvation through arsenic') by the German pharmaceutical company, Hoechst. This first 'magic bullet' (and, indeed, this was the first ever specific drug for a bacterial infection) was initially hailed as a remarkable success for the treatment of syphilis but it was fairly toxic and had some unpleasant side effects. A modified compound, Neosalvarsan, was produced but it was not until the introduction of penicillin in the 1940s that a real 'wonder cure' was available for both syphilis and gonorrhoea. Ehrlich often said that to achieve success one needed the four Gs (in German): *Geduld* ('patience'), *Geschick* ('intelligence'), *Geld* ('money') and *Glück* ('luck') – and, indeed, the history of medicine is full of stories of scientists who made great discoveries based on one or more of these attributes.

Madness and malariatherapy

'Though this be madness, yet there is method in't.' Polonius,
in William Shakespeare, *Hamlet*, II. ii.

Prior to the advent of penicillin as a treatment for syphilis, an
interesting idea came to the Austrian neurologist, Julius von
Wagner-Jauregg (1857–1940). Many people with late-stage
syphilis ended up in mental asylums suffering from 'general
paralysis of the insane' (GPI), the name given to the form of
mental illness caused by syphilis. In a psychiatric hospital in
Vienna, Wagner-Jauregg noticed that patients who also came
down with malaria (and developed a high fever) seemed to show
a marked improvement in their physical and mental health. It
was likewise observed that when *Treponema pallidum* was cultured in a test tube, it could be killed by heat. What if,
Wagner-Jauregg wondered, he gave his syphilitic patients a dose
of malaria? Might the resulting high fever get rid of the syphilis
germ?

The practice of inoculating patients with the malaria parasite,
Plasmodium vivax, seemed to work, at least by slowing the progress of dementia and other symptoms of late-stage syphilis.
Quinine was available to kill off the malarial parasites once the
experimental treatment had been given. Wagner-Jauregg was
awarded the Nobel Prize in 1927 for his novel 'discovery' of
using one disease to fight another, and malariatherapy was given
to thousands of GPI patients all over the world, until it was
superseded by early treatment with penicillin.

Guard against VD – prevention
during the two world wars

The First and Second World Wars saw a sharp rise in venereal diseases, as well as a real fear that soldiers returning from the theatres of war would spread the infections far and wide, as they had done in the late fifteenth century. The policies for dealing with the threat were quite different in each of the wars, and differed also from one country to another.

In the First World War, US soldiers who contracted either syphilis or 'the clap' lost their pay. Propaganda material warned the Allies that 'A German bullet is cleaner than a whore', and closing down brothels made sense to the American military at this time on the grounds that 'to drain a red-light district and destroy thereby a breeding place of syphilis and gonorrhoea is as logical as it is to drain a swamp and thereby a breeding place of malaria and yellow fever.' Although condoms were available as a preventative (the first rubber condoms had come on the market in 1855), these were strongly discouraged on the grounds that it would simply encourage licentious behaviour.

By the Second World War, there was less emphasis on the stigma and shame of VD and more concern for public health, family and social welfare. Campaigns aimed at servicemen began to promote ways to avoid the infection or seek treatment for it. Condoms were freely available and encouraged. Posters reminded soldiers to: 'Guard against VD. Keep straight – keep sober. You owe it to yourself, your comrades, your efficiency.'

A limerick published in an American medical journal in 1942 started with the lines:

> *There was a young man from Back Bay*
> *Who thought syphilis just went away,*
> *He believed that a chancre*
> *Was only a canker*
> *That healed in a week and a day . . .*

The poem continues for several more verses, describing the horrific effects of the disease. It was just one of many ditties aimed at warning against the follies of unprotected intercourse. At the end of the war there was also a powerful new drug – penicillin.

The story of penicillin

'It looks like a miracle.' Howard Florey, 1940

One of the most remarkable stories in the history of medicine was the discovery of penicillin and its development as an effective antibiotic for a range of bacterial infections, including syphilis, during the Second World War. Originally discovered as a mould by Alexander Fleming (1881–1955) in 1928, it was a team of Oxford scientists, including Howard Florey (1898–1968), Ernst Chain (1906–79) and Norman Heatley (1911–2004) at the Sir William Dunn School of Pathology, who first realized the clinical significance of penicillin in the early 1940s. From a momentous moment on 25 May 1940 when their experiments with mice suggested that 'penicillin could play a vital role in war medicine' to the first tests on humans and the first large-scale field trial in North Africa in 1943, Florey's prediction that 'it looks like a miracle' proved true.

Soldiers who would have previously lost limbs or died of gangrene survived with the help of penicillin. It was also used to treat cases of venereal disease which had been causing more casualties than the enemy forces, enabling men to be returned to the front fit for fighting. By the end of the war, there was no doubt that there was, at last, a powerful drug to treat a whole host of life-threatening bacterial infections. In October 1945, Fleming, Florey and Chain were jointly awarded the Nobel Prize in Physiology or Medicine and penicillin soon became the 'wonder drug' of the second half of the twentieth century. By the late 1950s, long-acting penicillin had completely replaced arsenic compounds for patients with syphilis, and penicillin still remains the main drug for the treatment of syphilis.

From VD to AIDS

In the second half of the twentieth century, a more open policy towards syphilis was established in many countries, with free VD clinics, posters to spread the message of prevention, and penicillin for those who needed it. The incidence of syphilis fell and, although it remained a dreaded disease, there was hope that it could be stamped out entirely.

One notorious episode in the twentieth-century history of syphilis, however, was the Tuskegee Syphilis Study in Macon County, Alabama. This became known as 'one of the most infamous medical experiments' ever carried out. Some 400 poor black male sharecroppers who had latent syphilis (but were told they had 'bad blood') were tracked and left untreated over a period of years from 1932 to 1972 so that the US Public Health Service could monitor the progress and effects of the disease. Even after penicillin came into use in the late 1940s, the men enrolled in this study were denied access to this effective cure. In 1997 President Bill Clinton formally apologized for this 'outrage to our commitment to integrity and equality for all our citizens', though by then many of those in the study, as well as their wives and children, had already died.

The recent HIV/AIDS pandemic has overshadowed the older fears of syphilis. Syphilis does, however, still remain a persistent, albeit easily diagnosed, preventable and treatable sexually transmitted infection (STI) in many parts of the world, with some 60 per cent of all deaths from syphilis being recorded in Africa. It is also an important cause of infertility. Congenital syphilis – now often called 'mother-to-child transmission of syphilis' to reflect the full spectrum of adverse outcomes, including stillbirths, neonatal deaths, premature and low birth weight infants, as well as deformities at birth – is a tragic and neglected public health problem, especially in the developing world.

The incidence of gonorrhoea is even higher than that of syphilis, and some countries are currently reporting strains of gonorrhoea which are resistant to front-line antibiotics. Antibiotic resistance for other STIs, though less common, also exists, making prevention and prompt treatment critical. Indeed, antibiotic resistance, a fear predicted by Alexander Fleming when accepting his Nobel Prize for penicillin, is a huge concern for many infectious bacterial diseases in the twenty-first century and has been described as a 'ticking time bomb' and the greatest 'global threat' of our time.

A newly emerging bacterial STI, chlamydia, is thought to be the most prevalent infectious disease in the USA after the common cold. Chlamydia leads to infertility in females if left undiagnosed and untreated. It is estimated that each year over 500 million people become ill with such STIs as syphilis, gonorrhoea and chlamydia, and some STIs can increase the risk of HIV acquisition three-fold or more. The direct physical, psychological and social consequences of STIs have a major impact on the quality of life. Yaws – a chronic bacterial infection caused by *T. pallidum* subspecies *pertunue* and related to syphilis (though spread through skin contact rather than sexual intercourse) – although massively reduced following campaigns to treat patients with penicillin in the 1950s and 1960s, still remains a serious and disfiguring disease especially amongst children in parts of the tropical world. It is the HIV/AIDS pandemic, however, with its devastating global impact, that looms largest in the public health arena of sexually transmitted diseases in the twenty-first century.

In retrospect, the emergence of the scourge of the 'great pox' in the 1490s bears frightening parallels with the escalation of HIV/AIDS in the late twentieth and early twenty-first centuries. The two diseases, while quite different from a pathological and immunological perspective, both share common risk factors, both have long, dormant periods during which patients show few symptoms, and both have generated huge debates about their origin, and how best to tackle treatment in the light of the associated moral issues.

TYPHUS

Typhus is an acute infectious disease that is transmitted by *Pediculus humanus corporis* – or, as it is more commonly known, the body louse. For centuries typhus was especially prevalent where there was overcrowding and poor standards of hygiene, causing horrible suffering and innumerable deaths. There are many graphic descriptions of epidemics during wars and famines, and on a number of occasions the disease has even changed the course of human history. However, a combination of vaccination, insecticides and antibiotics, as well as improvements in hygiene, has led to a decline in the incidence of typhus. It is now relatively uncommon, but does still occur in parts of Asia, Africa and Central and South America.

∾

In 1577 a Catholic bookbinder called Rowland Jencks was arrested for being 'foul-mouthed and saucy' and was tried in Oxford for distributing 'popish' books. His trial at the Assize Court at Oxford Castle attracted considerable interest from the citizens of the town and the dons of the university. The courtroom was crowded, stuffy and, above all, smelly. Jencks got off lightly. He was found guilty, had his ears cut off, and lived another thirty or so years. Many of the people who attended the trial, however, sickened and died from a horrible 'spotted fever'.

It is estimated that some 300 to 500 people, including many members of Oxford University, died during this episode, one of the so-called 'Black Assizes' that occurred in England during the sixteenth century.

Oxford's rival, Cambridge, also suffered, as a contemporary account from 1522 highlights: 'The justices and all the gentlemen, bailiffs and others, resorting thither, took such an infection, whether it were of the savour of the prisoners, or the filth of the house, that many gentlemen . . . thereof died, and almost all which were present were sore sick, and narrowly escaped their lives.'

These 'Black Assizes' occurred despite courtrooms being decked with aromatic herbs in the belief that it was the bad smells of the prisoners that caused contagion. Sweet-smelling scents, as well as the 'refreshing' vapours of garlic and vinegar, were thought to be the best way for the judges, jury and spectators to preserve their health and prevent 'jail fever' spreading from the felons in the dock to the assembled company.

A deadly nip

Historians suspect that the Oxford and Cambridge outbreaks, like many similar occurrences of 'jail fever', were caused by typhus – a disease that we now know is spread by body lice, or, more precisely, their infected faeces. Body lice live and lay their eggs in the warm clothes of humans (preferring woollen or cotton underwear to silk). They do not jump, hop or fly, but every now and again crawl out of the clothes onto the skin for a quick nip of blood. If the lice suck blood from a person suffering from typhus, they become infected and ultimately die from damage to their digestive organs. But – and this is the critical part – if they first move to another person (deserting the feverish or dead host) and then defecate, their infected excrement can easily be rubbed into the slightest scratch or wound, including those made by the louse itself. It is also possible for someone to be infected by sniffing or breathing in dried louse faeces in clothing or bedding; the typhus organism then enters the body via the mucous membranes in the nose or mouth.

Once infected with typhus, victims becomes feverish, even delirious; they experience an intense headache, with pains in the muscles and joints, and exhibit a vivid rash of bright red spots resembling flea bites. They also emit a vile stench – giving further credence to the formerly popular idea that bad smells cause disease. Death rates in untreated cases range from 10 to 40 per cent, increasing with age. Death results from toxaemia (the accumulation of toxic substances in the blood).

A 'hazy' disease

The term 'typhus' was first used in the eighteenth century. It is derived from the Greek word *typhos*, meaning 'smoky' or 'hazy', one of the characteristic symptoms of the disease being the stupor or dullness of mind experienced by its victims. It was not until the mid-nineteenth century, however, that typhus was clearly differentiated from typhoid and a number of other fevers. There are many accounts from the preceding centuries of foul and fatal epidemics variously known as 'spotted fever' in English, *fleck-fiëber* in German (after its characteristic rash), or *tabardillo* in Spanish (meaning 'red cloak'). The Veronese physician Girolamo Fracastoro in his 1546 book *De contagione et contagiosis morbis et eorum curatione* gives an account of a 'malignant and contagious fever' (most likely typhus) and describes the spots that appear on the arms and torso of the infected as *lenticulae* ('small lentils'), *puncticulae* ('small pricks') or *petechiae* ('flea bites'). One of his ideas about 'contagion', ironically, isn't far off the mark as far as typhus is concerned: 'I call fomites [from the Latin *fomes*, meaning 'tinder'] such things as clothes, linen, etc; which although not themselves corrupt, can nevertheless foster the *essential seeds* of the contagion and thus cause infection.' The disease was also named after the circumstances in which it broke out – hence it was known as 'jail fever', 'ship fever', 'famine fever' and 'camp fever'.

The close association of typhus with conditions of poor hygiene, overcrowding, cold, hunger and – above all – unwashed bodies and clothes, singled it out as a classic disease of dirt and distress. Along with the 'Black Assizes', typhus frequently broke out in prisons where the filthy and foul-smelling conditions of the wretched prisoners were deplorable. In the early part of the eighteenth century, for every person hanged at Tyburn, four would die of 'jail fever' in Newgate Prison before they could be executed. It also affected seafarers, beggars, slum dwellers and soldiers, and, in Europe from the late fifteenth century when the disease first made its appearance, it repeatedly devastated armies. Typhus – together with other pestilences such as dysentery (the 'bloody flux'), relapsing fever, scurvy and typhoid – was an almost invariable accompaniment of warfare, and such diseases accounted for far more losses than the actual fighting.

Battling typhus

One of the first documented typhus epidemics during wartime in Europe was in the late 1480s and early 1490s when, at the time of the Spanish siege of Granada, the last Moorish strong-hold in Spain, 'a malignant spotted fever' killed an estimated 17,000 Spanish soldiers. In the early sixteenth century, French troops near Naples lost some 30,000 soldiers to typhus. During the Thirty Years War in Europe (1618–48) typhus was a major problem. Both the Parliamentarian and Royalist armies in the English Civil War were ravaged by typhus in 1643, which spread throughout England, turning the country into 'one huge hos-pital'. A contemporary noted: 'This disease became so epidemical that a great part of the people was killed by it; and as soon as it had entered a house it ran through the same, that there was scarce one left well to administer to the sick.' Oliver Cromwell (1599–1658) and his army were paralysed by the 'Irish ague' (probably typhus) in Ireland in the winter of 1649. Throughout the eighteenth century, as national armies continued to fight, typhus took its inevitable toll in sedentary army camps and across Europe as marching armies spread the disease.

A 'murderous contagion'

One of the most striking epidemics of 'camp fever' occurred in 1812. That summer the French emperor Napoleon Bonaparte (1769–1821), with his 'Grande Armée' numbering more than half a million men, embarked on the ill-fated invasion of Russia. During the course of the advance many of his troops sickened or died of typhus and dysentery, and roughly constructed hospitals had to be erected en route for the wounded and the victims of disease. By mid-September, following the Battle of Borodino, Napoleon reached Moscow with a seriously depleted army. But the Russians were one step ahead of him. Taking with them most of the supplies and provisions, they had abandoned the city and put it to the torch. Napoleon entered a city that was silent, empty and smouldering. Despondent and wretched, the Grande Armée began its long retreat west as the ferocious Russian winter began to close in.

It was a bedraggled mob which started out on the long cold trek back to France. The hospitals set up on the outward march were by now in a deplorable condition – crowded, filthy, smelly and filled with unwashed, starving, diseased, frostbitten and emaciated men. They could hardly handle any more sick and dying soldiers. Horse meat became the staple diet of desperate soldiers – they even gnawed at leather or drank their own urine, for want of victuals. Some simply froze to death.

The Belgian military surgeon, J.R.L. De Kerckhove (1789-1867), in his account (published in 1836) of the campaign and the aftermath of the retreat from Moscow described typhus as a 'contagion meurtrière':

Typhus, which did not cease to reign with fury among our troops, spread more and more to the inhabitants, who, forced to give us shelter and food, were not only obliterated by our passage, but became prey to a murderous contagion, a fatal present that we gave them, and which equally caused a prodigious mortality amongst civilians.

Countless soldiers of the original Grande Armée (possibly as many as 400,000) died in this disastrous campaign. Napoleon's dream of a vast French empire extending to Russia and beyond had come to a staggering halt. Less than a quarter of the men had died as a result of enemy action; the rest had succumbed to a combination of disease, exhaustion, extreme cold and hunger, with typhus claiming the lion's share, and even changing the course of history.

Famine fever

Over the next few years, carried by the louse-ridden remnants of the Grande Armée and the equally infested Russian cavalry who pursued them, typhus spread far and wide across Europe. In 1815–19, the period immediately after the Napoleonic Wars, a combination of severe cold weather, widespread crop failure and the uprooting of starving peasants sparked another major epidemic in Europe, and many thousands perished.

Some decades later, Ireland was gripped by a terrible famine when a fungal blight destroyed the potato crop – the staple diet of the Irish peasantry. During the 'Great Irish Famine' (or the 'Great Hunger' as it was also known) of 1845–9, around a million people died – some from direct starvation, but the overwhelming majority from famine-related diseases such as typhus, relapsing fever and dysentery. Another million or so fled the country. Typhus was spread rapidly by bands of roving and ravenous beggars. Many of those still alive emigrated in desperation to England, Scotland, Canada and the United States, but great numbers fell sick in transit on what became known as the 'coffin ships'. The population of Ireland fell from possibly as many as 8.5 million to 6.5 million, and, while the exact figures remain subject to debate, one commentator noted that in some parts of the country the only living things left were the rats and dogs devouring the bodies of the dead.

The 'Irish fever' spread to the urban slums of England, and in North America raged amongst the immigrant population. In Quebec, Canada, a quarantine island, the Grosse-Île, located in the Gulf of St Lawrence, was used to receive surviving and sick passengers. Of those who reached the island in the summer of 1847, many, after their long voyage, were already in a deplorable condition and thousands quickly succumbed to 'ship fever' (typhus). They were buried in a mass grave during what became known as that 'summer of sorrow'. It has been said that: 'The Great Hunger began with an ailment of potatoes and ended with a pestilence of humans.'

The body louse revealed

The first breakthrough in the understanding of the epidemiology and ecology of typhus occurred in the United States. It had generally been assumed that typhus and typhoid were varieties of the same fever, until, in the winter of 1835–6, the American physician William Wood Gerhard (1809–72) studied an outbreak of typhus amongst recent Irish immigrants living in a slum in Philadelphia. In 1829 the French physician Pierre Louis (1787–1872) had coined the word 'typhoid' (meaning 'like typhus'), and Gerhard, who had previously worked in both Britain and France, had developed a hunch while he was in Paris that typhoid (common in France) was different from typhus (common in England and Ireland). Other leading physicians contributed to the debate, including London physician William Jenner (1815–98), who distinguished typhus clinically from typhoid, and by the 1860s most agreed that typhus and typhoid were distinct entities. A key feature showed up at autopsies: typhoid victims had inflamed lesions in their small intestines, but these were absent from typhus victims.

It took another seventy years or so before the final clue as to the cause of typhus came to light. In 1909–10 Charles Nicolle

(1866–1936), the French director of the Institut Pasteur in Tunis, North Africa, showed that it was the body louse – *Pediculus humanus corporis* – that was the main vector for the disease. He observed that patients who were stripped of their clothing, shaved and washed before entering the hospital in Tunis did not go on to infect others. He then went on to prove his hypothesis experimentally. Summing up his conclusions when he won a Nobel Prize in 1928, he recalled: 'It could only be the louse. It was the louse.'

However, at the time of his discovery of the louse, Nicolle and his colleagues had no idea what the actual infectious agent was. The American pathologist Howard Taylor Ricketts (1871–1910) and the eastern European zoologist Stanislaus J.M. von Prowazek (1875–1915) were both close to identifying the causative agent when they tragically died of typhus. In 1916 the Brazilian scientist Henrique da Rocha Lima (1879–1956) isolated and named the agent responsible for typhus as *Rickettsia prowazekii* in honour of their discoveries.

Since then a number of other so-called rickettsial diseases or 'spotted fevers' have been identified which are carried by lice, ticks, mites, fleas and other arthropods; these include Rocky Mountain spotted fever, endemic flea-borne typhus (murine typhus), and Queensland tick typhus. The disease-causing agents, or rickettsiae, are gram-negative bacteria and, like other bacteria, possess both DNA and RNA. However, they differ from most other bacteria in that they are incapable of living independently in the environment and grow only in cells.

Once the role of the body louse in the transmission of typhus was recognized, many of the patterns of past epidemics made sense: insanitary, crowded conditions, cold winters, thick layers of unwashed clothes, humans huddled together – all were ideal environments for the spread of typhus. While early attempts to clean up insanitary places affected by such diseases as typhus and cholera and encourage personal hygiene may have helped – including the work and influence of Florence Nightingale who had witnessed the appalling suffering from these 'filth diseases' in the Crimean War in 1854–6 – the discovery of the role of the louse and its mode of transmitting typhus now provided a vital key to prevention: delousing.

Two 'lousy' world wars

Typhus did, nonetheless, ravage Europe during both the First and Second World Wars. In both conflicts it seemed to have a very marked predilection for the Eastern Front. In 1914 typhus (like the war) erupted in Serbia, and within the first six months over 150,000 had died of typhus. Russia, too, was hit exceptionally hard, in spite of efforts to control the disease. Between 1917 and 1922 there were an estimated 25 to 30 million cases of typhus and 3 million deaths in eastern Europe and what, by the end of the period, had become the Soviet Union. This experience led the Soviet leader Vladimir Ilyich Lenin (1870–1924) to declare: 'Either socialism will defeat the louse, or the louse will defeat socialism.'

On the Western Front in the First World War strict measures were taken to prevent a catastrophic outbreak of typhus – and here an understanding of the vector and the mode of transmission certainly paid off. Mobile laboratories, laundries and delousing stations were set up, and soldiers and prisoners of war were bathed, disinfected and shaved. Bodies and clothing were deloused, a process involving steam treatment, fumigation and rubbing with anti-lice powders – getting rid of lice in the soldiers' underclothes became one of the daily rituals of life. It is said that the mortality of lice may have been the greatest in the history of the world.

Despite determined efforts, and almost no outbreaks of epidemic typhus on the Western Front, another louse-borne disease – which became known as 'trench fever' – tormented and incapacitated more than a million soldiers. Trench fever was a mild infection also spread by the body louse. Although it did not cause huge fatalities, the irritation from the louse was an ever-present nuisance even with the delousing measures, and soldiers often tried to rid themselves of infestation by stubbing their burning cigarette ends onto the lice. Trench fever caused a greater loss of manpower during the war than did any other malady except the Spanish flu (the 1918–19 influenza pandemic).

Between the First World War and the end of the Second World War there were two medical advances that became vital in preventing an escalation of typhus, especially amongst the Allied troops: a vaccine and an insecticide. In the early 1930s, the Polish biologist Rudolf Weigl (1883–1957) had developed the first vaccine against epidemic typhus; his vaccines were smuggled into Jewish ghettos. By the late 1930s Herald R. Cox (1907–86) of the US Public Health Service produced a different vaccine that, though not fully effective in preventing typhus, did at least reduce the virulence of the disease for those military personnel to whom it was administered in the last few years of the Second World War. Previous attempts to produce a vaccine, like Weigl's, had been based on grinding up the guts or faeces of infected lice. The 'Cox vaccine' – based on culturing *rickettsiae* in the yolks of hens' eggs – was the first effective and commercially viable vaccine for typhus.

Over the next few years the powerful insecticide DDT (dichloro-diphenyl-trichloroethane), first synthesized in 1874, was given its first airing. A typhus epidemic in recently liberated Naples in the winter of 1943–4 was brought to a halt with the use of DDT. The Italian population was living in abominable conditions, demoralized and often starving after years of war. So effective was the new insecticide that long queues of people formed at disinfecting stations eager to be given a thorough delousing. DDT, which could be used as a powder, was administered through 'blowing machines'. No longer did soldiers have to undress and have their underwear deloused – the blowing machines could direct DDT straight to the lice and zap them on the spot. During this epidemic, some 84,000 kgs (185,000 pounds) of DDT were used to delouse over 3 million people between mid-December 1943 and the end of May 1944. This wartime testing of DDT was followed immediately by the first large-scale use of DDT against malaria. Swiss chemist Paul Hermann Müller (1899–1965), who had discovered DDT's insecticidal action in 1939, was awarded a Nobel Prize in 1948.

Typhus did, however, continue to be a severe problem in the Nazi concentration camps, in spite of strict delousing measures for all POWs. The Jewish teenager Anne Frank (1929–45), who left a moving diary of her life and experiences, died in March 1945 in the Bergen-Belsen concentration camp, probably from a combination of typhus fever, hunger and maltreatment. Serious epidemics of typhus again struck the Eastern Front, while its relative, 'scrub typhus' or tsutsugamushi (a rickettsial disease spread by mites or 'chiggers') caused many casualties in the Pacific theatre of war.

Typhus today

By the late 1940s broad-spectrum antibiotics were proving effective against the rickettsiae that cause typhus. In many civilian settings, improvements in cleanliness – both personal and environmental hygiene – have also helped to reduce the prevalence of body lice infestation and the spread of typhus. Globally typhus is now fairly rare, but there are pockets of the disease in some colder, mountainous or poverty-stricken areas of central and eastern Africa, Central and South America, and Asia. In recent years, most outbreaks have taken place in Burundi, Ethiopia and Rwanda. Epidemics may continue to occur during war and famine and in conditions of overcrowding and poor hygiene, such as in prisons and refugee camps.

'Feeling lousy' – nit-picking and head lice

When most people think of lice they now think of head lice (*Pediculus humanus capitis*) and their tiny eggs, known as nits. According to the prevailing medical view today, head lice do not carry typhus or any other infectious disease (although some of the scientists who worked on typhus in the early twentieth century thought otherwise). Head lice are about 3mm in length; they grip tightly onto the hairs of the head and feed on human blood. Itching from head lice bites can be intensely irritating.

Head lice infestations – so common today among young schoolchildren – date back thousands of centuries, as the many ancient nit combs found by archaeologists attest. The expression 'going over it with a fine-tooth comb' serves as testimony to our long and uncomfortably intimate relationship with lice. Humans are also host to pubic or crab lice (*Phthirus pubis*) and researchers have found both head and pubic lice on South American mummies dating back 2,000 years. Egyptian priests, according to Herodotus in the fifth century BC, were required to wear freshly washed linen clothes, fumigate their orifices and shave their bodies all over every day 'to keep off lice or anything else unpleasant'. The Roman naturalist Pliny the Elder (AD 23–79), who died during the eruption of Vesuvius, suggested bathing in viper broth as a cure, while Montezuma (1466–1520), the Aztec emperor, paid people to pick nits off his subjects. He then had the nits dried and saved them in his treasury.

Louse infestation was a major problem in medieval times. Etiquette lessons were given to young members of the nobility as to when and how to dispose of one's lice. It was very much frowned upon to scratch or attempt to remove one's lice while in company, except in the most intimate circles. However, for some, lice were called 'pearls of poverty' and a mark of saintliness. After Archbishop Thomas à Becket (*c.*1118–70) was murdered in Canterbury Cathedral on 29 December 1170, his body, in its many layers of clothing, lay in the cathedral all night. One chronicler noted that, as the corpse began to grow cold, 'the vermin boiled over like water in a simmering cauldron and the onlookers burst into alternate fits of weeping and laughter.'

But others continued to complain. One Renaissance writer noted that both men and women 'swarmed with fleas and lice, some stank at the armpits, others had stinking feet and the majority were foul of breath.' Samuel Pepys recorded in his diary on 23 January 1669: 'When all comes to all she [Pepys' wife] finds that I am lousy having found in my head and body above twenty lice little and great, which I wonder at, being more than I have had I believe these twenty years.' Pepys changed his clothes and cut his hair short, 'so shall be rid of them.' Frustratingly, he also found nits in his newly purchased wig, which, he wrote, 'vexed me cruelly.' Amongst popular remedies at the time was that suggested by Nicholas Culpeper (1616–54), the English herbalist, who recommended tobacco juice to kill lice.

Scientists tried to understand the life cycle of these wretched creatures. Some seventeenth-century observers realized that nits on the head were eggs cemented onto the hairs of the scalp while those on the body were attached to clothing or sometimes body hairs. The famous Dutch microscopist Antonie van Leeuwenhoek (1632–1723) was interested in observing lice. He experimented by placing two lice on top of a black stocking on his leg and observed about ninety eggs ten days later followed by twenty-five lice another ten days later (after the eggs had hatched). He was so disgusted at the sight of so many lice that he threw his stocking containing them into the street.

The British scientist Robert Hooke (1635–1703) published in 1665 a book called *Micrographia* detailing his studies with the microscope. He provided an excellent illustration of a louse clutching a hair and wrote: 'this is a creature so officious that 'twill be known to everyone at one time or another, so busie and so impudent, that it will be intruding itself into everyone's company . . . and will never be quiet till it has drawn blood.'

Over the following centuries, people scratched their heads to come up with an ultimate solution to the ubiquitous head louse. In Victorian England, various 'sanitary associations' were formed to offer help to mothers, including 'delousing' their children. By the early twentieth century, school nurses began to play a role in children's health. The 'Nitty Nora' image of the 'nit nurse' visiting schools brandishing her nit comb will be familiar to many British readers. Although 'nit nurses' were phased out in the 1980s and '90s, some parents and teachers have recently called for their return as head lice infestation continues to plague youngsters.

Meanwhile, for domestic use, there is a range of treatments for head lice including the application of topical insecticides, such as pyrethrin or permethrin, as well as medicated shampoos and various herbal remedies. Special nit combs, not unlike those used in ancient times, continue to be a popular way of detecting and removing the lice and nits from children's hair.

Indeed, visitors to the newly opened Mary Rose Museum in Portsmouth Historic Dockyard will be struck by the similarity of the old and the new methods of 'delousing'. Tudor nit combs (including 500-year-old Tudor nits!) can be seen amongst arte-facts on display recovered in 1982 from Henry VIII's flagship, the *Mary Rose*, which was built in 1510 and sank in 1545.

Rats, Lice and Zinsser

'Swords and lances, arrows, machine guns, and even high explosives have had far less power over the fates of the nations than the typhus louse, the plague flea, and the yellow-fever mosquito.' Hans Zinsser, *Rats, Lice and History*, 1935

For anyone itching to read more about lice, the classic book by Hans Zinsser (1878–1940), *Rats, Lice and History*, first pub-lished in 1935, remains a gripping read. Zinsser, an American bacteriologist, was an authority on typhus and, together with Nathan Brill (1860–1925), is remembered by the eponymous Brill-Zinsser disease, a delayed recrudescence of epidemic louse-borne typhus. In his book, also known as a 'biography of typhus', Zinsser recounts the fate of many who over the centuries succumbed to the torture of the human body louse (as well as many other nasty bugs) and he reminds us, too, that the louse itself comes to a miserable end: 'in eight days he sickens, in ten days he is in extremis, on the eleventh or twelfth his tiny body turns red with blood extravasated from his bowel, and he gives up his little ghost'. A sobering thought.

Although typhus poses less of a threat today than when Zinsser was studying and writing about the disease, recent studies have suggested that the flying squirrel (*Glaucomys volans*) in North America acts as host to the *Rickettsia prowazekii* bacteria – adding a new dimension to our understanding of the disease. We should perhaps heed Zinsser's concluding warning in *Rats, Lice and History*: 'Typhus is not dead. It will live on for centuries . . .'

CHOLERA

Cholera is an extremely unpleasant and potentially fatal disease caused by the bacterium *Vibrio cholerae*. The symptoms are hideous: victims are convulsed with pain, and suffer violent vomiting and uncontrollable watery diarrhoea. Many, if their severe dehydration is not treated, turn blue and die within a short time. In the nineteenth century, pandemics of cholera spread out from the Ganges Delta in the Indian subcontinent, killing millions of people around the world. Cholera became one of the most feared and terrible scourges to emerge after bubonic plague. John Snow's request for the authorities to remove the handle of the Broad Street pump in London in 1854, based on his ideas that the disease was waterborne, is one of the most famous public health interventions of the Victorian era. In the latter part of the nineteenth century, scientists were, eventually, able to identify the bacterium and confirm that cholera is spread when drinking water or food becomes contaminated with faecal matter containing cholera bacteria. Improvements in sanitation have made cholera uncommon in the Western world, but it still poses a threat to many people in parts of Asia, Africa and Latin America.

∾

In October 1831 a local newspaper in the port of Sunderland in north-east England warned its readers of a dangerous new epidemic heading their way: Asiatic cholera. Its early symptoms, according to the *Sunderland Herald*, included: 'a sick stomach . . . vomiting or purging of a liquid like rice-water . . . the face becomes sharp and shrunken, the eyes sink and look wild, the lips, face and . . . whole surface of the body a leaden, blue, purple, [or] black.' The reporter noted that there was, as yet, no specific treatment for the disease, but reassured readers that, 'the greatest confidence may be expressed in the intelligence and enthusiasm of the doctors of this country who will surely find a method of cure.'

Sunderland was hit by cholera in the following months. Isabella Hazard, aged twelve years, who lived in Low Street near Fish Quay in Sunderland, where her parents ran a pub popular with ship-workers, was one of its first victims in England. After twice attending church on Sunday, 16 October 1831, she was suddenly struck down with vomiting, torrents of watery diarrhoea and an unquenchable thirst. Her eyes were sunk in their sockets, her features were unrecognizable, her legs seized with terrible spasms, her pulse scarcely perceptible and her whole body freezing. Most alarmingly, her skin had turned a terrible dark blue. She died soon after the onset of her symptoms.

This was Asiatic cholera's first visitation to the Western hemisphere and, despite the Sunderland newspaper's optimism, there was no cure.

Asiatic cholera: a 'new' disease?

The word 'cholera' is derived from the Greek *cholē*, meaning 'bile', and *rhein*, 'to flow'. The term (or the fuller Latin term *cholera morbus*) had been used since ancient times to describe any sporadic diarrhoeal affliction – though diarrhoea (also from the Greek, and meaning 'to flow through') is a symptom of many diseases. However, the devastating and unstoppable diarrhoea (described as 'rice-water' stools) that characterized the Asiatic cholera was believed to be quite unlike anything that had been experienced before. Indeed, we now know that its watery contents contain bits of the body's gut as well as swarms of cholera bacteria, and it is rapid dehydration that leads to the shrunken features and the bluish tinge, accompanied by shock and, finally, death.

It is hard to say for sure whether the cholera pandemics that erupted and spread over the globe in the nineteenth century were different from earlier episodes of *cholera morbus*. Contemporaries, and historians since, have generally agreed that the origin of the so-called 'modern' great pandemics of cholera lay in the populous Ganges-Brahmaputra Delta in India (where the disease had probably been endemic since ancient times) – hence, the adoption in the West of the term 'Asiatic cholera'. The first pandemic began in 1817 when cholera spread from its natural heartland across much of India to China, Indonesia and the Caspian Sea. It did not, however, continue to move any further west, and by 1825 it had petered out, though by this time some 1 to 2 million had died of the disease. Since then there have been six other pandemics, including the most recent beginning in the early 1960s. Many mysteries still surround the sudden eruption and cessation of these pandemics.

It was the second pandemic (*c.*1827/8 to *c.*1836/8) and subsequent pandemics of the nineteenth century that engulfed nearly all the populated regions of the world. Indeed, in 1831 the British medical journal *The Lancet* produced a 'Map of the

Progress of Cholera in Asia, Europe and Africa' highlighting its trajectory and predicting its imminent arrival in England itself. This was one of the earliest (and, for the time, quite remarkable) maps to document the spread of disease in both 'time' and 'space'. With expanding empires and towns and cities interlinked through long-distance trade networks, the threat of a 'new' disease reaching the shores of England was terrifying, as one doctor emphasized when cholera did first strike in 1831/2: 'Our other plagues were home-bred, and part of ourselves, as it were . . . but the cholera was something outlandish, unknown, monstrous . . . a terror which . . . seemed to recall the great epidemics of the Middle Ages.'

In the 1830s, by the time the disease had reached Moscow, Hamburg, Sunderland, London, Paris, Quebec and New York City, Asiatic cholera was well and truly on the world map. Carrying a mortality rate of at least 50 per cent, and conveyed unwittingly over land and sea by traders, soldiers, sailors, pilgrims, refugees and migrants, the nineteenth-century pandemics (lasting from five to thirty years) followed a somewhat different trajectory. But all who found themselves in the path of the dreaded disease – or 'King Cholera' – were terrified that they would be the next victim. At the end of March 1832, as the people of Paris were enjoying a carnival, one of the harlequins suddenly collapsed. Underneath his merry mask his face had shrivelled and turned a violet blue. Laughter and dancing ceased as other masked entertainers succumbed to the same dreadful fate. They were quickly carted off – many still in their costumes – to the Hôtel-Dieu Hospital, to suffer the gruesome and humiliating death of the cholera victim. The London journal *Quarterly Review* of 1832 described cholera as 'one of the most terrible pestilences which have ever desolated the earth.'

Cholera created mass panic across Europe and North America. In New York City in 1832, for example, when it first hit the continent, thousands either fled or died from the disease. The medical profession had little to offer, though a wide variety of nostrums and quack remedies were tried, including all the common therapies from bloodletting, purging and steam baths to opiates, alcohol and infusions of mercury and arsenic. A disease producing such radical changes in the body was seen to require equally radical therapies – however bizarre and dangerous they may seem to us today.

Cholera hospitals were set up and the sick were 'carted' away, much to the horror of relatives who, as in Liverpool in 1832, feared their loved ones would be deliberately killed so that doctors could use the corpses for anatomical dissection. Desperate citizens reacted angrily, and 'Cholera Riots' broke out in Liverpool as well as in Paris and elsewhere in Europe. In some places police and troops had to be brought in to enforce isolation and quarantine regulations – scenes reminiscent of Ebola when it first erupted in West Africa in 2014.

Homeopaths in the mid-nineteenth century offered 'alternative' forms of treatment. Homeopathy (based on the principle of 'like cures like' and the law of 'infinitesimals' (serial dilution) – the smaller the dose, the more potent the medicine) had been introduced by the German physician Samuel Hahnemann (1775–1843). Like a number of physicians, Hahnemann had been horrified at such 'heroic' practices as bloodletting and the use of toxic drugs, and wanted to focus instead on using the healing powers of nature. During epidemics such as that of cholera in London in 1854, statistics indicated that mortality rates in homeopathic hospitals were lower than those in conventional medical hospitals where the treatments were often harmful and did little or nothing to combat the disease.

Trying to understand the cause of cholera – a miasmatic or contagious disease?

Cholera affected young and old, rich and poor, but its striking epidemiological characteristic in the nineteenth century was its devastating impact on centres of pilgrimage such as the Ganges and Mecca, and on the stinking slums of the rapidly expanding industrial towns of Europe and North America. The shock of the disease – its sudden onslaught and the haste with which death followed – was matched by its foul symptoms. Vomit and profuse diarrhoea produced a sickening and humiliating stench, and when cholera struck the burgeoning towns of Europe and the USA it added one more intolerable smell to the noxious vapours already oozing from dung-fouled streets, festering tenements, unwashed bodies, belching factories, stinking slaughterhouses, putrid rivers, overflowing cesspools and open sewers that were so often features of everyday life. Words cannot adequately evoke the stenches that assaulted the noses of our nineteenth-century forebears.

The doctors who sought to understand and deal with cholera were totally confused as to how and why this 'new' disease was spreading. Furious debates ensued. The miasmatists (or anti-contagionists) were convinced that, like other epidemic fevers that afflicted the poor, cholera's root lay in the stench and squalor of the slums. Edwin Chadwick (1800–1890), the English social reformer and sanitarian, wrote: 'All smell is, if it be intense, immediate, acute disease; and eventually we may say that, by depressing the system and rendering it susceptible to the action of other causes, all smell is disease.' In 1842 he published his influential *Report of an Inquiry into the Sanitary Conditions of the Labouring Population of Great Britain*, recommending improvements in sewerage, water supply and drainage.

William Farr (1807–83), the English medical statistician, said that lethal miasmas were like a mad dog prowling forth from the city's cesspools and sewers. Chadwick, Farr and others in Europe and the USA, including Lemuel Shattuck (1793–1859) in Boston, amplified their arguments with 'sanitary' or 'effluvia' maps, graphs, tables and vital statistics. They looked for correlations between the distribution of cholera cases and deaths and a range of factors – from meteorological variables to altitude and elevation above sea level and rivers, and from the number of inhabitants per house to income and value of houses.

Their findings, in particular, showed a clear association between the filthiest, most overcrowded, lowest-lying or poorest parts of the cities and the highest mortality rates. In Bethnal Green in London, the average age of death was sixteen years. In the more salubrious areas, it was forty-five years. Infant mortality rates in the worst parts of London, Liverpool, Manchester, Paris, New York and elsewhere were shocking – as many as one in three or four babies dying before their first birthday. Life expectancy was very low – little more than twenty to thirty years among the working classes. Cleaning up the squalor, washing the 'Great Unwashed', sorting out the stenches and foul sanitation of urban and industrial areas and reducing poverty by, first, combating infectious diseases such as cholera, were high on the agenda of the nineteenth-century miasmatists and social reformers.

Their 'opponents' – the contagionists – observed and also mapped the path of Asiatic cholera as it tracked its way from east to west, from ports to inland towns, via ships, river boats, canals, wagon trains and (later) railways. The contagionists believed that the disease must be transmitted by some poison passed from person to person. The only way to prevent the disease spreading, they argued, was through strict quarantine measures. However, this posed a threat to the commercial activities of the industrializing nations, and international sanitary conferences were set up to debate the question. In 1851 delegates from a number of countries met in Paris for the first international convention on quarantines. A second followed in 1866 in Constantinople – though their agenda, to create a single system of maritime quarantine that might halt the spread of cholera (as well as bubonic plague), floundered on disagreements over what cholera was, how it was spread, and therefore how it might be stopped. In fact, there was often confusing overlap between the ideas of the miasmatists and the contagionists, with some joining the debate as contingent-contagionists.

There were even others who saw cholera as just one aspect of the moral and physical degradation of the working classes. Wherever there was rottenness, drunkenness and uncleanliness, there poverty and disease struck most viciously and – they argued – deservedly. Countering such arguments, humanitarians tried to convince their contemporaries that the poor were diseased not because of their immoral state of mind or body but because they were living and working in conditions of appalling filth, hunger and wretchedness. Cholera, with its spectacularly ghastly effects, was evidence not of moral justice but of human injustice.

In his 1845 book, *The Condition of the Working Classes in England*, Friedrich Engels (1820–95), the German political theorist, described a typical urban scene in Manchester. Everywhere he went he met 'pale, lank, narrow-chested, hollow-eyed ghosts' cooped up in houses that were mere 'kennels to sleep and die in': 'Passing along a rough bank, among stakes and washing lines, one penetrates into the chaos of small one-storied, one-roomed huts, in most of which there is no artificial floor; kitchen, living and sleeping-room all in one'. Engels went on to note the piles of residue and offal, and the constant disgusting stench. Others depicted the miserable conditions of the hordes of people who were crammed into basement rooms through which the effluence from outside privies oozed. Such conditions aroused horror and indignation in Engels and other sympathetic observers.

Even the poor themselves recognized the threat that cholera posed, given their appalling insanitary conditions, as one appeal printed in *The Times* in 1849 made clear:

Sur
May we . . . beseech your proteckshion and power. We are Sur, as it may be, livin in a Wilderness, so far as the rest of London knows anything of us, or as the rich and great people care about. We live in muck and filth. We aint got no priviz, no dust bins, no drains, no water-splies, and no drain or suer in the hole place. The Suer Company, in Greek Street, Soho Square, all great, rich powerfool men take no notice watsomdever of our complaints. The Stenche of a Gulley-hole is disgustin. We all of us suffer, and numbers are ill, and if the Cholera comes Lord help us.

The diseases that afflicted the poor in such slums were numerous – typhus, typhoid, smallpox, tuberculosis, measles, dysentery, infantile diarrhoea, diphtheria, scarlet fever, rickets, whooping cough, bronchitis, pneumonia, to name but a few. Many also met their end in accidents, especially in factories and mines. Some were poisoned by industrial toxins and adulterated food, or exhausted by hard labour and hunger. But it was 'King Cholera' with its sudden and dramatic impact (although overall accounting for a lower demographic toll than some other diseases) that prompted the greatest concern and confusion. What was its cause and how was it transmitted? As an editorial in *The Lancet* in 1853 questioned: 'What is cholera? Is it a fungus, an insect, a miasma, an electrical disturbance, a deficiency of ozone, a morbid off-scouring of the intestinal canal? We know nothing; we are at sea in a whirlpool of conjecture.'

As the debates rumbled on, one man found the answer – or thought he had.

Dying for a drink and 'turning off' the cholera

'According to the present system of London Water Supply, a portion of the inhabitants of the metropolis are made to consume, in some form or another, a portion of their own excrement, and moreover to pay for the privilege.' Arthur Hassall (1817–94), British physician and microscopist, 1850

In 1849 the satirical magazine *Punch* printed a cartoon entitled 'Mistaking cause for effect', in which a young boy comments to his little friend as he watches a man pumping drinking water from a street standpipe: 'I say, Tommy, I'm blow'd if there isn't a man a turning on the cholera.' In that year, with cholera once more raging (in its third pandemic, *c*.1839–61), a British doctor, John Snow (1813–58), had published a short pamphlet (*On the*

Mode of Communication of Cholera) – setting out the radical idea that cholera was spread through contaminated drinking water. In 1854 Snow attempted to 'turn off the cholera' by requesting the removal of the handle of the Broad Street pump in Soho, London.

Born in York, Snow had witnessed the horrors of the second cholera pandemic in a mining village near Newcastle-upon-Tyne in late 1831, shortly after its initial outbreak in nearby Sunderland. He later established himself in London as an expert on anaesthesia. His practice was close to the bustling but squalid Golden Square area of Soho, where people were crammed into overcrowded housing – eating, sleeping, washing, drinking and defecating within 250 yards of the Broad Street pump. Snow became convinced that cholera might be caused by swallowing 'some as-yet-unidentified' infective particle in sewage-contaminated water. The River Thames was, as Snow observed, in effect an open sewer into which excrement was discharged.

Most people in Victorian cities like London relied on using a privy – variously known as the gong house, bog house, place of easement or temple of convenience – which was often shared by as many as forty people. Night-soil men (known from medieval times as 'gong-fermors') collected the contents of privies from some houses and dung heaps – usually at night. Human excrement was sold and recycled as fertilizer for farmers' fields. Privies in poor districts were rarely emptied, however, and invariably seeped into underground pits or cesspools, from where they eventually contaminated water supplies. In the early nineteenth century in London, flushing water closets (WCs) were installed in the houses of the rich. Unfortunately, without a functioning sewerage system to connect to the WCs, their contents made their way back into the drinking water supplies, making matters even worse. There was little in the way of piped water to houses, and people queued, drew and paid for their water from street standpipes – such as the Broad Street pump – which often contained the recycled contents of both the privies and new WCs.

The year 1854 proved to be one of the worst years in the global history of cholera. In the oppressively hot August of that year, the baby daughter of Thomas and Sarah Lewis of 40 Broad Street, Soho, fell ill with vomiting and green watery stools that emitted 'a pungent smell'. Sarah, desperately trying to cope with her baby's soiled nappies, washed them in a bucket and threw some of the water into a cesspool in the basement at the front of their house. The following day their upstairs neighbours fell ill, and a few days later whole families in the surrounding area began to sicken – often dying together in their dark, squalid rooms. Within ten days, upwards of 500 local residents were dead.

John Snow inspected with meticulous detail the drinking habits of the victims of this outbreak. He noted that most of those who caught cholera were drawing their drinking water from the Broad Street pump – which was right outside No. 40 Broad Street. In a nearby workhouse and brewery, both of which had their own private water supplies, there were almost no casualties. On 7 September 1854, two weeks after the local outbreak began, Snow persuaded the authorities to remove the Broad Street pump's handle, which they did the following day.

When John Snow showed the Reverend Henry Whitehead (1825–96) his now famous 'ghost map' of the cholera deaths and the location of the water pumps in the Golden Square area, drawn up in the autumn of 1854, he too became convinced by Snow's theory. Whitehead, a young curate who had tirelessly worked to mitigate the worst effects of the outbreak, conducted his own bit of detective work. He interviewed residents and drew up his own map, and discovered in the death registers the tragic record of the little baby, who, he subsequently concluded, was the first case and 'cause' of the transmission of cholera. The cause of her death was given as follows: 'At 40, Broad Street, 2d September, a daughter, aged five months: exhaustion, after an attack of diarrhoea *four days previous to death*.' Sarah Lewis, her mother, survived, but the father, Thomas, also caught cholera and died two weeks later. Sarah continued to throw contaminated excreta – this time her husband's – into the cesspool, but, fortunately for others, by this time the Broad Street pump had been temporarily turned off (and, although subsequently restored, was eventually closed down in 1866).

Today, next to the site of the pump in Broad Street (now Broadwick Street) is the John Snow pub, which commemorates the significance of Snow's discovery. It was, however, his next piece of epidemiological mapping – his experiment 'on the grandest scale' – that for Snow confirmed his waterborne contamination hypothesis. He investigated the more widespread but less sensational outbreak of cholera that occurred in London south of the River Thames between July and October 1854. He compared the number of cholera victims whose drinking water was supplied by two competing water companies – one of which (the Southwark and Vauxhall company) drew its water from a polluted stretch of the Thames downstream from several London sewers; the other (the Lambeth company) had, since Snow's first 1848/9 study, moved its works upstream out of reach of sewage. Death rates for the Southwark and Vauxhall customers were considerably higher than those of the Lambeth customers (by at least fourteen-fold during the early phases of the epidemic) and

Snow's findings again showed that cholera deaths were linked to water contaminated with sewage.

Where the miasmatists had been convinced that all smell was disease, Snow was now able to pinpoint, in the case of cholera, one particularly noxious source of disease – foul water, not foul air. And while the contagionists had provided a strong case for the infectious nature of the disease, Snow showed that cholera (which affected the intestines rather than the lungs) was not directly transmitted through airborne particles, but by drinking contaminated water. The cycle of cholera was clear, but more subtle than hitherto suspected: what was evacuated in faeces and flushed into the cesspools or rivers contained the infective (albeit then 'invisible') particles that then made their way back into the pumped drinking water and the gastrointestinal tracts of its victims.

Sanitary reform and the sewers of London

The removal of the Broad Street pump handle has now become perhaps the leading symbol of public health action in the mid-nineteenth century. What in retrospect could have been a 'magic' medical breakthrough was not immediately appreciated, however. Indeed, some (including Snow) thought that by the time the Broad Street pump handle had been removed, cholera in Soho was already on the wane. Many others expressed scepticism – wasn't this just a coincidence? But, although Snow's clever medical detective work, and the publication of his expanded second edition of *On the Mode of Communication of Cholera* in 1855 containing the results of his 'grand experiment', did not immediately lead to a widespread acceptance of his waterborne theory, there were other forces at work that continued to convince 'sanitarians' in many parts of the Western world that the populous towns, as well as the countryside, needed a big clean-up.

The 'Great Stink' of London in the summer of 1858, when the House of Commons had to break off its proceedings and soak the curtains in chloride of lime to cover up the stench, showed that the time was ripe for drastic sanitary reform. One of the key developments that followed this 'miasmatic scare' was the construction of underground sewers in London. Joseph Bazalgette (1819–91), Chief Engineer to the Metropolitan Board of Works, was put in charge of this project and created an ambitious and complex system of effective sewers and pumping stations in London between 1859 and 1875.

His operations were designed to remove the 'stink' and incidence of cholera by taking the sewage eastwards to be discharged into the River Thames downstream and away from heavily populated areas. Although this was based on the miasmatic rather than Snow's (correct) waterborne theory, it has been seen as one of the sanitary marvels of the Victorian age, and a number of scholars have suggested that Bazalgette can be credited with saving more lives than any other Victorian public health official.

Cholera and the Crimea

At the same time as John Snow was coming up with his waterborne theory and others were still dealing with foul stenches, another key figure in the story is Florence Nightingale (1820–1910). In 1854, during the Crimean War (1854–6), Florence Nightingale took a team of thirty-eight nurses to Scutari in Turkey where cholera, typhoid, typhus and dysentery were rampant.

Nightingale and her nurses did their best to care for many casualties of the war, who were also sick and dying of the so-called 'filth diseases', by insisting on cleanliness, ventilation and light to reduce death and disease. In the following year, a British Government Sanitary Commission was sent out to help. Underneath the dilapidated Barracks Hospital in Scutari appalling conditions were found: 'Sewers of the worst possible construction, loaded with filth, mere cesspools, in fact, through which the wind blew sewer air up the pipes of numerous open privies into the corridors and wards where the sick were lying'. In Nightingale's subsequent report about the Crimean War she produced a set of 'pie charts' or Coxcomb diagrams (her own invention) to prove that the majority of soldiers in the Crimean War died not of war wounds but of fever, cholera, diarrhoea and dysentery, which could be prevented by improved hospital hygiene. While historians continue to debate her legacy and contributions to reducing mortality amongst the British troops in the Crimean War, Nightingale (the legendary 'Lady with the Lamp'), on her return to Britain, became an advocate for improvements in sanitation and one of the pioneers of the modern nursing profession.

The cause of cholera is discovered

In spite of a move towards public health reforms in Britain, the USA and elsewhere, cholera, nevertheless, continued its terrifying march across the globe. The fourth pandemic (c.1863–79) was perhaps the most widespread of them all. Spreading from India (where millions succumbed to the disease) it went on to affect large parts of the world, including Europe, the Americas and sub-Saharan Africa (the latter for the first time, where a significant piece of epidemiological investigation, similar to but less well-known than that of John Snow, was conducted by James Christie (1829–92) in East Africa).

It was not, however, until the 1880s that the critical piece of the cholera puzzle, which had eluded Snow and others, was finally fitted into place. The fifth cholera pandemic of 1881–96 spread westward from the Indian subcontinent just like the previous ones had done and, although it did not reach the shores of Great Britain, its severity elsewhere prompted scientists to investigate its cause. French and German bacteriologists, including Louis Pasteur and Robert Koch, had already put forward the 'germ theory' of disease in the 1860s and 1870s, but the 'germ' causing cholera remained a mystery. This was despite the fact that in 1854 an Italian scientist, Filippo Pacini (1812–83), had observed the microbes that cause cholera in the excreta and intestinal contents of victims. Unfortunately, his valuable work had been overlooked by other scientists.

In 1883, unaware of Pacini's observations, two rival teams – one French, one German – were dispatched to Alexandria in Egypt, where cholera had been introduced by pilgrims returning from Mecca. The French 'Pasteurians' performed a number of autopsies and examined stool specimens from cholera patients but could not isolate a cholera 'pathogen'. They also attempted, using specimens, to reproduce the disease in animals. As cholera has no mammalian host outside the human body, their efforts failed, and when one of their team succumbed to cholera the disheartened scientists returned to France.

The German team, headed by the famous bacteriologist Robert Koch, (who had identified the tubercle bacillus in 1882) had more success. They performed autopsies on ten cholera victims and there, in walls of the intestines, they identified under the microscope a short, curved, 'comma-shaped' bacillus. Koch was initially cautious but he confirmed his findings the following year in the teeming, cholera-infested suburbs of Calcutta (now Kolkata), where he found the same cholera bacillus (*Vibrio cholerae*) in both water tanks contaminated with 'choleraic discharges' and the 'rice water stools' of victims. Koch and his team made a triumphant return to Germany.

John Snow had been right – although it is claimed that Koch did not know of his work any more than he was aware of Pacini's. Cholera was, indeed, a waterborne disease, communicated mainly by polluted water and transmitted through the faecal-oral route. But now scientists could 'see' the swarms of bacteria that invaded and multiplied in the guts and gushed out with the watery 'rice water' diarrhoea of its victims.

Almost immediately after Koch's discovery, attempts were made to produce a vaccine. In 1885, Spanish physician Jaime Ferrán (1851–1929) tried out a vaccine against cholera, first testing it on himself and then inoculating around 30,000 people. In India, Waldemar Haffkine also began a large-scale vaccination programme at the end of the nineteenth century. The immunity provided by the vaccines was, however, only partial and short-lived (and, to this day, vaccination has not played a major role in cholera prevention). More significantly, Koch's confirmation of the mode of communication of cholera gave a further and much-needed impetus to the authorities to put in place measures for disease prevention and control through environmental and hygienic improvements.

A cocktail of cholera and death in Hamburg

However, not all were convinced by Koch's findings. One of Koch's sceptical German colleagues was the Munich hygienist

Max von Pettenkofer (1818–1901). Although he believed in constructing proper sewers, Pettenkofer adhered to a complex theory of the cause of cholera which combined both the role of miasmas and ground-water levels. In 1892, he decided to test Koch's theory that cholera was caused by a 'germ'. He asked Koch to send him a flask containing a culture infected with cholera 'germs' and, in an extreme form of public testing, proceeded to swallow it. Following just a mild bout of diarrhoea, he sent Koch a polite message: 'Herr Doctor Pettenkofer presents his compliments to Herr Doctor Professor Koch and thanks him for the flask containing the so-called cholera vibrios, which he was kind enough to send. Herr Doctor Pettenkofer has now drunk the entire contents and is happy to inform Herr Doctor Professor Koch that he remains in his usual good health.' How he survived his 'cocktail' remains an enigma. He may have been one of the fortunate ones to be protected from this deadly disease, perhaps because he had unusually high levels of stomach acid which can kill the germs before they do their damage, or perhaps he had partial immunity by previous exposure to the disease.

However, Pettenkofer's lucky escape was marred by a terrible epidemic of cholera which hit Hamburg in 1892, claiming over 7,500 lives (mostly among the working-class poor) and causing the panicked flight of some 40,000 middle-class citizens. Even the 'model hospital' of Eppendorf, based on Florence Nightingale's design of pavilion-style hospitals to maximize cross-ventilation, was overwhelmed with cholera and around half of all patients died. One volunteer nurse recalled that:

In the large, airy rooms, there lay, in bed after bed in a row the poor patients, here contorted in powerful muscular convulsions, there begging the nurse for a bedpan or a drink; some had violent attacks of vomiting and befouled the bed and the floor in a nauseating manner; others lay in their last moments, a loud death-rattle in their throats, and many passed on in my very presence.

Koch was called to Hamburg to consult and was appalled by the state of public hygiene, especially in the slum quarters, and the absence of a water treatment system (which had been installed in nearby Altona, which was spared the disease). This epidemic, in the end, led to major sanitary and public health improvements, including a sewage system and a sand-filtering plant for drinking water in Hamburg. In other cities in the West, filtration and chlorination of urban water supplies gradually proved a major barrier to cholera, and as additional improvements in personal hygiene, nutrition, practical domestic measures (including boiling water) and better standards of housing and indoor plumbing were encouraged to enhance the health and hygiene of citizens, cholera ceased to wreak its havoc on the industrialized world.

The last serious outbreak of cholera in western Europe was in 1910–11. This claimed many lives, notably in Italy. Venice was affected and is the setting for Thomas Mann's famous novella, *Death in Venice* (first published in 1912). Naples was also badly hit – and with thousands sick or dead, the outbreak was accompanied by 'cholera riots'. Cholera then spread to the USA when the steamship *Moltke* brought infected people from Naples to New York City. But cholera was soon to fade into history in the 'advanced' countries of the world.

Effluence and affluence

Many people, when asked to name the greatest medical break-throughs of the past, think of such discoveries as the germ theory, anaesthesia, penicillin or vaccination. But in a UK poll of the medical profession and the public, conducted by the *British Medical Journal* in 2007, it was in fact the 'sanitary revolution' (the introduction of clean water and sewage disposal) that topped the list of the greatest fifteen medical milestones since the 1840s. Turning on the cholera had been easy. Turning it off was more problematic, but improvements in sanitation over the course of the second half of the nineteenth century and the twentieth century in the industrialized world eventually con-tributed to a decline in cholera. In other parts of the globe, the story has been very different.

During the sixth cholera pandemic (1899–1947), India was once more devastated by the disease. It is estimated that deaths from cholera had exceeded 15 million between 1817 and 1860 in the first three pandemics and another 23 million died between 1865 and 1947. Its impact on eastern Europe was also severe. More than half a million people died of cholera in the Russian empire during the first quarter of the twentieth century, a time of major social disruption associated with the First World War and the 1917 revolution. Mecca in the Arabian Peninsula remained a hot spot for cholera, and many epidemics were recorded among pilgrims to Mecca from the nineteenth century to the 1930s. In 1905 a new strain of cholera, the *Vibrio El Tor* strain, was isolated from the bodies of six Muslim pilgrims housed in the El Tor quarantine station outside Mecca.

This 'new' El Tor strain has largely featured in the seventh (and ongoing) pandemic of cholera which, beginning in the early 1960s, has been easily and rapidly conveyed by air, land and sea. Unlike all previous pandemics, this started in Indonesia, rather than the Indian subcontinent, and then spread to many regions of Asia, the Middle East, Russia and parts of southern Europe, reaching West Africa in 1971. As Myron Echenberg recounts in his book, *Africa in the Time of Cholera* (2011), while Asia had been the 'cradle' of cholera, and parts of North Africa (including Mecca in Saudi Arabia, as well as Egypt) had also long been affected by cholera through trading and pilgrimage connections, the more recent impact on sub-Saharan Africa has been especially traumatic. Cholera has taken a huge toll on people living in squalid slums with little access to safe water, and on those forced into overcrowded and foetid refugee camps during natural disasters, such as drought, flooding and famine, or at times of societal breakdowns produced by civil strife and wars.

A complex disease

The seventh pandemic witnessed not only the accelerated spread of the El Tor strain (albeit milder than the 'classical' strain) but the emergence in the early 1990s of another new strain of cholera, called the *Vibrio cholerae 0139* Bengal serotype, which is currently confined to South-east Asia. On the other side of the globe, the seventh pandemic of cholera reached Peru in 1991 after an absence from the Americas of some eighty years.

During this current pandemic, there have been significant new findings about the disease. Since Koch's announcement of the causative organism of cholera in 1883/4 it had been thought that there was no natural reservoir of the pathogen outside the human intestinal tract (unlike many 'zoonotic' diseases which have another mammalian host). It was, however, recently discovered that some cholera vibrio can survive in an aquatic milieu – the bacteria adapt well to the brackish water of estuaries, attaching to microscopic zooplankton and surviving in the guts of clams, mussels, oysters and other crustaceans. As an estuarine and marine organism, it means that there may be permanent niches all over the world (and global warming may create favourable environments for the cholera vibrio to flourish in its natural habitat). This adds to the complexities of 'where' the bacteria might lurk in between explosive pandemics, and how the disease might be originally transmitted by consumption of water containing the vibrio before spreading via the human intestinal tract and sewage-contaminated water and food.

A simple solution?

Improvements in sanitation and the provision of safe water are still desperately needed in much of the developing world (see below). There is now, however, one cheap and simple method of treating those who are infected with cholera: oral rehydration salts (ORS) solution. Originally suggested in the early nineteenth century and used intravenously from the early twentieth century, a solution of clean water, salt and sugar – promoted in the 1970s as 'oral rehydration therapy' and easily administered – can drastically reduce the mortality rate of cholera, from 50–60 per cent in untreated cases to as little as 1 per cent for those given ORS.

The cholera bacteria produce and secrete toxins that trick the cells of the intestines into expelling prodigious quantities of water. Dehydration and the resulting loss of essential water and salts lead to rapid death. Antibiotics can help reduce the numbers of *Vibrio cholerae* in the intestines and shorten the period of communicability, but ORS, by replacing the lost fluid and salts, can change cholera from a life-threatening condition to a disease that can be quickly treated at home. In the severe outbreak of cholera in Peru in the 1990s, deaths were kept down by ORS – which were called *'bolsitas salvadoras'*, little packets of salvation.

ORS is also invaluable for those dehydrated by other severe diarrhoeal diseases, such as rotavirus infections. It is estimated that the use of ORS (with zinc tablets as an additional supplement) has saved countless lives over the past few decades and has been described as 'one of the most important medical advances of the twentieth century' with its potential to prevent many deaths at little cost.

Cholera and diarrhoeal disease: the 'forgotten killers'

Cholera continues to threaten the poorest and most vulnerable areas of the world. There are an estimated 3 to 5 million cases and 100,000 to 120,000 deaths due to cholera every year. Sub-Saharan Africa together with parts of Asia and South America are the most severely affected regions. The disease garners public attention when outbreaks affect disaster-struck populations, as in the tragic situation in Haiti following the 2010 earthquake where over 700,000 cases of cholera and 8,555 deaths were reported between October 2010 and April 2014. But cholera in the twenty-first century is often neglected by comparison with many other major diseases. Moreover, diarrhoea (a symptom of an infection in the intestinal tract) can be caused by a variety of bacterial as well as viral and parasitic organisms. As a group, 'diarrhoeal disease' (known in Bantu-speaking East and Central Africa as 'snake in the belly') is, after pneumonia, the second leading cause of death in children under five and, although its incidence has declined in recent years, globally one in ten childhood deaths still results from diarrhoeal disease. Frequent bouts of diarrhoea are also a major cause of childhood malnutrition in the developing world. There are effective vaccines for rotavirus, one of the most common causes of severe dehydrating diarrhoea, but 95 per cent of rotavirus-related deaths in young children occur in low-income countries in Africa and Asia, where lifesaving care can be limited or unavailable.

While these 'forgotten killers' warrant more attention, concern over the lack of provision of safe water and sanitation is well recognized. Some 2.5 billion people worldwide lack access to improved basic sanitation (functioning toilets and safe means to dispose of human faeces) and over 780 million people are still without access to safe drinking water. The nineteenth-century pioneering sanitary reformers would be shocked by these global statistics. Improvements in sanitation are vital, and many international health organizations are doing all they can to address this challenge. The contribution of ORS to the reduction in mortality has already been seen as a success story, and its use needs to be promoted and extended further, ensuring ready availability of this simple, cheap and effective solution to those most in need.

Reflecting on the global history of cholera, 'sanitation and health for all' – or WASH (water, sanitation and hygiene) – will remain an ultimate goal and aspiration for the impoverished parts of the world in the coming decades of the twenty-first century.

TYPHOID

Typhoid fever is one of those unpleasant diseases that are spread when food or water becomes contaminated with human faeces – a mode of transmission known as the faecal-oral route. The causative agent is a bacterium, *Salmonella typhi*, and this can spread rapidly in areas of poor sanitation and inadequate hygiene. Typhoid causes a range of symptoms, including abdominal pain, blinding headaches, rashes and a high fever. If left untreated, it can be fatal in about 10 to 20 per cent of cases. The disease has undoubtedly been around for centuries, but when looking back it is difficult to differentiate typhoid fever from many other 'fevers' of the past. Improvements in public health, water supply and food hygiene have helped reduce its incidence in the industrialized world. Today, there are also antibiotics and vaccines for typhoid, but in some parts of the world with inadequate sanitation it continues to claim many lives.

∾

In London during the long, hot summer of 1858 the stench of untreated sewage floating in the River Thames was so horrendous that it was becoming almost impossible for members of the House of Commons to conduct their business. The windows were draped with curtains soaked in chloride of lime. But even that was not enough. The smell was sickening. Politicians choked and retched and threatened to leave London. It was, moreover, generally believed that the very smell itself was the cause of the deadly fevers that continually plagued the city. This 'Great Stink' would, it was feared, lead to further outbreaks of pestilence. As the physician William Budd (1811–80) remarked: 'Stench so foul, we may well believe, had never before ascended to pollute this lower air. Never before, at least, had a stink risen to the height of an historic event.'

At the time of the Great Stink, Queen Victoria (r.1837–1901) was on the throne – just entering the twenty-second year of her reign and deeply in love with her husband, Prince Albert (1819–61). There had, a few years earlier, been a fever scare at their royal castle at Windsor but it had come to nothing. Britain was moving into the new age of flush toilets and industrial innovation. In 1851 Prince Albert had masterminded the Great Exhibition at the Crystal Palace, where for the first time visitors had enjoyed an opportunity to 'spend a penny' in one of the latest attractions of the Industrial Revolution – the paying public toilet. Back home, Prince Albert had tried to sort out fifty-three overflowing cesspools at Windsor Castle, but whenever the Thames rose and saturated their lawns with raw royal sewage, the royal gardeners had simply raked up the filth and shovelled it back into the river.

Three years after the Great Stink, Prince Albert was fighting for his life. He was running a high fever and was violently sick, while on his torso there appeared a few rose-coloured spots. The royal physicians, James Clark (1788–1870) and William Jenner (1815–98), were in constant attendance. They diagnosed a 'bowel fever' (probably typhoid), but they could do little for him. On 14 December 1861, following a crisis the day before, Prince Albert died, aged only forty-two. Queen Victoria was inconsolable, and dressed in black for the rest of her long reign. To the public she became the 'Widow of Windsor'.

Foul and fatal fevers

'To get into them [the worst slums in London] you have to penetrate courts reeking with poisonous and malodorous gases arising from accumulations of sewage and refuse scattered in all directions and often flowing beneath your feet . . . you have to grope your way along dark and filthy passages swarming with vermin. Then, if you are not driven back by the intolerable stench, you may gain admittance to the dens in which these thousands of beings . . . herd together.' Andrew Mearns, *The Bitter Cry of Outcast London: An Inquiry into the Condition of the Abject Poor*, 1883

London in the nineteenth century was not so different – in terms of its poor sanitation – from other major European and American cities of the period. It was also not so very different in this respect from many of today's rapidly expanding cities in Asia, South America and Africa. In London the Great Stink alerted physicians and the government to the appalling state of squalor and sanitation in both the towns and the countryside. Fevers, it seemed, accounted for a huge proportion of all deaths – especially amongst the poor. But, as Prince Albert's death showed, fevers could attack anyone. So what caused these fevers, and were they all from the same source?

There were many febrile and deadly diseases at the time.

Some like smallpox, yellow fever and cholera were reasonably well recognized and defined (if not understood), but many others were lumped together or described by their feverish symptoms and fatal effects rather than by their causative agents. For many physicians the overpowering stench of their environs suggested that the real cause of most fevers must lie in the noxious vapours or miasmas emitted by the stinking ordure, stagnant marshes, overflowing cesspools, raw sewage and foul industrial waste that contaminated the fields, streets and waters of both towns and countryside. 'All smell is disease,' claimed Edwin Chadwick, the pioneering English campaigner for improvements in sanitary conditions. 'Effluvia' that arose from the sick and poisoned the air were also blamed for the contagions.

The 'miasmatic theory' of disease was so in vogue with many scientists throughout much of the eighteenth and early nineteenth centuries that the term 'mal'aria' (from the Italian *mala aria*, 'bad air') began to be used as a catch-all description of the cause of disease. In 1827 John MacCulloch (1773–1835) wrote an influential book entitled *Malaria: An essay on the production and propagation of this poison and on the nature and localities of the places by which it is produced.* The book is not simply a description of the mosquito-borne disease we now call malaria. In it MacCulloch, like others of his time, sets out to show that any number of diseases – in all sorts of 'poisonous' localities – are caused by 'mal'aria', or foul air.

Two diseases that became especially muddled and mired in this 'miasmic mess' were typhoid and typhus – both clearly associated with filth, poverty, poor sanitation and, above all, poisonous stenches.

Typhoid – like typhus?

In 1829 the French physician Pierre Louis coined the term 'typhoid' – meaning 'like typhus' (from the Greek *eidos*, 'like'). The disease Louis called typhoid was common in Paris, and appeared to some scientists to be different from typhus, which was especially common in England and Ireland. Louis did not draw any conclusions about the real difference between typhoid and typhus. (To make matters even more confusing, 'paratyphoid' was identified in 1902 as a separate but milder disease that was 'like typhoid'.)

It took another fifty or more years after Louis' work before the real culprits were tracked down and a distinction between typhoid and typhus was conclusively drawn on scientific grounds. Three Williams – the American physician William Wood Gerhard, the British royal physician William Jenner who attended Prince Albert and who himself contracted both typhoid and typhus, and the British epidemiologist William Budd – all played a crucial role in coming up with an answer to the puzzle.

William Budd, in particular, was intrigued by the Great Stink of 1858 and the dire predictions that the overpowering stench would lead to a huge rise in mortality. But when in 1873 he examined the reports for sickness and death in the years 1858–9 he noted:

> Strange to relate, the results showed, not only a death-rate below the average, but . . . a remarkable diminution in the prevalence of fever, diarrhoea, and the other forms of the disease commonly ascribed to putrid exhalations.

Budd – like John Snow in his investigations of cholera in London – had already begun to suspect from his epidemiological investigations that it was not the smells that caused disease, but something in contaminated water. He was later proved right. In the 1880s the typhoid bacillus was described, identified and cultured by a group of German scientists, including Karl Eberth (1835–1926) and Georg Gaffky (1850–1918). This was one of the first discoveries of a bacterial agent as a cause of disease and was later named *Salmonella typhi* after the American veterinary surgeon Daniel Elmer Salmon (1850–1914). It took a while longer for the cause of typhus (transmitted by the body louse) to be elucidated.

Towards the end of the nineteenth century the germ theory of disease – first put forward by Louis Pasteur in the 1870s – was becoming more widely accepted, although even in the 1890s Charles Creighton (1847–1927), in his two-volume *History of Epidemics in Britain* (1891–4), still adhered to the miasmatic theory of disease. But by 1900 over twenty micro-organisms had been identified as the cause of specific diseases, and the germ theory had become firmly established. Typhoid had its own distinct identity and also a diagnostic test – the Widal test, developed by Georges-Fernand Widal (1862–1929) in 1896. This was too late to say for sure whether Prince Albert had died from typhoid (and some historians have recently suggested that he died either from Crohn's disease or cancer of the stomach), but in time to sort out a new puzzle – the case of 'Typhoid Mary'.

A human reservoir and the healthy carrier

In the early twentieth century it was recognized that typhoid is transmitted by the faecal-oral route: the bacterium responsible can move from the gut of an infected individual into the faeces or urine, which can then contaminate water and food and so enter the mouth of the next victim. In principle the cycle of typhoid is one of the simplest. There is no other reservoir except for humans, and breaking the cycle should be possible by strict hygiene – for example, washing hands before handling food, and providing pure water supplies. Flies feeding on faeces may also occasionally transfer the bacteria to food. Before the arrival of the motor car and trams, horse-drawn vehicles dumped piles of manure in city streets which swarmed with flies in the hot summer months and may have been an important source of spreading the typhoid bacillus.

But there was one more intriguing puzzle about the infectious nature of typhoid. In 1873 William Budd had already made an important observation when he noted:

> The precise date at which the fever patient ceases to give fever to others is not easy to define. But I have seen so many in which fever had broken out in a family living in a previously healthy neighbourhood soon after the arrival of a convalescent, that I am quite sure that patients so far recovered cannot always be safely allowed to mix with others without precaution.

In 1902 the German bacteriologist Robert Koch also proposed that convalescing patients could still shed the bacterium in their faeces and so act as a source of infection even after they had recovered from the disease. In an era when there was no treatment, the key question was: how long could such survivors continue to be a source of infection?

The answer – possibly a lifetime – came with the famous investigation and incarceration in New York in the early decades of the twentieth century of the Irish cook Mary Mallon – known to posterity as Typhoid Mary. Wherever Mary went, typhoid was sure to follow . . .

The Tale of Typhoid Mary

'The Most Harmless and yet the Most Dangerous Woman in America,' headline from *New York American* magazine, 1909

In the summer of 1906 Henry Warren, a wealthy New York banker, was enjoying a vacation with his family in Oyster Bay, Long Island. They felt especially fortunate to have as their cook a young Irishwoman, Mary Mallon (*c*.1869–1938). Mary, a large, somewhat uncommunicative person, could produce dishes to die for. Her 'peaches on ice' were a particular specialty. But something that summer prompted Mary to move on and find employment elsewhere. Then, for the Warren family, disaster struck. Within a few weeks of Mary's departure, six of the eleven members of the household came down with typhoid. It was a terrible shock – surely this was an affliction of the filthy urban slums, not the scrupulously clean summer residences of the rich?

Warren called in the New York sanitary engineer George Soper (1870–1948) to investigate. As chance would have it, Soper had read Koch's paper on healthy carriers of typhoid fever. Once he had ruled out various other possibilities, he began to suspect the Warrens' former cook. Soper tracked her down to her new home in New York. He also looked into her employment record: she was esteemed as an excellent cook, but wherever she had been, cases of typhoid – including some deaths – had followed. He decided it was time to check her out:

I was as diplomatic as possible, but I had to say I suspected her of making people sick and that I wanted specimens of her urine, faeces and blood. It did not take Mary long to react to this suggestion. She seized a carving fork and advanced in my direction. I passed rapidly down the long narrow hall, through the tall iron gate, out through the area and so to the sidewalk. I felt rather lucky to escape.

Soper's next attempt was met by 'a volley of imprecations from the head of the stairs'. He called in reinforcements – the public health inspector S. Josephine Baker (1873–1945) and five New York policemen. But Mary Mallon had disappeared. After a three-hour search, she was discovered cowering in an outdoor closet, and was dragged out kicking and cursing. Her stools proved positive – they were teeming with typhoid bacilli. She was, as Soper suspected, a healthy carrier of typhoid. Mary Mallon spent the next three years of her life at the Riverside Hospital, an isolation hospital on North Brother Island in New York's East River.

The London magazine *Punch* published a ditty on Typhoid Mary in 1909:

> *In the U.S.A. (across the brook)*
> *There lives, unless the papers err,*
> *A very curious Irish cook*
> *In whom the strangest things occur:*
> *Beneath her outside's healthy glaze*
> *Masses of microbes seethe and wallow*
> *And everywhere that MARY goes*
> *Infernal epidemics follow.*

In 1910, after a public outcry, she was released – on condition that she had her gall bladder removed (*Salmonella typhi* appear to concentrate in the gall bladder) or stopped working as a cook. She did neither, and then the health authorities lost track of her. In 1915 an outbreak of typhoid erupted in the Sloane Maternity Hospital in Manhattan. Investigations revealed that the hospital's cook, Mrs Brown, was in fact none other than Typhoid Mary. She was sent once more to North Brother Island, and here she spent the rest of her life in the company of her dog until her death in 1938.

The story of Mary Mallon showed that in a small number of cases – perhaps 2 or 3 per cent of those who contract typhoid and then fully recover – subjects can remain carriers of this disease for the rest of their lives.

Sanitation and vaccination

The horrors of the so-called 'filth' diseases of the nineteenth century – such as typhoid, dysentery, typhus and cholera – eventually led to huge campaigns by diverse groups of 'sanitarians' and reformers – from doctors to engineers – to clean up the deplorable state of many cities, In Europe there were a number of public health acts and a massive drive to separate water contaminated with sewage from drinking water. The USA followed suit. Even seemingly small and simple measures – hand-washing, boiling drinking water, protecting food from flies, improved inspection and handling of food and milk, the provision of dustbins with lids – may well have had a substantial impact. 'Swat the Fly' signs were put up in public places, and the idea of germs, albeit invisible but perhaps conveyed by flies, began to capture the public imagination. Unclean domestic kitchens, toilets and washbasins were viewed as dangerous havens for bacteria, and housewives were encouraged to ensure that their homes were free from flies and germs.

In the industrial nations typhoid declined significantly in the early twentieth century. However, the disease remained a serious threat in times of war. Troops in the Second Boer War (1899–1902) in South Africa were seriously affected by typhoid. In the Spanish-American War of 1898 there were over 20,000 cases of typhoid and 1,500 deaths among a total of 100,000 US troops. Walter Reed (1851–1902) – head of the army's typhoid commission – inspected army camps in the USA where typhoid was rampant and found the state of sanitation to be appalling. He also demonstrated the role that flies could play in moving improperly treated waste matter to the mess tents. To make his point, he sprinkled lime into the filthy latrines, then watched as flies trailed their lime-covered feet over the men's food.

In the late nineteenth and early twentieth century, a number of scientists, including Richard Pfeiffer (1858–1945) and Wilhelm Kolle (1868–1935) in Germany, had begun work on developing a vaccine for typhoid. Another key figure was the British scientist Almroth Wright (1861–1947), known by his critics as 'Sir Almost Wright', or even 'Sir Always Wrong' – and caricatured as Sir Colenso Ridgeon in George Bernard Shaw's 1906 play *The Doctor's Dilemma*. Wright's vaccine was first deployed on a mass scale by the British army during the First World War. Mandatory typhoid immunization as well as better military sanitation were measures that may well have prevented many cases of typhoid in the trenches.

A typhoid vaccine was also used extensively during the Second World War, and with the introduction in the late 1940s of an effective antibiotic drug – chloramphenicol – there was for the first time a treatment for typhoid, although by this time the disease was already on its way out in some parts of the world.

Typhoid today

'Gone are the days when the disease decimated armies and rampaged through the filthy streets of 19th-century London, New York, and other large cities of the Western world, taking the lives of rich and poor alike. Today, it is the poor, the poorest of the poor, living in the slums of the developing world, who bear the full brunt of the mortality and morbidity ... wrought by *Salmonella typhi*.' *The Lancet*, 2012

There have been a small number of typhoid outbreaks in Europe and the USA in the last few decades, including an alarming epidemic in Aberdeen, Scotland, in the early summer of 1964 – attributed to cans of corned beef imported from Argentina. After processing under sterile conditions, the tins had been cooled in a sewage-laden river where microscopic cracks in the seams of the cans permitted contamination. But for the most part, typhoid is a disease of the past in the developed world.

Typhoid does, however, remain a huge problem in the poorer countries, and is endemic throughout most of Central and South America, as well as much of Africa and Asia. Worldwide, the annual incidence of typhoid is estimated by the WHO to be about 21 million cases, with approximately 216,000 to 600,000 typhoid-related deaths a year. Although there are drugs and improved vaccines, one particularly worrying development is that typhoid strains are becoming resistant to some of the key antibiotics in several areas of the world. Improvements in sanitation and public health, which have proved so effective in eliminating the disease from most developed countries in the past century, are urgently needed to prevent the incidence of typhoid and many other water- and food-borne diseases in the developing world, where supplies of clean water and effective sewerage are by no means the norm. As the African proverb has it, 'Filthy water cannot be washed.'

TUBERCULOSIS

Tuberculosis – or TB – is a chronic bacterial infection that has probably plagued humankind since antiquity. It can be transmitted by both humans (via *Mycobacterium tuberculosis*) and cattle (via *Mycobacterium bovis*), and may affect almost any tissue or organ of the body. Identifying many of the past forms of tuberculosis can be confusing. The great variety of names – such as scrofula, phthisis, consumption, graveyard cough and the 'White Death' – mirrors the myriad symptoms of this varied and deadly disease. The most common form is pulmonary tuberculosis, which affects the lungs and is spread from person to person through airborne droplets. This form of tuberculosis became one of the greatest scourges of the industrial towns and cities of the nineteenth and early twentieth centuries. Despite the development of a vaccine in the 1920s and an effective cure in the 1940s, there was an alarming resurgence of tuberculosis in the second half of the twentieth century, and in 1993 the WHO declared TB a global emergency. Today, with an estimated 1.5 million deaths per year, the fight against the disease poses great medical challenges: drug-resistant TB microbes, a synergistic association with the HIV/AIDS pandemic, and the need for new diagnostics, therapies and vaccines. There is also the need to address the social and economic antecedents to TB and its links with poverty and deprivation.

∾

In 1924 the German novelist Thomas Mann (1875–1955) published what many believe to be his masterpiece, *The Magic Mountain*. The novel is an evocative depiction of life and death in a TB sanatorium in the Swiss Alps at the turn of the twentieth century.

> 'The highest of the sanatoriums is the Schatzalp – you can't see it from here. They have to bring their bodies down on bob-sleds in the winter, because the roads are blocked.'
> 'Their bodies? Oh, I see. Imagine!' said Hans Castorp. And suddenly he burst out laughing, a violent, irrepressible laugh, which shook him all over and distorted his face, that was stiff with the cold wind, until it almost hurt.

Tuberculosis – as Castorp soon discovers – is no laughing matter. It is not laughter that distorts the faces of those racked by the terminal stages of TB, but the violent, bloody cough, the breathlessness, the pain, the night sweats, the slow, insidious wasting and decay of young, tormented bodies. Castorp, whose failing health obliges him to stay in the sanatorium for seven years, comes to understand 'that one must go through the deep experience of sickness and death to arrive at a higher sanity and health'.

While the history of tuberculosis may conjure up images of health-restoring sanatoria and pale-faced, slender, love-sick men and women, below the 'Magic Mountain', in the squalor and filth of overcrowded slums across the world, lies the grim reality of a disease that over the course of the last few hundred years has destroyed the lives of millions, and which today once again ranks as one of the most devastating infectious diseases in the world.

Phthisis and the mysteries of antiquity

When, where and how humans were first infected with tuberculosis is a mystery. It is likely to have been around for at least 3,000 years in its varied forms. Ancient Egyptian paintings show hump-backed figures typical of those with spinal TB. Scars on the lungs of Egyptian mummies reveal signs of the pulmonary variety of the disease, and the DNA of *Mycobacterium tuberculosis* has recently been extracted from mummified human remains. Clay tablets in Mesopotamia dating from the seventh century BC describe lists of ailments, including one in which the patient coughs continually. 'What he coughs up is thick and frequently bloody,' says the tablet. 'His breathing sounds like a flute. His hand is cold, his feet are warm. He sweats easily, and his heart activity is disturbed.'

Whether the human form of the disease evolved from an animal form (bovine tuberculosis) – possibly through the consumption of infected dairy products after people began to domesticate animals – or whether humans gave it to their herds, has been a much debated question. It is now thought that, unlike many human diseases which have jumped from animals to humans (zoonoses), the human form of tuberculosis (*Mycobacterium tuberculosis*) may actually be much older than its cattle equivalent (*Mycobacterium bovis*), and some researchers have traced the evolutionary history of human tuberculosis back to hunter-gatherer groups in Africa 70,000 years ago. As TB infected people and spread across the world, the pathogen eventually evolved into at least seven families, or lineages.

By the time of the Greek physicians Hippocrates (*c.*460–*c.*365/370 BC) and Galen (AD 129–*c.*216), pulmonary tuberculosis – or 'phthisis' as it was known (meaning 'dwindling' or 'wasting away') – was clearly recognizable. The Greeks ascribed the disease to 'evil airs'. The Romans recommended bathing in human urine, drinking elephants' blood or devouring wolves' livers. Arab physicians treated the disease with asses' milk and powdered crab shells. Bloodletting, purging, exercise and a host of different herbal remedies, including opium, were also tried. Some ancient and early medieval doctors advised the patient to seek a change of air – a practice that was revived in the nineteenth and twentieth centuries.

Varieties of tuberculosis

Most people with normally functioning immune systems appear to have a good natural resistance to TB: only a minority of those infected develop the active form of the disease, but it is the 5 to 10 per cent in whom the disease moves from initial infection to clinical TB that is the problem. Pulmonary tuberculosis, which progressively destroys the lungs, is the most common form of TB, and once a person begins to show active symptoms – coughing up blood, night sweats, wasting and general debility – it can soon prove fatal. Tuberculosis can also affect many other parts of the body. In the medieval period a disease known as scrofula may have been the glandular form of the disease. The word 'scrofula' is the diminutive of the Latin *scrofa*, meaning 'a breeding sow' – the puffy appearance of someone with swollen lymph glands in the neck apparently resembled a 'little pig'. This form of tuberculosis was also known as the 'King's Evil'.

For centuries, French and English kings and queens claimed to be able to cure those suffering from scrofula or the 'King's Evil' by the Royal Touch. They believed this power was vouch-safed by God only to the true line of kings, and ceremonies involving the Royal Touch were used to legitimate those who acceded to the throne. But why scrofula should have been singled out for royal attention is puzzling.

In England, Edward the Confessor 'touched' numerous people during his reign (r.1042–66). Charles II (r.1660–85) is said to have 'laid hands' on nearly 100,000 subjects. At his coronation in 1722, Louis XV of France (r.1715–74) touched over 2,000 scrofula victims. In England, the last person to receive the Royal Touch in Queen Anne's reign (r.1702–14) was the young Samuel Johnson (1709–84) who went on to become one of the great literary figures (although it is not certain that Johnson, or anyone else, was really 'cured'). The practice died out in England in the eighteenth century, but continued in France until 1825, when Charles X (r.1824–30) gave the last performance.

The King's Evil and scrofula were amongst any number of names once used to describe the various forms of tuberculosis. While for many centuries phthisis remained the term applied by physicians to pulmonary tuberculosis, the popular equivalent was 'consumption', a word that aptly captured the way victims seemed to be literally consumed by the disease, becoming pale, weak and emaciated. 'Galloping consumption' and 'graveyard cough' signalled imminent death. *Lupus vulgaris*, 'the common wolf', was the name given to tuberculosis of the skin, which causes horrible disfigurement, especially of the face. Tuberculosis of the spine became known as Pott's disease, after Percivall Pott

(1714–88), and tuberculosis of the cortex of the adrenal glands was named Addison's disease after another English physician, Thomas Addison (1793–1860).

The range of names used in the medieval and early modern period makes it difficult to conclude with any certainty the full impact of the disease. In the London Bills of Mortality in the seventeenth century, however, even during the terrible plague year of 1665, 'consumption and tissick [phthisis]' claimed the lives of 4,808 Londoners, third only to plague and fevers, while another 86 died from the 'King's Evil'. During the seventeenth and eighteenth centuries, as many as one-quarter of all deaths in Europe may well have been due to consumption.

It is not surprising that the English author John Bunyan (1628–88) in his book *The Life and Death of Mr. Badman* (1680) should famously call consumption the 'captain of all these men of death':

I cannot so properly say that he died of one disease, for there were many that had consented, and laid their heads together to bring him to his end. He was dropsical, he was consumptive, he was surfeited, was gouty, and, as some say, he had a tang of the pox in his bowels. Yet the captain of all these men of death that came against him to take him away, was the consumption, for it was that that brought him down to the grave.

The White Death

'I know the colour of that blood! It is arterial blood. I cannot be deceived . . . That drop of blood is my death warrant. I must die.' John Keats in 1820, a year before his death at the age of twenty-five

In the nineteenth century and the first half of the twentieth century, tuberculosis – especially the pulmonary variety – probably killed millions of people. It became known as the 'White Death' or the 'White Plague', referring to the characteristic pallor of its victims, and was, though in a very different way, as devastating as the Black Death of half a millennium earlier. For unlike bubonic plague, the White Death did not come and go in epidemic waves. It was ever present, sapping the energy and destroying the lives of young men, women and children across the globe.

The poet John Keats (1795–1821) lost his mother and his brother to tuberculosis. In his 'Ode to a Nightingale' he refers to the symptoms of the disease, the 'weariness, the fever, and the fret', and yearns to escape a world 'Where youth grows pale, and spectre-thin, and dies'. When, in 1820, the year he published his great poem, he saw blood on his handkerchief, he knew that he too had contracted the disease and did not have long to live. John Keats exemplified the 'Romantic' tuberculosis patient – creative, ethereal and dead at an early age. He was one of a number of poets, writers and artists who died from tuberculosis. But dying from TB was not a romantic end. Exhausted sufferers coughed, spat out blood, sweated, and saw their flesh waste. The Polish composer Frédéric Chopin (1810–49), in a letter shortly before his death, possibly from TB, wrote:

One [doctor] sniffed at what I spat out, the second tapped where I spat it from, the third poked about and listened how I spat it. One said I was going to die, the second that I was dying and the third that I was dead . . . All this has affected the Preludes, and God knows when you will get them.

The list of famous names who suffered or are believed to have had tuberculosis is long, and includes several members of the Brontë family as well as Robert Louis Stevenson, Anton Chekhov, Franz Kafka, Katherine Mansfield, George Orwell and Albert Camus. Characters suffering from 'consumption' also make frequent appearances in the novels, plays and operas of the period. Among the notable ones are: Mimi in Puccini's *La Bohème*, Violetta in Verdi's *La Traviata* (inspired by the fate of Marguerite Gautier in *La Dame aux Camélias* by Alexandre Dumas), Fantine in Victor Hugo's *Les Misérables*, and Smike in Charles Dickens' *Nicholas Nickleby*. TB was, as one scholar has written, 'once responsible for no less than one in seven deaths – and a good many more if novels and operas are included.'

A slow and silent killer

'Tuberculosis is a Plague in disguise. Its ravages are insidious, slow. They have never roused people to great, sweeping action. The Black Plague in London is ever remembered with horror. It lived one year; it killed fifty thousand. The Plague Consumption kills this year in Europe over a million; and this has been going on not for one year but for centuries. It is the Plague of all plagues – both in age and power – insidious, steady, unceasing.' American journalist, Ernest Poole, early twentieth-century

John Keats, like others racked with the early stages of consumption in the nineteenth century, sought refuge in 'healthier' climes, away from the polluted air of cities such as London. For some it was already too late. After Keats died in Rome in 1821, his apartment at the foot of the Spanish Steps was fumigated and his furniture burnt in the hope that this would destroy whatever it was that caused this mysterious, deadly infection. But for many a change of air was not an option, and it was in the filthy and crowded slums and factories of Europe and North America that this slow and silent killer had its greatest impact.

Tuberculosis, along with a host of other 'crowd' diseases, wiped out generation after generation of people in their prime of life – depriving children of parents, families of breadwinners, lovers of sweethearts. Life expectancy among the labouring classes was little over thirty years in some industrial towns, and tuberculosis ranked high as a cause of death in the mid-nineteenth century, probably killing one in four adults in Europe and the USA. Even in the early twentieth century, TB still killed more people worldwide than any other infection. In many cities during this period, autopsies suggested that a high proportion of the urban population were, at some point in their lives, infected with the bacillus – with perhaps 10 per cent going on to develop the active form of the disease, and 80 per cent of those ultimately dying from tuberculosis.

Naming and identifying the disease

Beginning in the Renaissance and gathering pace in the early modern period, there was a new quest to understand the human body. Dissections and autopsies were conducted with increasing frequency and physicians in Europe began to correlate symptoms of hospitalized patients who had died with pathological changes which could be detected when the body was opened up in the morgue. Dutch physician Franciscus Sylvius (1614–72) identified during an autopsy hard nodules in the lungs of one of his patients and associated them with the symptoms of phthisis. Thomas Willis (1621–75), famous for his description of the arrangement of arteries at the base of the brain still known as the Circle of Willis, added further insights based on autopsies. The British physician Richard Morton (1637–98) in his treatise of 1689, *Phthisiologia*, was the first to state that tubercles – from the Latin *tuberculum*, the diminutive of *tuber*, meaning 'lump' or 'bump' – were always present in this disease. These were the tiny nodules of inflamed tissue which he saw under the microscope in the lungs of patients who had died of phthisis.

In 1816 the French physician René Théophile Hyacinthe Laënnec (1781–1826) – who himself probably died of tuberculosis – invented a device that made it possible to diagnose the disease in those who were still alive. This was the stethoscope, and with it doctors could listen to the amplified sounds of breathing, the noise of blood gurgling round the heart, and the distressed state of the lungs. The word stethoscope derives from Greek *stēthos*, 'chest', and *skopein*, 'to look at'. Laënnec had wanted to listen to the heart of a young, somewhat plump, female patient, but felt it inappropriate to do anything as intimate as putting his head so close to her bosom. So he rolled up his notebook and put one end on the young lady's chest and the other to his ear. He could clearly hear not only the sounds of her heart, but also her breathing. Soon after this the stethoscope became a hollow tube of wood, and later many new designs were created, including the flexible form with two earpieces that became one of the physician's most useful diagnostic tools and remains to this day one of the most recognizable symbols of the medical profession.

Laënnec also observed, at post-mortems, that the characteristic tubercles of pulmonary phthisis found in the lungs could be identified in other organs – such as the brain, the intestines, and the liver – suggesting that the disease, while affecting different parts of the body, might have a single cause, thus unifying a disparate group of pathologies. It was not until the 1830s, however, that the term 'tuberculosis' (the Greek suffix *-osis* denotes a diseased condition) was introduced into medical parlance by Johann Lukas Schönlein (1793–1864), professor of medicine at Zurich. In the 1840s the German physician Philipp Klencke (1813–81) showed that the disease could be transmitted experimentally. In 1865 the French physician Jean Antoine Villemin (1827–92) also succeeded in transmitting matter from tubercles into experimental rabbits and is usually credited as one of the first to demonstrate that tuberculosis was an infectious disease, although his findings were ignored by the scientific community at the time.

The credit for definitively isolating and identifying the bacillus that causes TB – *Mycobacterium tuberculosis* – is attributed to the great German bacteriologist Robert Koch. (The abbreviation TB itself originally stood for 'tubercle bacillus'.) Koch presented his new findings to a stunned audience in Berlin on 24 March 1882, complete with paraphernalia from his laboratory: microscopes, test tubes with cultures, glass slides with stained bacteria, dyes and glass jars with tissue samples. The young Paul Ehrlich was in the audience and later described it as 'the most important experience of my scientific life.' This still ranks as one of the most profound achievements in the history of medicine, and helped to usher in the germ theory of disease more generally.

Koch's work on tuberculosis had consisted of three steps: identification of a bacterium in infected tissues, cultivation of the suspected pathogen and successful animal experimentation thereafter. Epitomized as Koch's Postulates, the same method-ology was subsequently – with various modifications – applied to many other bacterial infections. Koch was awarded the Nobel Prize in Physiology or Medicine in 1905 for 'his investigations and discoveries in relation to tuberculosis.'

Following Koch's discovery it was eventually recognized that the human form of tuberculosis – capable of invading different organs and tissues – was a contagious airborne bacterial infec-tion spread by coughing, sneezing and spitting, usually after prolonged and close contact with an infected person. Bovine tuberculosis, which damages the internal organs and the bones of the spine, was subsequently shown to be transmitted to humans through infected cows' milk and meat (and is currently in the UK a source of concern because of its link with badgers in the wild who carry the pathogen and can transmit the disease to domestic cattle).

Sanatoria, and isolating the infectious

'In the future struggle against this dreadful plague of the human race, one will no longer have to contend with an indefinite something, but with an actual parasite.' Robert Koch

Koch's discovery in 1882 of the tubercle bacillus and the infec-tious nature of the disease quashed some of the older theories about the cause of the disease: some had suggested a hereditary 'consumptive disposition', others blamed the 'indigent' habits of the poor or the 'sorrowful passions' of young lovers. The fact that Koch showed TB to be an infectious bacterial disease in many ways confirmed what had been suspected and observed all along: the disease hit hardest at those whose lives were blighted by poverty and poor nutrition, and worked in badly ventilated, overcrowded, cold, damp or dusty conditions.

Tuberculosis in the late nineteenth and early twentieth centuries figured largely as a disease of the urban poor. It became clear that the bacilli spread rapidly and easily when people lived or worked in close proximity, breathing in one another's airborne particles from coughs, sneezes and sputum. Those most likely to succumb to the symptoms were people with little resistance to fight off the infection. Isolating the infected and giving them the opportunity to rest became the preferred way of dealing with the disease, for which there was as yet no cure.

The old idea of seeking 'healthy airs' – whether in spas, by the seaside or in the mountains – gave rise to a great expansion of institutionalized sanatoria. The first sanatorium had been opened in 1854 by the physician Hermann Brehmer (1826–89) in Görbersdorf, Silesia (now Poland). Influenced by its ideals and success in treating TB with the 'rest cure', Edward Trudeau (1848–1915), who like Brehmer was a TB sufferer, established the first sanatorium in the USA in 1885 – the Adirondack Cottage Sanitarium, at Saranac Lake, New York. Many others followed in Europe and America. Located in isolated mountainous and rural settings, they had bed-lined verandas offering patients 'cool and fresh air' for diseased lungs, as well as a regime of nourishing food, rest and moderate exercise. Health professionals in Europe believed that the clean, cold Alpine air was the best treatment for lung diseases, and many sanatoria were opened there, including the Schatzalp Sanatorium in Davos, Switzerland, the setting for Thomas Mann's novel, *The Magic Mountain*. In the USA, warm and dry climates were favoured, with California, New Mexico and Arizona becoming known as the 'Lands of the New Lungs' from the early twentieth century.

And it was not just the wealthy 'lungers' (as they were known) who benefited; the 'contagious' poor were also encouraged or even pressurized (to segregate those spreading the germs from the rest of society) to enter one of the state- or charity-run sanatoria. By the 1930s in Britain there were 420 sanatoria with 30,000 beds in hilly or rural settings, offering 'cool and fresh air' for diseased lungs. Papworth Sanatorium, near Cambridge, was founded by Pendrill Varrier-Jones (1883–1941) in 1916 and developed into a 'village settlement' known as the Cambridgeshire Tuberculosis Colony. It became famous for its treatments and for helping people to return to work after convalescence. Papworth is now one of the leading hospitals for heart and lung transplants.

Apart from rest and a range of tonics, there were few effective cures. However, a surgical technique known as artificial pneumothorax became popular, whereby a diseased lung was collapsed with the idea of giving it a period of 'resting' and 'healing' – a procedure endured most famously by the writer George Orwell (1903–50) in 1947 when he was writing *Nineteen Eighty-Four*. Artificial ultraviolet light therapy was also recommended for tuberculosis of the skin (as well as for rickets) using the Finsen lamp, invented by Faeroese physician Neils Ryberg Finsen (1860–1904) for which he was awarded a Nobel Prize in 1903.

Prevention and diagnosis: 'No spitting', and screening

'An X-ray will show it before you know it.'

Public health campaigns, often spurred on by local and national TB societies, also instructed people on how best to avoid contracting or spreading tuberculosis. The US declared a 'War on Consumption' beginning in the early 1900s. This consisted of vigorous anti-TB campaigns, the most famous being the adoption of the Danish idea of Christmas seals by adding an extra charitable stamp on mailed holiday greetings during Christmas to raise money for TB.

One clear public health directive was 'no spitting in public places', and spittoons were provided to try to limit the spread of airborne bacilli. Ordinances against spitting go back a long way, but with the fear of TB in the early twentieth century spitting became a major public health concern. In 1908 a health inspector in Massachusetts was shocked to find that spitting on the floor was common in most tailors' shops. The shop owners, however, merely responded with: 'of course they spit on the floor; where do you expect them to spit, in their pockets?' In New York City spitting became a punishable offence, and by 1916 nearly 200 American cities had rules in force against spitting in public. Linoleum – invented in the mid-nineteenth century – became popular as a cover for wooden floors to protect people from TB. It was believed that the germs hid in the cracks between the planks, and 'lino' was widely advertised as a sanitary alternative.

The discovery of X-rays in 1895 by Wilhelm Röntgen (1845–1923), professor of physics at the University of Würzburg in Bavaria and winner of a Nobel Prize in 1901, enabled doctors to get a clearer picture of the lungs of tuberculous sufferers. In the early twentieth century TB became a notifiable disease in a number of countries, and from the 1920s, mass X-ray screenings were undertaken to detect those likely to be 'infectious'.

A vaccine and three drugs

'If you know tuberculosis, you know Medicine.' James
Supramaniam (1921–2008)

While many of these measures were designed to prevent tuberculosis from escalating out of control, the search for an effective
vaccine or therapeutic drug was far more problematic. Koch
himself was convinced that he had found a glycerine extract to
treat tuberculosis, which he called 'tuberculin'. He kept his
remedy secret for a while but, when he announced his exciting
'cure' in 1890, it failed to live up to its promise (though it was
subsequently used as a valuable diagnostic test for both humans
and cattle).

Development of a TB vaccine (based on a weakened strain of
M. bovis – the bovine form) was eventually achieved in the early
1920s by two French scientists – Albert Calmette (1863–1933)
and Camille Guérin (1872–1961) – and called BCG (Bacillus
Calmette-Guérin). This vaccine – one of the major medical
breakthroughs of the early twentieth century – was first tested
successfully on a baby in 1921 at the Charité Hospital in Paris.
Further children were vaccinated and the acceptance of BCG
grew, particularly in France and Scandinavia. There was a set-
back when a contaminated batch led to the deaths of around
seventy babies in the German city of Lübeck in 1930. Public
confidence was eventually restored and the BCG vaccine was
widely used in many countries after the Second World War,
although it was less popular in the USA. It is estimated that more
than four billion doses of the BCG vaccine have been administered since its introduction.

The BCG vaccine was followed in the 1940s by the discovery of the first antibiotic effective against TB – streptomycin. The soil microbiologist Selman Waksman (1888–1973) was a Ukrainian-born American who in 1941 used the term 'antibiotic' in its medical sense (from the Greek *anti-*, 'against' and *biotos*, 'the means of life'). He and his colleagues at Rutgers University in the USA, with the financial support of the drug company Merck, screened thousands of soil microbes in the hope of finding an effective drug for TB (which did not respond to penicillin). One of Waksman's Ph.D. students, Albert Schatz (1920–2005), had a lucky 'hit'. In 1943 he isolated streptomycin from a mould growing in the throats of chickens that had been reared in a heavily manured field. For this discovery, Waksman (though not Schatz) was awarded the Nobel Prize in Physiology or Medicine in 1952. The first reported modern randomized controlled trial (RCT) of any drug was conducted in Britain in 1947–8 on streptomycin as a treatment for pulmonary tuberculosis.

Two other drugs – para-aminosalicylic acid (PAS) and isoniazid – were subsequently combined with streptomycin as a way of preventing resistance to any one single drug. This triple therapy, developed by John Crofton (1912–2009) and his team in Edinburgh in the 1950s, became known as the 'Edinburgh method'. Combination therapy, based on this model, has since been used for a number of other diseases, including cancer, leprosy, HIV/AIDS and malaria. Other physicians, notably James Supramaniam in Singapore and Wallace Fox (1920–2010) in Africa and India, also pioneered the use of antibiotics for TB. Together with newer TB drugs (including rifampicin in the 1960s) these drugs proved spectacularly successful in treating TB, and over the following decades saved millions of lives globally.

Pasteurization of milk and keeping cattle herds free of TB, with the aim of reducing the incidence of bovine tuberculosis, also became important in the post-war era. With a vaccine to prevent TB and powerful antibiotics to treat anyone who contracted it, there was by the mid-twentieth century tremendous optimism that this disease could be eliminated, and by the early 1960s many sanatoria had already closed. Indeed, over the next few decades the incidence of tuberculosis fell dramatically, to a point in the 1980s when it was no longer considered a public health threat in the West.

The declining incidence of TB

As historians have looked back at the changing death rates of TB over the previous century and a half, they have noticed that (notwithstanding the huge toll exacted by TB until well into the twentieth century) the downward trend of mortality from TB had begun long before the introduction of these 'magic bullets', and some time before Koch's discovery of its causative agent. Indeed, three-quarters of the reduction had occurred before the BCG vaccine or antibiotics were introduced.

The reasons for this change have puzzled historians and generated much interest. If vaccination and therapeutic medicine played no role in the earlier stages of the decline of TB, what else might have helped? Some have argued that improved nutrition was a key factor, enabling people to cope better with the infection. Others have pointed to broader public health measures, including the isolation and care of the sick in hospitals and sanatoria, along with a concerted effort to prevent the spread of infection and to provide supportive health care measures for chronic sufferers. Social and economic improvements – better housing (especially reduced domestic crowding) and working conditions for the poor – are yet other factors likely to have contributed to the downward trend. The decline in the 'filth' diseases such as cholera and typhoid, related to improved sanitation, may also have had a synergistic impact on the mortality trends of TB. Or, possibly, there was a decline in the virulence of the disease over the course of the nineteenth and twentieth centuries.

Tuberculosis is a disease with many complex pathways and manifestations, and it is likely that some combination of these factors was responsible for the decline, a trend that was then accelerated with the introduction and widespread use of screening, vaccination and antibiotic treatment. Whatever the exact chain of events, the decline of TB in the Northern hemisphere was hailed as a huge victory, and by the 1980s TB had become in the Western world a 'plague' of the past. In some countries, vaccination was no longer even seen as necessary.

The disease that never went away

The declining incidence of tuberculosis in the West is only one part of the global story. Beyond western Europe and the USA lay a world where TB was slowly, silently and often needlessly destroying millions of lives. In the poorer countries of Africa, Asia and South America, TB became an increasingly serious problem over the course of the twentieth century, and around the world it has recently shown a terrifying resurgence. It has turned out to be the disease that never went away.

It took another major epidemiological tragedy to bring tuberculosis back onto the international health agenda – HIV/AIDS. In the mid-1980s cases of TB in the USA began to surface in inner-city areas amongst the homeless, drug users and prison inmates, as well as amongst foreign-born individuals. In eastern Europe and the former USSR following the fall of communism, cases of TB soared in the wake of social and economic dislocation, wars and ethnic conflict. In western Europe, in cities like London, TB cases also began to rise amongst immigrant and refugee populations. But it was the AIDS pandemic, coupled with the emergence of multi-drug resistant (MDR) strains of TB, that catapulted the disease back into the limelight. The most alarming development was the phenomenon of parallel epidemics of AIDS and TB in the developing world, especially in Africa and South-east Asia. For patients with HIV/AIDS the immune system is seriously compromised, and those living with the disease are at risk of developing 'opportunistic' infections, of which TB has proved the most common and worrying.

In 1993 the WHO declared TB a 'global emergency' as the staggering and emerging number of new cases became apparent. In the mid-1990s, the WHO launched a new global TB strategy and a method of monitoring and following up drug treatment, known as 'directly observed treatment, short-course (DOTS) strategy', which became the internationally recommended strategy for TB control. The aim of DOTS was to ensure that all detected cases were given appropriate anti-TB drugs and that infected patients continued to take these drugs – usually for six months. Further campaigns and partnerships in the twenty-first century have been established to extend the DOTS strategy and 'Stop TB'. TB was included in the UN's Millennium Development Goals (MDGs) of 2000–15 with the aim of reversing the spread of TB by 2015, and in 2002 the Global Fund to Fight AIDS, Tuberculosis and Malaria (GFATM) – the 'Big Three' – was set up.

The good news is that, globally, TB mortality rates have fallen by 45 per cent since 1990 and the world is on track to achieve the global target of a 50 per cent reduction by 2015; an estimated 56 million people have been cured of TB and 22 million lives have been saved since the mid-1990s. China has made huge strides in reducing its number of TB cases based on the DOTS programme.

However, one of the most worrying aspects has been the rise in the number of cases that have proved resistant to the standard drugs, often as a result of inappropriate or incorrect use of anti-TB treatments. This has become known as multi-drug resistant TB or MDR-TB. Patients need to be given second-line drugs (including injectable antibiotics) that are more costly, cause more severe side effects and must be taken for up to two years. In 2006, cases of extensively drug-resistant TB or XDR-TB emerged in which the disease cannot be controlled by either the first-line antibiotics or the more expensive second-line anti-TB drugs. Indeed, resistance to antibiotics for many bacterial infections poses a 'major global threat', according to a 2014 WHO report, while the chief medical officer for England, Sally Davies, has warned that the rise in drug-resistant infections is comparable to the threat of global warming.

Recent statistics highlight the current crisis of TB: one-third of the world's population is infected with TB bacilli; 9 million new cases of TB were detected worldwide in 2013 and there were around 1.5 million deaths from TB including 360,000 people who had been HIV positive; there are an estimated half a million cases of MDR-TB in the world; XDR-TB has been reported by 92 countries; an estimated 3 million people with active TB are either not diagnosed or are diagnosed and go unreported, and continue to spread the disease in the wider community; people living with HIV and infected with TB are 20 to 30 times more likely to develop active TB disease than people without HIV. A 'cascade-of-care' approach is desperately needed, which includes early diagnosis, treatment, management of TB and HIV co-infections, and also encompasses the tragic fact that many patients will need palliative care.

The TB burden is widespread worldwide but most evident in the poorest countries of the world; over 95 per cent of TB deaths occur in low- and middle-income countries. Swaziland in southern Africa is known as the epicentre of MDR-TB. But even in wealthier nations, there are pockets of TB amongst the most deprived sectors of society that are a serious cause of concern. London has the highest rates of all European cities, and some boroughs have rates of TB greater than in parts of sub-Saharan Africa. As in the past, TB remains a biological expression of social inequality, and the link between deprivation, malnutrition and multiple infections is strikingly clear. Improving the social conditions of the poorer sections of society is vital in reducing rates of the disease in all countries, whatever their income level.

Scientists are trying to understand more about the different genetic strains of TB – one of which appears to be surprisingly virulent and prone to drug resistance, and especially well-suited to spreading the disease in our interconnected, densely populated world. Such research has implications for the design and development of new vaccines, new therapies and new diagnostics. The BCG vaccine, dating back to the 1920s, is still the only vaccine available for preventing TB. However, its efficacy is variable and its use varies from country to country. Moreover, while it offers some protection against severe forms of paediatric TB, it is unreliable against adult pulmonary TB. Major international

research efforts are underway to improve the existing BCG vaccine or develop new vaccines; several candidates are in
early-stage clinical trials and there is optimism that there will be
at least one new vaccine within the next decade. Many of the
drugs are over forty years old, but novel TB drugs, such as
bedaquiline for multi-resistant TB, are being developed. And
there are new diagnostic tools such as the GeneXpert MTB/RIF
automated molecular assay for rapid diagnosis of drug-
susceptible and drug-resistant TB.

All these offer hope of fresh solutions. But in the meantime,
tuberculosis – the disease that never went away – is currently the
second greatest killer disease from a single infectious agent
(after HIV/AIDS), and remains a major global health problem
in the twenty-first century.

PUERPERAL FEVER

Puerperal fever – or childbed fever – was for several centuries the most common cause of maternal death following childbirth, reaching epidemic proportions in the lying-in hospitals of Europe and the United States in the nineteenth century. *Streptococcus pyogenes*, the bacterium responsible for puerperal fever, was discovered in 1879, but it was not until the 1930s, following the introduction of the first anti-bacterial drugs, known as sulphonamides and then the antibiotic penicillin in the mid-twentieth century, as well as improved maternity care, that puerperal fever ceased to be a major problem in developed countries. However, puerperal sepsis, as it is now known, still remains a serious threat for mothers in parts of the world with limited health facilities.

∾

In 1797 Mary Wollstonecraft (1759–97), pioneering feminist and author of *A Vindication of the Rights of Women*, gave birth to her second child at home with the assistance of a midwife from the Westminster Lying-in Hospital in London. On Wednesday, 20 August, a healthy baby daughter was born. Following some difficulties with the placenta, Mary was attended by a doctor from the hospital. A few days later she developed a 'shivering fit', followed by a high fever and agonizing abdominal pain. She died on Sunday, 10 September, aged thirty-eight. Her daughter, also Mary, later married the poet Shelley, and achieved enduring fame in her own right with the novel *Frankenstein*. Her mother was just one of countless women who, several days after the joy of giving birth, died of puerperal fever.

A female event

Puerperal fever was first identified as a specific disease in the eighteenth century – its name being derived from the Latin *puer*, 'boy', and *parere*, 'to bring forth'. The term 'puerperium' was used to denote the period immediately following childbirth – the 'lying-in' or 'confinement'. Puerperal fever had probably been a cause of maternal mortality for centuries, but it was not until the eighteenth and nineteenth centuries that it captured the attention of the medical profession.

Giving birth had always been an ordeal, a risky time for both mother and child. With no anaesthetics apart from opiates and alcohol, no antibiotics and little in the way of antiseptics, the risk of infection was high. In the medieval and early modern periods, most mothers gave birth at home – sometimes alone, sometimes with a group of other women or 'gossips', and occasionally with the assistance of the local (untrained but often experienced) midwife. It was an exclusively female event.

Only in the case of difficult deliveries would a male practitioner be summoned. Fathers and siblings would huddle outside the birth chamber in hushed silence, listening to the screams of the mother, and anxiously awaiting the first cries of the new baby.

Hotbeds of infection

'Epidemics of puerperal fever are to women as war is to men. Like war, they cut down the healthiest, bravest, and most essential part of the population; like war, they strike their victims in the prime of their lives.' Jacques-François-Édouard Hervieux (1818–1905)

The eighteenth century witnessed the beginnings of lying-in (maternity) hospitals. These hospitals, often run as charitable institutions, offered poor women or unmarried mothers a comfortable place to give birth, providing them with free food, warmth and shelter. The delivery was handled by skilled medical accoucheurs (male midwives). Ironically, it was these very maternity hospitals that gave rise to some of worst outbreaks of puerperal fever.

In some of the larger lying-in hospitals, 5 to 20 per cent of mothers died from puerperal fever, and in the smaller hospitals severe outbreaks might kill as many as 70 to 100 per cent of lying-in women. In the early nineteenth century, the risk of dying from puerperal fever in Queen Charlotte's Maternity Hospital in London – one of the most prestigious of its kind – was seventeen times as high as it was for a woman delivered at home in the worst slums of the East End of the city. The lying-in hospitals soon gained a reputation as 'slaughterhouses' or 'necropolises'.

The more enlightened physicians tried fumigating the wards and the women's clothing, and recommended regular washing and good ventilation. Various concoctions of herbs were tried to help the mothers once infection set in. Purging, venesection (copious bleeding using a lancet) or applying leeches to the mother's abdomen were also popular – but did nothing to stem the tide of death. Doctors grappled with the question as to why so many mothers were dying under their care. Was it a miasma or poison in the atmosphere of the hospitals? Was it some noxious influence that seeped out of soiled bedclothes, or the invasion of the womb by putrid matter? Or was it some inherent complication of pregnancy, labour and birth?

Death in the hands of doctors and midwives

Only a small proportion of mothers actually gave birth in these charitable institutions, and epidemics of puerperal fever could as easily happen outside the hospitals. The disease seemed to affect indiscriminately the rich and the poor, the robust and the weak, younger mothers and older mothers, and could follow both normal and abnormal labours. As doctors began to look more closely at the outbreaks, however, they came up with findings that were uncomfortable for their own profession. It became clear that there was some kind of link between women who contracted puerperal fever and certain birth attendants – whether midwives or doctors – who came to be seen as 'harbingers of death'. One of the first to point out this connection was Alexander Gordon (1752–99), following an epidemic of puerperal fever in 1789–92 in Aberdeen, Scotland. By 1795 Gordon had come to a disturbing conclusion:

'It is a disagreeable declaration for me to mention,' he confessed, 'that I myself was the means of carrying the infection to a great number of women.'

One doctor in Philadelphia, Dr Rutter, was so distressed at the number of cases of puerperal fever in his practice that he became fastidious about washing, shaving, and changing his clothes, and even made sure he used a fresh pencil to take notes while attending a new case. Yet, despite his efforts, the disease seemed to follow him wherever he went and, in the end, like others who found themselves in such a situation, he was forced to give up his practice.

From corpses to confinements

In 1843 Oliver Wendell Holmes (1809–94), a young physician and poet in Boston, documented a number of cases which, he believed, illustrated the 'contagious' nature of puerperal fever, its links with another infection – erysipelas – and the possibility that the infection was carried by doctors from corpses to confinements. His observations were reprinted in 1855 as a pamphlet, *Puerperal Fever as a Private Pestilence*, in which he wrote:

> In view of these facts, it does appear a singular coincidence that one man or woman should have ten, twenty, thirty, or seventy cases of this rare disease, following his or her footsteps with the keenness of a beagle through the streets and lanes of a crowded city, while the scores that cross the same paths on the same errands know it only by name.

Holmes cited one distinguished doctor who removed the pelvic organs at the post-mortem of a patient who had died of puerperal fever. He then put them in his coat pocket before going on to deliver a number of women – all of whom subsequently died.'

Such practices, Holmes argued, were criminal, and should be banished. He also recommended that anyone attending an autopsy, or a case of puerperal fever or erysipelas, should take sensible precautions to avoid conveying the contagion to a midwifery case.

James Young Simpson (1811–70), who first used chloroform as an anaesthetic for women in labour in 1847, noted the similarity between hospital gangrene (or 'surgical fever') and puerperal fever.

Wash your hands

'I make my confession that God only knows the number of women whom I have consigned prematurely to the grave.' Ignaz Semmelweis (1818–65)

It is the Hungarian physician Ignaz Semmelweis who has gone down in history for making the critical connection between corpses and confinements. In 1846 Semmelweis was an assistant in Vienna's famous teaching hospital, the Allgemeines Krankenhaus. There were two obstetrical clinics in the hospital, and expectant mothers were randomly allocated to either one on alternate days. The one where Semmelweis worked was used for teaching young male medical students, the other for training female midwives. Semmelweis discovered that cases of puerperal fever and mortality rates were far higher in the clinic with the medical students. When a good friend, Jakob Kolletschka, who was professor of forensic medicine in Vienna, died at the age of forty-three, Semmelweis read the autopsy report. His friend had been nicked by a scalpel while conducting an autopsy, and the report suggested that he had died from the same disease as women who died in childbirth. Semmelweis had a sudden insight. He scrutinized the practices of the doctors in his clinic and observed that they would often go straight from assisting with autopsies to carrying out vaginal examinations of women in labour – without washing their hands or changing their clothes. There had to be a connection.

Semmelweis, unaware of Holmes' paper, put forward his 'cadaveric theory', suggesting that infectious particles from patients who had died of, or were infected with, the fever were conveyed to healthy lying-in women on the hands of the students. He insisted that the students and physicians, when returning from the mortuary and in between examinations of every patient, washed their hands and scrubbed their nails in a bowl of chloride of lime placed at the entrance to the ward, so that 'not the faintest trace of cadaver aroma' would be left. Cases of puerperal fever on the ward fell dramatically.

This simple and effective method for preventing the spread of puerperal fever was not taken up more widely, however, and mortality from puerperal fever in many countries actually rose in the following years. It was not until some twenty years after his death in 1865 in a lunatic asylum that the significance of Semmelweis' findings was widely realized, and he became hailed as an unsung hero. In the meantime, there had been an important breakthrough in identifying the cause of puerperal fever as well as the introduction of antisepsis in surgery and a more general adoption of asepsis practices.

Germs – from sepsis to antisepsis and asepsis

'All that would be needful would be to purify the surface of the skin of the part to be operated upon by means of some efficient antiseptic, to have my own hands, and those of my assistants, and also the instruments, similarly purified; and then the operation might be performed without the antiseptic spray ... and no one would rejoice more than myself to be able to dispense with it.' Joseph Lister, 1875

The identification of the causal agent of puerperal fever is usually credited to Louis Pasteur, who in 1879 described the bacterial micro-organisms responsible as *microbes en chapelet* ('microbes like a rosary'). His finding was confirmed by others, and the bacterium causing puerperal fever was subsequently named *Streptococcus pyogenes* (from the Greek *streptos*, 'twisted like a chain', *coccus*, meaning a 'berry', and *pyogenes*, translated as 'pus-producing'). *Streptococcus pyogenes* is a spherical, gram-positive bacterium that is the cause of group A streptococcal infections; we now know that it can lead to many important human diseases, ranging from mild superficial skin infections to life-threatening systemic diseases.

As Pasteur, Robert Koch and others identified a range of disease-causing bacterial germs, a number of physicians and nurses were finding ways to prevent the spread of germs in hospitals. The British surgeon Joseph Lister (1827–1912) is best remembered for his pioneering use of antisepsis (Greek *anti-*, 'against' and *sēpsis*, 'putrefaction') in surgery. He first used carbolic acid as an antiseptic on a young boy, James Greenless, who in 1865 had been run over by a cart and had sustained a compound fracture of the left leg and a nasty open wound where the broken bone had perforated the skin. Lister, who was then Regius Professor of surgery at Glasgow University, had been intrigued by some of the early ideas published by Pasteur – in particular his ideas that microscopic living organisms, carried from place to place by the air, caused putrefaction. By dressing James' wound with lint soaked in carbolic acid (in the form of 'German creosote'), he was able to save the boy's leg. Lister's famous aerosol spray of carbolic acid was used throughout operating theatres in an attempt to kill germs in the air, and the strong smell of disinfectant also began to pervade some of the maternity wards.

Not everyone was initially convinced by the antiseptic methods of using chemicals, preferring to use water to clean wounds and the 'Nightingale' principle of keeping hospitals clean and well ventilated. Florence Nightingale, who returned to London a heroine from the Crimean War of 1854–6, worked endlessly to reform hospital and nursing care and encourage good hygiene in hospitals. In 1860, she set up the Nightingale School of Nursing as part of St Thomas' Hospital in London, and a new profession of nursing was established. She also promoted a healthy, airy style of 'pavilion' hospital design 'to keep the wards perfectly sweet'. Their location and design aimed to maximize cross-ventilation, reduce contagion and eliminate 'corrupt airs'. Nightingale reiterated an old Hippocratic saying when she wrote: 'It may seem a strange principle to enunciate as the very first requirement in a Hospital that it should do the sick no harm.'

Nightingale's ideas were based on the miasmic theory of disease. But as an understanding of germ theory spread among a new generation of bacteriologists, it was eventually accepted within the field of surgery that bacteria in wounds were the cause of suppuration and infection. In 1874 Lister wrote to Pasteur: 'Allow me to take this opportunity for thanking you most heartily for having shown me, by your brilliant investigations, the truth of the germ theory of putrefaction, and having thus acquainted me with the one principle which can lead the antiseptic method to final success.'

This 'antiseptic method' also encouraged the more wide-spread principle of 'asepsis' (Greek *a-*, 'without' and *sēpsis*, 'putrefaction'), with the aim of excluding germs in the first place without the skin irritation of chemical antiseptics. Dramatic blood-encrusted frock-coats smelling of that 'good old surgical stink' were gradually abandoned in favour of clean surgical gowns, caps, gloves and masks, and the steam sterilization of surgical instruments and dressings. In the best-managed mater-nity hospitals, too, everybody and everything – from the mothers in labour to the doctors and midwives (in their clean caps, gowns, masks and gloves), and all the instruments used to assist the birth – were washed down with soap and hot water or doused in disinfectant or sterilized in heated autoclaves. Those suffering from puerperal fever were isolated. By the 1880s, once the sig-nificance of these methods was recognized, puerperal fever was seen as eminently preventable. The effect in some lying-in hos-pitals as well as in home deliveries, especially in continental Europe, was startling.

In the early twentieth century, the majority of women in Europe continued to give birth at home. In Scandinavia, Belgium and the Netherlands home deliveries were attended by midwives strictly trained and fully aware of the vital importance of pre-venting the spread of puerperal fever, and there was a marked reduction in maternal mortality in these countries. There was also a tradition of minimum surgical interference, rather than the use of forceps in home and hospital deliveries in north-west Europe.

Two other success stories stand out. In England and Wales, the rural nurse midwives of the Queen's Nursing Institute (a charity originally founded in 1887 to train district nurses) was an organization of highly trained and supervised nurses and midwives which was particularly active between the 1920s and 1940s and achieved very low rates of maternal mortality similar to, if not better than, the rates achieved in the northwestern European countries.

Similar low levels of maternal mortality were achieved in Kentucky, USA, during the 1920s and 1930s by a remarkable service in the history of maternal care that was founded by Mary Breckinridge (1881–1965). Midwives in the Kentucky Frontier Nursing Service travelled on horseback to assist with deliveries, which, in poor rural farming communities, were all at home. During its first several years of operation, mothers and babies of eastern Kentucky experienced substantially lower mortality rates than the rest of America.

However, the fear of death in childbirth remained, and there were wide variations in the adoption of the principles of antisepsis and asepsis. In many maternity hospitals in the USA and Britain, birth attendants continued to practise without the necessary preventive measures. In the USA, where many deliveries took place in hospitals, one-quarter of a million mothers died in childbirth in the 1920s. Even by the 1930s there were still no masks, gloves or sterilized instruments in Queen Charlotte's Maternity Hospital, London. It has since been shown that wearing a mask is one of the most effective preventive measures, as the streptococcal bug is transmitted primarily by carriers via respiratory droplets exhaled onto patients.

Notwithstanding some success stories, in Great Britain in the first half of the 1930s the risk of women dying from puerperal fever was as high as they had been in the 1860s. Ironically, it was often the upper social classes who suffered most, as they were likely to be delivered by physicians and experience unnecessary interference. One other key development in nineteenth-century surgery had been anaesthesia (from the Greek, *an-*, 'without', and *aísthēsis*, 'feeling or sensation') which was first tried out in dental surgery, using nitrous oxide or laughing gas, by the American dentist, Horace Wells (1815–48) in 1844. Two years later William Morton (1819–68) successfully and famously used ether in an operation at the Massachusetts General Hospital, Boston. In 1847 Scottish physician James Young Simpson gave another anaesthetic, chloroform, which he believed was pleasanter and more potent than ether, for the first time to a woman in labour. John Snow (of cholera fame) administered chloroform to Queen Victoria during the birth of her eighth child – Prince Leopold. She described the effects as 'soothing, quieting and delightful beyond measure.'

But some questioned this practice, and in Britain the widespread use of chloroform and forceps by doctors in uncomplicated deliveries was described by one observer as a tendency a 'little short of murder' and said to account for many unnecessary deaths, with puerperal fever remaining the most common cause of maternal mortality. The British obstetrician, Grantly Dick-Read (1890–1959), was greatly concerned about the increasing use of anaesthesia, twilight sleep (using narcotics to relieve the pain of childbirth) and obstetric intervention, and was a leading advocate of natural childbirth. His 1940s book, *Childbirth Without Fear*, became an international best-seller.

With wide geographical and social variations in the risk of contracting puerperal fever, and associated variations in rates of maternal mortality, historians have concluded that the main determinant of these disparities was the overall standard of maternal care provided by birth attendants. It took another medical revolution to reduce maternal mortality radically across the Western world.

A new era: antibiotics

'Today, antibiotics are as common as a cup of coffee. In the 1950s they were relatively new . . . they really were a miracle drug.' Jennifer Worth, *Call the Midwife: A True Story of the East End in the 1950s*, 2002

The introduction of anti-bacterial drugs was the greatest advance for the treatment of bacterial infections in the history of medicine. The first drugs to be used for puerperal fever, in the late 1930s, were the sulphonamides. Their discovery came about after a number of experiments with the red-orange textile dye Prontosil. In December 1935 the six-year-old daughter of Gerhard Domagk (1895–1964), research director at Bayer laboratories in Germany, was seriously ill after contracting a streptococcal infection when a needle went though her hand. Domagk administered Prontosil and she recovered. A year later, at Queen Charlotte's Maternity Hospital in London, British physician Leonard Colebrook (1883–1967) demonstrated the dramatic effect of Prontosil on puerperal sepsis. Scientists at the Institut Pasteur in Paris were able to show that Prontosil was broken down in the body and that its active principle was not the dye but the colourless compound p-aminobenzene-sulphonomide (sulphanilamide). New 'sulphonamide' or 'sulpha' drugs proved highly effective against group A streptococcal infection, and mortality from puerperal fever dropped dramatically.

With the availability of the antibiotic, penicillin, from the mid-1940s a new era dawned. Penicillin was more active and less toxic than the sulphonamides, and could also treat a rarer cause of puerperal fever, *Staphylococcus aureus*. Midwifery was also becoming increasingly professional, and in both hospitals and the home, childbirth was infinitely safer than it had been in the past. Mothers in labour could at last be reasonably optimistic that they would live to see their newborn infants grow up. By the 1950s puerperal fever in the Western world was no longer a life-threatening disorder, and its very name now has an old-fashioned ring to it.

Maternal mortality – from all causes – continued to fall sharply over the second half of the twentieth century, and death in childbirth is now the exception rather than the half-expected outcome. Puerperal fever went from being the main cause of maternal mortality in the 1870s to being a subordinate cause by the 1970s. Today, in the developed world, professionally trained midwives – either in maternity hospitals or in the home and community – play a major role in childbirth, while district nurses, health visitors and social workers provide a continuum of care for mothers and babies.

The continuing tragedy of death in childbirth

Sadly, this is not the case in many of the poorer countries of the world, where mothers often give birth in the harshest conditions and without any means to prevent or treat infections. Indeed, the maternal mortality rate in developing regions is fourteen times higher than that of the developed world and 99 per cent of global maternal deaths occur in developing countries. Puerperal sepsis (a term now used to cover a number of causal infectious agents) continues to threaten the lives of mothers and babies, especially in Africa and parts of Asia. Over a quarter of a million mothers still die every year, often from preventable causes related to pregnancy and childbirth. Puerperal sepsis, which can be prevented with good hygiene and early treatment with antibiotics, is one of the major causes, and accounts for 15 per cent of all maternal deaths in developing countries. If it does not cause death, puerperal sepsis can cause long-term health problems such as chronic pelvic inflammatory diseases and infertility.

We know from the history of puerperal fever that skilled care, good hygiene and nutrition before, during and after childbirth can save the lives of women and newborn babies, and midwifery services need to be a pivotal and core part of universal health coverage. Yet, still, more than half of births among the rural poor in low-income countries take place without a skilled birth attendant. This means that millions of births are not assisted by a midwife, a doctor or a trained nurse. The United Nations made a commitment, as part of its Millennium Development Goals 2000–2015, to reduce maternal mortality. And, indeed, some of the world's poorest countries have managed to cut maternal and young child mortality rates by half or more. The importance of breastfeeding infants is also being widely promoted. Momentum is gathering, but there is still a need to move faster. The number of mothers and babies dying from preventable infections and complications of pregnancy (including those leading to premature births) remains one of the great tragedies of the modern world.

ENCEPHALITIS LETHARGICA

Encephalitis lethargica – or the 'sleepy sickness' – is a mysterious affliction that spread as a pandemic around the globe from around 1916 to the 1930s. Sufferers experienced a range of bizarre symptoms and devastating after-effects. The disease attacked the brain, leaving its worst-affected victims motionless and speechless. About one-third died during the acute stages of the disease, but thousands of others were left in a somnolent state that subsequently progressed to a condition known as post-encephalitic Parkinsonism. There are still a number of sporadic cases of encephalitis lethargica (possibly following a streptococcal bacterial infection), but what it really was, whether it was connected to the Spanish flu pandemic of 1918–19, and why it hit the world with such force in the early twentieth century remains one of the great unsolved modern medical mysteries.

∽

One of the first physicians to describe – and the first to name – encephalitis lethargica was Baron Constantin von Economo (1876–1931), a Romanian-born neurologist (of Greek parentage) working in Vienna, Austria: 'Some died within a few weeks, others lingered for weeks or months, falling into periods of deep sleep punctuated by comas ... The most affected surviving patients ... sit motionless, aware of their surroundings, but lethargic and unresponsive, like extinct volcanoes.' Von Economo observed his first cases of this mysterious disease in the wards of the Wagner-Jauregg Clinic for Psychiatry and Nervous Diseases in Vienna in the winter of 1916–17, while the European powers were mired in the horrors of the First World War. Other similar but equally ill-defined cases had been noted in France in the winter of 1915–16, and it is likely that earlier cases had occurred in central Europe some two or three years previously.

Soon after von Economo's description, the disease appears to have spread in waves across the world. It was described in Australia in late 1917, in England in early 1918 (where it was at first attributed to botulism – a severe form of food poisoning) and in North America by late 1918 to early 1919. It continued to take its toll during the 1920s and was reported in many parts of the world. By the 1930s the pandemic had seemingly come to an end – almost as quickly as it had arrived.

The symptoms of those stricken were so varied and so complex that the medical establishment had no idea whether they were dealing with one disease or a thousand different ones. One feature, however, seemed to unify all those affected – lethargy (*encephalitis lethargica* literally means 'inflammation of the brain that makes you tired'). In spite of various speculations at the time, its cause was, and still remains, a mystery.

The baffling nature of encephalitis lethargica

'Young people ... now appear senile, emaciated, bent, with a demented "greasy face", dripping mouth and trembling chin, and drag themselves along with a hesitating gait. To look at these people of twenty and thirty years of age is most terrible for the physician.' From the 1931 English translation of Constantin von Economo's monograph *Encephalitis Lethargica* (2nd edition, 1929)

In the period 1916–27, anywhere between half and 1 million people (some estimates put it as high as 5 million), of all ages but especially young adults, were affected by encephalitis lethargica. Possibly as many as one-third died quickly after the acute phase, either in a 'deep sleep' or in a state of insomnia. Patients displayed a baffling range of peculiar symptoms – sore throats, headache, fever followed by severe lethargy, insomnia, tremors, hiccoughs, tics, twitching and disturbances of eye movement (including 'oculogyric crises', in which the eyeballs are fixed in one position for a period of time). Some of those who were afflicted by the complaint recovered after a few days or weeks, but many others became lethargic and unresponsive, and unable to interact with or participate in the world around them.

Many of the long-term survivors were affected, some time after the original infection, by a condition known as post-encephalitic Parkinsonism, similar in presentation but unrelated in origin, to Parkinson's disease, which was named after the British surgeon, James Parkinson (1755–1824), who is most famous for his 1817 work, *An Essay on the Shaking Palsy*. Many of those in this chronic phase experienced severe neurological problems, psychotic episodes, personality changes and behavioural disturbances. Some were confined to institutions, where they existed like living statues, unaware of their surroundings or the passage of the years.

L-dopa and the awakenings

In the 1960s a new drug, L-dopa, seemed to offer exciting possibilities as a treatment for those suffering from Parkinson's disease, and it is still used for this condition today. Oliver Sacks (b.1933), a British neurologist working at the Beth Abraham Hospital in New York, was among the first to try out L-dopa on a group of patients with post-encephalitic Parkinsonism, who, as Sacks put it, had been 'frozen and hidden for decades – profoundly isolated – half-forgetting, half-dreaming of the world they had once lived in.'

In his 1973 book *Awakenings* (which was made into a feature film in 1990), Sacks recounts the moving stories of some of his patients – their amazing and miraculous 'awakenings' when first treated with L-dopa in the spring of 1969, and then the subsequent bizarre effects when the drug failed to live up to expectations. He writes: 'The central themes of *Awakenings* – falling asleep, being turned to stone; being awakened decades later, to a world no longer one's own – have an immediate power to grip the imagination. This is the stuff that dreams, nightmares, and legends are made of – and yet it actually happened.'

One patient, known as Rose R., who had been struck by a virulent form of encephalitis lethargica in 1926, had been in the hospital since 1935. In 1969 she 'came joyously to life' after being given L-dopa. But she was entirely engrossed in her memories of the 1920s, seeing herself still as a flapper girl, in love with the music of Gershwin. But then, as L-dopa proved less and less effective, her mood began to veer from elation to anxiety. The world of 1969, into which she awoke, was not real. 'Is 1926 now?' she asked. In the end, Rose – a Sleeping Beauty whose 'awakening' was too unbearable for her – wanted never to be awoken again.

Another patient, Leonard L., made a miraculous recovery after he was first given L-dopa. But it became harder and harder to find an optimal dose to keep him awake and to stop him from regressing. When, some years later, ailing and very frail, he was given a final dose of L-dopa, his 'awakening' response was to question why he should be 'resurrected' when it was already too late.

What was encephalitis lethargica?

'As far as the historical record of the disease was concerned, this malady was something new, mysterious in its
onset, and appalling in its destruction. Its etiology was a
matter of conjecture, its pathology merely guessed at, and
its sequelae undreamt of.' A. Pool, 1930; quoted in Joel A.
Vilensky (ed.) *Encephalitis Lethargica: During and After
the Epidemic*, 2011

Encephalitis lethargica in both the acute and chronic phase was a kaleidoscope of symptoms. How was it possible to have an epidemic of sleepiness, insomnia, paralysis, hyperactivity and hysteria all at once? Were these protean cases triggered by an infection? If so, what? And was this really a new disease?

As Joel Vilensky has discussed in the first comprehensive study of the disease in seventy-five years, physicians, at the time of the pandemic, were desperate to come up with answers. A massive search was undertaken to find the organism that might be causing the disease. Tissues (typically brain) and fluids (cere-brospinal fluid, blood and nasopharyngeal washings) from victims were injected into the brains of a large variety of animal species (especially rabbits) in attempts to develop an animal model of the disease and isolate the causative agent – either a bacterium that could be cultured or a 'filterable' virus that could pass through the smallest pores of available filters (viruses were not actually identified as structures until 1935, following the invention of the electron microscope). One group of researchers who focused on the search for a bacterium suggested the possibility that a streptococcal infection could be the culprit. On the basis that it was caused by an infectious agent, vaccines were developed and given to patients who already had the illness rather than unaffected individuals who were at risk.

Von Economo and his contemporaries also trawled though the historical literature to see if they could find evidence of similar outbreaks of a sleepy sickness in the past. Indeed, there have been a number of neurological conditions in the past as mysterious as encephalitis lethargica. Some began with manic dancing, followed by stupor, death or permanent tremors in survivors. In the 1370s in the Rhine basin of Germany and the Low Countries, there was an epidemic of what is known as St Vitus' Dance. It involved groups of people joining hands and dancing wildly for hours in a delirium, until they fell exhausted to the ground. During the sixteenth century there were mysterious outbreaks of 'sweating sickness' in England, characterized by somnolence as well as sweating. Europe in the 1580s was swept by a serious febrile and lethargic illness, leading to neurological complications.

A century later, Thomas Sydenham (1624–89) described an unusual epidemic, which occurred in London in 1673–5, as 'febris comatosa'. Symptoms included fever, sleepiness and hiccoughs, and chiefly infected 'the brain and nervous system'. He also wrote about St Vitus' dance, which is now known as Sydenham's chorea. This is characterized by rapid uncoordinated jerking movements, motor weakness and behavioural disorders, possibly occurring as a latent effect of a streptococcal infection. It has been suggested that this might have an aetiology (cause) similar to encephalitis lethargica. Germany experienced another strange outbreak in 1712 known as the *Schlafkrankheit* ('sleeping disease') in which the afflicted also showed signs of morbid changes in the structure of the brain.

Von Economo himself was intrigued by hearing stories of a mysterious and severe somnolent illness known as *nona* which occurred in Italy, following an influenza pandemic in 1889–90. The symptoms sounded hauntingly similar to the cases he was seeing in his clinic. Indeed, since he first identified cases of encephalitis lethargica and even down to the present day, there have been speculations that influenza might have played a role in the encephalitis lethargica pandemic. Was encephalitis lethargica a type of post-viral syndrome afflicting influenza sufferers?

With the current fear of another major pandemic of human influenza following the recent outbreaks of bird and swine flu, this is an important medical issue. The most obvious link is the fact that the encephalitis lethargica pandemic occurred during approximately the same time period as the devastating Spanish flu pandemic of 1918–19. However, so far there is no concrete scientific evidence for an aetiological connection. For example, recent examination of archived encephalitis brain material from the 1920s has failed to demonstrate influenza RNA. Moreover, the onset of the pandemic of encephalitis lethargica seems to have preceded the influenza pandemic, and it continued to rage for at least ten years after the influenza pandemic had receded.

The debate on whether there is a relationship (either causal or, simply, coincidental) between the two pandemics continues.

In the meanwhile, some scientists who have re-examined the historical evidence, as well as studying current sporadic cases, have suggested that encephalitis lethargica was triggered not by a viral infection but rather by a bacterium, in which the body's immune system reacts violently to a throat infection (possibly streptococcal) by attacking the nerve cells of the brain. Even if this line of inquiry proves to be correct, it does not tell us why the disease erupted so violently, and why it then, after a decade, apparently almost disappeared.

For those who died or suffered a lifetime of frozen 'sleep', any retrospective diagnosis is too late. Today, there are still occasional cases in young people of what appears to be encephalitis lethargica, so understanding the causes of the disease, and finding an effective treatment, remains critical – especially as it is impossible to say if or when there will be another sudden violent eruption of this mysterious disease.

Parasitic Diseases

MALARIA

Malaria is a life-threatening, parasitic disease transmitted from person to person by the bite of an infective female *Anopheles* mosquito. It is one of the most significant health problems in the world today, killing an estimated 627,000 people, mostly infants and children, every year. Malaria is one of the oldest diseases in human history, and in the past it ranged from Archangel in the Russian Arctic to Australia and Argentina in the Southern hemisphere. It is thought that malaria has killed more people than any other single infectious disease over the past few millennia. The development of effective tools for preventing malaria and reducing its effects on human health awaited the discovery of malaria parasites and the role of anopheline mosquitoes in their transmission at the end of the nineteenth century. The disease is now largely confined to around a hundred countries in the tropical and subtropical regions of Africa, Asia and Latin America, where it still causes immense suffering in some of the poorest areas of the world. Ninety per cent of the world's malaria deaths are in Africa. Scientists and international health organizations are giving much-needed attention to malaria as a serious global health problem, with increased commitment and funding to treat and prevent the disease with effective drugs and vector control, as well as through the promotion of insecticide-treated bed nets. It is hoped that a malaria vaccine – the first vaccine for any parasitic disease – will be approved in 2015.

∾

In 1937 the American malariologist Lewis Hackett (1884–1962) articulated the complex and variable nature of malaria: 'Everything about malaria is so moulded and altered by local conditions that it becomes a thousand different diseases and epidemiological puzzles. Like chess, it is played with a few pieces, but is capable of an infinite variety of situations.' The pieces involved in this deadly game comprise the mosquito, the parasite that causes the disease, and the human host. However, there are in fact thirty to forty species of the mosquito genus *Anopheles* capable of transmitting malaria, each with its own breeding preference in different types of water, and there are five species of the protozoan parasite that infect humans: *Plasmodium falciparum* (the deadliest form), *P. vivax*, *P. ovale*, *P. malariae* and *P. knowlesi*. Susceptibility in the human host can be determined by factors such as immunity, nutritional status and overall health, while exposure to malaria infection is linked to broader social and economic forces that drive the epidemiology of the disease. This multiplicity results in a wide range of possible variations in the local pattern of disease transmission and clinical symptoms.

Life cycle and symptoms

When a female mosquito carrying plasmodium parasites bites a human being, the parasites are injected into the blood. The parasites then rapidly enter cells in the liver and change into new forms that invade red blood cells. Every forty-eight or seventy-two hours (depending on the species), the parasites complete a cycle of multiplication in the red blood cells and then burst out, inducing the periodic fevers that characterize the disease. Any female mosquito biting an infected person itself becomes infected, so continuing the cycle.

The clinical course of malaria is characterized by a range of symptoms. These can include alternate bouts of hot and cold sweats, high fever, headache, malaise, and aches and pains. Malaria can be mild, chronic or fatal. In severe cases the disease may lead to chronic anaemia, and complications such as coma and cerebral malaria can be fatal. The fatality rate among untreated children and non-immune adults may be 10–40 per cent or higher. Pregnant women are at high risk of dying from the complications of severe malaria. Malaria is also a cause of spontaneous abortion, premature delivery, stillbirth and severe maternal anaemia, and is responsible for about one-third of preventable low birth-weight babies. Even for those who survive their early episodes of malaria, the disease can still be severely debilitating.

The stench of the swamp

The role of the mosquito and its parasite in transmitting malaria was not unravelled until the late nineteenth century. In previous centuries people ascribed the disease to a range of factors and called it by a host of different names, including 'ague', 'tertian fever', 'quartan fever', 'malignant fever', 'marsh fever', 'swamp fever', 'autumnal fever', 'Roman fever' or 'the shakes'.

In many parts of the world people noticed that the disease was found near foul-smelling stagnant marshes and swamps. This led to the idea that the disease was caused by poisonous or noxious vapours emanating from the marshes. The Italians in the sixteenth century gave the disease the name '*mala aria*', literally meaning 'bad air'. The word 'malaria' was adapted into the English language in 1740 by Horace Walpole (1717–97). While travelling in Italy, he wrote home: 'there is a horrid thing called the mal'aria, that comes to Rome every summer and kills one.' Edward Hasted (1732–1812) in his *History and Topographical Survey of the County of Kent* (1797–1801) reminds us of the miasmatic connection: '[In Romney Marsh, Kent] the large quantity of stagnating waters engenders such noxious and pestilential vapours as spread sickness and frequent death on the inhabitants . . . the sickly countenances of them plainly discovering the unwholesome air they breathe in.'

Malaria in the ancient and early modern worlds

In the past malaria had a much wider distribution than it does today, and was, for example, a common disease around the Mediterranean basin from ancient times to the mid-twentieth century. Hippocratic writings dating from the fifth century BC described malarial symptoms, including the enlarged spleens of people who lived in marshy areas, and fevers were classified as quotidian, tertian and quartan depending on their periodicity. Some scholars have even speculated that the disease played a role in the decline of both ancient Greece and the Roman empire.

The exact chronology and geographical distribution of the disease in ancient times are currently the subject of historical investigation, but the existence of genetic traits that confer some protection against malaria, such as sickle-cell anaemia and thalassaemia, indicates a long evolutionary history, and it is likely that malaria has plagued humans for more than 6,000 years.

In the early modern period, in areas of Italy such as the Po Valley, the Pontine Marshes, the Roman Campagna and the Mezzogiorno region of the south, malaria was a serious problem with major social and economic consequences until its final eradication in the mid-twentieth century. One nineteenth-century Italian writer described its impact:

Malaria penetrates your bones with the bread that you eat and every time you open your mouth to speak, whilst walking along the stifling streets choked with dust and sunlight, when you feel your knees buckling under you, or you slump on the pack saddle of an ambling mule, head hung low ... For malaria seizes the inhabitants in the empty lanes or strikes them down by the sun-bleached house door, shaking with fever in their overcoats, with all the blankets in the house heaped on their shoulders.

It was also a serious disease in parts of France, as another writer noted:

The inhabitants of the Dombes, that vast filthy marsh from which emanates the poisoned gas they ... inhale ... have pale, livid complexions, dull, downcast eyes, swollen eyelids and lined wrinkled faces; their shoulders are narrow, their necks elongated, their voices high pitched, their skin is either dry or soaked in debilitating sweat and they walk slowly and painfully ... they are old at thirty, and broken and decrepit at forty or fifty. They live out their brief miserable life on the edges of a tomb.

In areas of southern Europe the most dangerous form of malaria, falciparum malaria, was endemic. The vivax form of malaria also appears to have become endemic in parts of the temperate world. Capable of being transmitted in areas where average summer temperatures are over 16°C (61°F), the *P. vivax* parasite is generally known as producing the 'benign' or milder form of the disease. Yet historical accounts from northern Europe suggest that even this form of the disease was anything but mild. In the marshes of Kent and Essex and the eastern fenland counties of England, where the disease was endemic in some localities up until the early twentieth century, one in three babies died before their first birthday – with malaria partly contributing to the high death toll.

From the Old to the New World

Although some have suggested that malaria was already present in the New World prior to 1492, it is more likely that travellers from northern Europe carried the *P. vivax* parasite to the New World after that date. The local mosquitoes would have become infected, passing on the disease in turn to the indigenous populations and early colonists. In New England in the seventeenth century the disease was popularly known as the 'Kentish ague'.

Travel and trade between the Americas and southern Europe – and the importation of slaves from Africa – brought the more deadly *P. faliciparum* parasite to the subtropical and tropical parts of the New World. The southern regions of North America and parts of South and Central America became severely affected, and malaria had also reached the Mississippi valley by the nineteenth century. In southern Illinois, during the summer of 1865, one doctor noted that 'every man, woman and child . . . at least within my range shook with the ague every other day'.

The area all along the watercourses from the Mississippi to the Potomac was described in the early nineteenth century as a 'graveyard', and it was suspected by one authority that 'no changes and no cultivation will ever bring it into a state of salubrity'. One account from the 1830s describes an exchange between the captain of a boat on the Ohio River and the mother of two young children. The children had crawled out into the warm sun – shivering and with chattering teeth – to watch the boat go past. Their mother, uncertain as to the cause of their fever, was told by the captain of the boat:

> If you've never seen that kind of sickness I reckon you must be a Yankee. That's the ague. I'm feared you will see plenty of it if you stay long in these parts. They call it here the swamp devil and it will take the roses out of the cheeks of these plump little ones of yours mighty quick. Cure it? No, Madam. No cure for it: have to wear it out.

The 'White Man's Grave'

Sailors used to sing a shanty containing the warning lines:

> Beware, beware the Bight of Benin,
> For there's one that comes out for ten that goes in.

In the past, Europeans penetrating the continent of Africa were frequently struck down by violent fevers. Some may have had immunity to the northern European or vivax form of malaria, but when exposed to the more deadly falciparum form for the first time, it soon proved lethal. The coast and rivers of West Africa proved particularly deadly, and the area around the Bight (bay) of Benin became known as the 'White Man's Grave'. Almost half of the British soldiers stationed in Sierra Leone between 1817 and 1836 died, mostly from malaria. In India, too, epidemics of malaria repeatedly struck with a vengeance, affecting and killing both local and European populations and accounting possibly for some 1.3 million deaths a year by the 1890s.

Early remedies

Early remedies for the treatment of malaria included all sorts of herbal remedies as well as other speculative ideas – for example, wearing a large fish tooth as an amulet or eating spiders whole in butter. Purging and bleeding were thought to rectify imbalances in the body's 'humours', and were frequently resorted to in order to get rid of the 'bad blood'.

Opium has been used for medicinal and recreational purposes since ancient times. In the nineteenth century much of the opium used in Britain was imported from India, and it came as a surprise to some to discover that in the marshy Fens of eastern England – where malaria was formerly endemic –the locals actually grew their own opium poppies. Opium was said to prevent the shivering fits of the 'ague', and the local beer was laced with it, while infants were dosed with poppy-head tea.

In 1864 a doctor was shocked to discover that 'there was not a labourer's house in which the bottle of opiate was not to be seen ... it is also sold in pills or penny sticks, and a well-accustomed shop will serve 300 or 400 customers with the article on a Saturday night'. Opium-eating infants were described as 'wasted ... shrank up into little old men ... wizened like monkeys'. As a consequence of both malaria and narcotic poisoning, the infant mortality rate in the Fens was exceptionally high.

However, some early cures proved highly effective. In the early seventeenth century Jesuit missionaries in South America noticed that the indigenous people used the bark of a native tree to control fevers (or so the story goes, as there are many myths about the discovery of the bark). The Jesuits sent the bark – known by a number of names, including cinchona bark (after the Spanish Countess of Chinchón, the wife of the Viceroy of Peru), Peruvian bark, Jesuits' bark and *quinquina* – back to Europe. It was introduced into England in the 1650s, where the Puritan Lord Protector Oliver Cromwell called it the 'Devil's Powder' because of its association with the Catholic Church. He refused to use it despite suffering badly from malaria, which he probably contracted in the English Fens. Robert Talbor (1642–81), an English quack, however, made his fame and fortune using a 'secret remedy' based on the bark to cure European royals and nobility.

The Scottish physician William Buchan (1729–1805) came up with a remedy in the 1780s that sounds like the first recipe for gin and tonic: 'Take an ounce of the best Jesuits bark, Virginian snake-root, and orange-peel, of each half an ounce; bruise them all together, and infuse for five or six days in a bottle of brandy, Holland gin, or any good spirit; afterwards pour off the clear liquor, and take a wine-glass of it twice or thrice a day'. In 1820 the alkaloid quinine was extracted from the bark by two French chemists, Pierre-Joseph Pelletier (1788–1842) and Joseph Caventou (1795–1877). With the recognition that this was the most effective anti-malarial agent within the cinchona bark, botanical explorations into the South American interior were undertaken to find quinine-yielding cinchona trees with the added aim of establishing plantations in other parts of the world. Charles Ledger (1818–1905), a British merchant, with the help of his faithful servant, Manuel Mamani, a Bolivian *cascarillero* (who made a living stripping the bark from the cinchona trees), obtained seeds in 1865 from a rare Bolivian species with one of the highest quinine contents. However, when Ledger and his brother, George, tried to sell these to the British government their offer was rejected and it was the Dutch government which – for a mere 100 guilders – purchased most of the seeds and established valuable plantations in Java in the Dutch East Indies. Quinine is still used as a treatment today, as well as in tonic water.

Unravelling the mystery

'What malaria is nobody knows ... there is no doubt, however, that malaria is some mysterious poison in the atmosphere, and that it is confined strictly to certain localities.' *Scientific American*, 1861

In the late nineteenth century, faced with the enormous global toll of malaria, scientists started to unravel the cause of the disease. Was it really spread from the foul vapours of the swamps and marshes? Alphonse Laveran (1845–1922), a French army surgeon in Algeria, recognized, under the microscope, malaria parasites in the blood film of a patient in 1880. He subsequently meticulously examined the blood of other patients and observed the crescent-shaped bodies in all cases of malaria but never in those cases without malaria. With further research he was convinced that the blood parasites were the cause of malaria. Although his initial communications on the malaria parasite were received with much scepticism, this was the first time that a protozoan parasite had ever been identified, and in 1907 Laveran was awarded the Nobel Prize in Physiology or Medicine. In the 1880s the Italian scientists Ettore Marchiafava (1847–1935) and Angelo Celli (1857–1914) also identified parasites under the microscope and gave the organism its generic name, *Plasmodium*. Other Italian scientists, including Camillo Golgi (1843–1926), distinguished three different forms of the plasmodium – which are now known as *P. vivax, P. falciparum* and *P. malariae*. But how did the parasite spread from one human to another?

Patrick Manson (1844–1922), a Scottish doctor, became known as 'Mosquito Manson' after he discovered the role of the mosquito in lymphatic filariasis (elephantiasis) in 1877. But it was his protégé, a British army doctor called Ronald Ross (1857–1932), who went down in history as the first scientist to make the connection between mosquitoes and malaria.

While stationed at Secunderabad in India, Ross, inspired by Manson's ideas of a mosquito connection, dissected and examined the stomachs of thousands of mosquitoes in a cramped, hot, humid laboratory until, almost exhausted, he eventually found 'pigmented cysts' – evidence of the malaria parasite – protruding from the stomach wall of a 'dapple-winged' (i.e. an *Anopheles*) mosquito that had fed on a patient with malaria. In 1897 Ross reported his remarkable discovery, and in the following year, in Calcutta, was able to elucidate the entire malaria-mosquito cycle of avian malaria.

Ross – who was something of an amateur poet – celebrated his eureka moment on 20 August 1897, known afterwards as 'Mosquito Day', with the following words:

This day relenting God
Hath placed within my hand
A wondrous thing; and God
Be praised. At His command,

Seeking His secret deeds
With tears and toiling breath,
I find thy cunning seeds,
O million-murdering Death.

I know this little thing
A myriad men will save.
O Death, where is thy sting
Thy victory, O grave?

Italian scientists were hot on Ross's heels, and by 1898 Giovanni Battista Grassi (1854–1925), Amico Bignami (1862–1929) and Giuseppe Bastianelli (1862–1959) had shown experimentally that malaria was transmitted to humans by *Anopheles* mosquitoes. Ross was awarded the Nobel Prize in Physiology or Medicine in 1902, but the Italians, justifiably, felt that their vital contributions had been overlooked.

Mosquito brigades

Once it was understood that mosquitoes carried the parasite, it seemed all too certain that a way of breaking the cycle would follow. For the first time in history, it was thought that if the mosquito vector could be eliminated, malaria transmission could be prevented and this 'million-murdering' death could be conquered. Ross later recalled his hopes:

In a few more months, perhaps in a year, or in two years, the death-dealing pests would begin to come under control, would begin to diminish entirely in favourable spots; and with them, slowly, the ubiquitous malady would fly from the face of civilization – not here or there only, but almost throughout the British Empire – nay, further, in America, China, and Europe.

Fired with optimism, 'mosquito brigades' drained swamps and other breeding sites of the mosquito, and sprayed them with chemicals such as Paris Green (a larvicide prepared from copper acetate and arsenic trioxide) and from the 1930s pyrethrum (a powdered extract from the chrysanthemum flower). Mosquito brigades went into action in India, Malaysia and elsewhere, and even attempted (albeit unsuccessfully) to eliminate the indigenous *Anopheles* mosquito from the marshes of Kent in south-east England. People in malarial areas were advised to use bed nets, screens and head nets. Ross himself claimed he was scrupulous in using a bed net to avoid getting malaria: 'I myself have been infected with malaria only once in spite of nineteen years' service in India . . . I attribute this good fortune to my scrupulous use of the bed net'– advice that still holds good today.

A successful campaign against both the malarial mosquito and the yellow fever mosquito allowed the Panama Canal to be completed by 1914. Following a major malaria outbreak in 1938–9 in north-east Brazil, Fred Soper (1893–1977), a member of the Rockefeller Foundation and one of the leading forces behind vector control, successfully led a campaign to rid the area of the *A. gambiae* mosquito – one of the most efficient malaria vectors in the world – which had been accidentally imported from West Africa. By focusing primarily on larviciding all potential habitats, he averted a major public health disaster. Soper continued to advocate what was known as 'species eradication'.

Quinine – attacking the parasite

Some scientists, including the German bacteriologist Robert Koch, advocated a different tack. Rather than trying to eliminate the mosquito, it would be better, they claimed, to attack the parasite in the human body using the drug quinine.

Quinine had been the mainstay of malaria prevention and treatment since the early nineteenth century, and was widely used in the tropics. The Scottish explorer and missionary David Livingstone (1813–73), took quinine with him on his expeditions into the African interior. Combined with jalap, rhubarb, calomel and tincture of cardamom, he called his little pills 'rousers' from 'their efficacy in rousing up even those most prostrated.' Burroughs Wellcome & Co later marketed the formulation as 'Livingstone's rousers'. In British India the bitter-tasting quinine was added to Indian tonic water – the basis of the ever popular gin and tonic. During the US Civil War (1861–5), every Union soldier in malarial regions was given a daily dose of quinine sulphate dissolved in whiskey.

With the discovery of the malaria parasite and its transmission via the mosquito, the Italians, in particular, promoted mass 'quininization' of the populations of malarial areas – either as a preventive or as a treatment. The Italian government established a monopoly over the marketing of quinine, subsidizing the cost through a 'quinine tax', and making it available to those who could not afford even the low subsidized price, through a network of some 1,200 rural health centres constructed by the beginning of the First World War.

Integrated approaches and malaria as a 'social disease'

Many campaigns in the early twentieth century combined both anti-mosquito and anti-parasite approaches. Integrated measures of larval mosquito control, swamp drainage, quinine prophylaxis and treatment, together with community education – were the most successful. One striking example was the malaria eradication programme of Israel Kligler (1888–1944) who in the early 1920s emigrated from the United States to Mandate Palestine, a land of people dying of malaria. Kligler had previously been a member of the Rockefeller Institute's Yellow Fever Commission, working in Mexico and Peru before he moved to Mandate Palestine. He built upon his experience in the laboratory and the field to design an integrated programme to attack the problem on all fronts: the parasite, the mosquito and the people. It was noted that following the commencement of the anti-malaria work: 'malaria has been robbed of its mystic attribute, its inevitability: it has been revealed as a preventable – and eradicable – disease.' Kligler's model, with its special attention to local sets of conditions, anti-larval measures and education, was praised by the Malaria Commission of the League of Nations in 1925 as one that could be applied to malarious areas in other parts of the world.

From the 1920s some malariologists began to think of malaria as a 'social disease', to be reduced only by improving the social and economic conditions in poverty-stricken areas through rural 'bonification' schemes to augment overall health and wealth. They based their arguments on the fact that malaria had declined in parts of the temperate north following improvements in agriculture and living standards, and prior to any knowledge of its transmission by mosquitoes, or, as an Italian saying goes: 'Malaria flees before the plough'. One of the most ambitious and successful programmes of integrated rural development linked to malaria control was initiated in the US under the Tennessee Valley Authority (TVA) in the early 1930s. The eventual eradication of malaria from the USA and much of Europe by the mid-twentieth century confirmed that ecological transformations brought about by socio-economic development played a key role.

But in many parts of the tropics and subtropics, the mosquito and the parasite outwitted any attempt at control. The ecology of malaria and its vectors proved far more complex than anticipated. Even in the USA during the early twentieth century, around one million cases of malaria occurred every year among a population of 25 million in the twelve southern states. In 1922–3 one of Europe's most devastating malaria epidemics in the modern era spread across Russia from the central Volga basin and reached as far north as the Arctic Circle, with an estimated 7 to 12 million people infected and thousands of deaths.

The first synthetic antimalarials

During the Second World War, Germany captured Dutch quinine reserves in Holland, and the Japanese, occupying Java, seized their overseas plantations along with the bulk of the world's supply of quinine. New antimalarials were desperately needed. One of the first synthetic drugs, mepacrine (Atabrine), had been first approved as an antimalarial drug in the 1930s. A daily dose did have some effect in keeping troops fit for active service, but it turned the skin yellow and was rumoured to cause impotence. The most effective of the new synthetic drugs was chloroquine, which was synthesized in the 1930s in Germany but not developed until after the Second World War – too late to help the huge numbers of servicemen and civilians affected by malaria during the conflict. Malaria outbreaks caused serious problems for Allied troops fighting in the Middle East, North Africa and, especially, the Pacific. In many theatres of operations in both the First and Second World Wars, malaria often proved a greater threat than enemy action.

DDT and the promise of eradication

'The sulfonamides, penicillin, radioactive isotopes, DDT ... foreshadow a new move forward, a new renaissance, a new period in human development when the imagination is endowed with wings'. Rockefeller Foundation, 1948

First discovered in 1874 and synthesized in 1939 by the Swiss chemist Paul Müller, the insecticide DDT was used towards the end of the Second World War for destroying body lice in typhus epidemics. It was heralded by some as a 'miracle', and by the late 1940s it was thought to have enormous potential in the campaign against malaria. In 1950 at a malaria conference held in Kampala, Uganda, a debate ensued about the possibilities of embarking on a global programme to eradicate malaria. At the end of the heated discussion, one of the delegates, Leonard Bruce-Chwatt (1907–89) 'poured oil on troubled waters' and folding his hands said quietly, 'Let us spray.'

Malaria-control programmes using systematic household

spraying with DDT, together with chloroquine, began to be implemented in a number of countries, and in the mid-1950s the WHO endorsed a programme for the Global Eradication of Malaria. Optimistic that global eradication was possible, but also aware that mosquitoes were beginning to build up some resistance to DDT, the aim was to move forward quickly. 'Time is of the essence,' the director-general of the WHO urged. This was the first international disease programme ever to consider 'global' eradication. However, in a much less well-known twist on this story, a number of malariologists at the time argued that the complexities of malaria in Africa, the most intensely malarious area of the world, were too great for the continent to be included in the goal of eradication. Though this was hotly debated, in the end only a few pilot projects were implemented in sub-Saharan Africa to test the feasibility of 'control'. 'Wait and study' were the operative words in this paradoxical situation.

Elsewhere, there were some initial and quite spectacular successes, and DDT was instrumental in eliminating malaria from much of southern Europe, helping to stimulate economic growth in Greece, Spain and Italy during the late 1940s and into the 1950s. The combination of DDT and chloroquine had dramatic early results in India, reducing malaria incidence from an estimated 75 million cases in the 1950s to only 50,000 cases by 1961. But by the late 1960s the 'global' eradication programme had floundered and in 1969 the WHO acknowledged that it had failed to reach its goal. In India, for example, there were again tens of millions of cases in the 1970s.

The reasons for the shortcomings of the campaign are complicated, and the subject of much discussion. The programme experienced a wide array of biological, social, political, economic and cultural difficulties. The costs and technical obstacles were far greater than anticipated. In some countries, control measures were stopped too soon after early successes had been achieved. As early as 1951 it had been observed that mosquitoes built up a resistance to DDT, and at the same time some species developed the uncanny ability to alter their resting behaviour to avoid the irritation caused by DDT sprayed onto the walls of huts and houses. The parasite also evolved a resistance to drugs such as chloroquine. The failure of DDT and antimalarial drugs to fulfil the promise of global eradication led to one of the greatest medical disappointments of the second half of the twentieth century.

From the 1970s onwards malaria resurged dramatically in many subtropical and tropical areas, although it had by this time been virtually eliminated from both the USA and Europe, most probably as a by-product of improved living conditions, increased wealth and a decline in other infectious diseases and nutritional deficiencies which can interact with malaria, as well as through malaria-specific interventions.

The complexities and tragedy of malaria

'There is no golden Yale key to open all the doors to all the problems in malaria . . . It is more like a labyrinth of many doors to many problems, and each key is only the opening of one door to one problem.' N.H. Swellengrebel (1885– 1970), Dutch malariologist, in 1938

The late twentieth century was the low point in the drive to control malaria. In many countries in the developing world malaria bounced back to unprecedented levels. In sub-Saharan Africa it was estimated that in the 1970s a child died of malaria every twelve seconds, and there were several million deaths a year globally from the disease.

Why was the control of malaria proving so difficult? The answer lies, in part, in the puzzling and complex interactions of the mosquito, its parasite and human biology. This was further compounded by problems of resistance to drugs and insecticides, as well as pressure from the environmental lobby since the 1960s to ban DDT, necessitating the use of expensive alternatives (especially following Rachel Carson's 1962 book, *Silent Spring* – although her target was primarily DDT's overuse in agriculture). In many parts of Africa, political and economic turmoil, civil wars, refugee problems, weak health infrastructures and the pressures of globalization caused health concerns to be pushed to the side. In some places, rapid and intensive agricultural development opened up forests, creating additional breeding sites for the mosquito vector and leading to epidemics of so-called 'man-made' malaria. The pandemic of HIV/AIDS, especially in sub-Saharan Africa from the 1980s, also exacerbated the problem. The combination with HIV infection can increase the risk of severe effects of malaria, particularly in children and pregnant women. Neglect by international health agencies of tropical diseases that were no longer seen as a direct threat to the developed world has, too, been cited as a factor in its resurgence.

Roll back malaria?

'SMALL BITE: BIG THREAT' World Health Day slogan, 2014

Today, fortunately, malaria is attracting more attention as a serious global problem and, in spite of its current impact, it is no longer seen necessary to include it in the long list of remaining twenty-first century Neglected Tropical Diseases (NTDs). In 1997 international agencies established the Multilateral Initiative on Malaria (MIM) and in 1998 the WHO launched its Roll Back Malaria Partnership with the aim of halving the burden of malaria by 2010. The United Nations and its member states in 2000 endorsed their commitment to key Millennium Development Goals – a set of global goals (including reducing the burden of malaria) to lift millions of people out of extreme poverty. The Global Fund to Fight AIDS, Tuberculosis and Malaria (GFATM) was established in 2002 to prevent an annual 5.6 million deaths from these three leading infectious diseases. An extraordinary symbol of commitment was the 2005 'Africa Live Roll Back Malaria Concert' in the Senegalese capital, Dakar, which brought together the greatest African musicians and a wide audience to promote a single message on the need to roll back malaria. The 2008 Global Malaria Action Plan (GMAP), developed by the Roll Back Malaria Partnership, has taken this drive forward towards global malaria control and elimination.

A huge amount of international funding, including major contributions from the Bill & Melinda Gates Foundation and the US President's Malaria Initiative (set up in 2005 by President Bush), has now been targeted towards solving the malaria crisis. Even the concept and long-term vision of 'eradication' (the 'e-word') is back on the international health agenda, promoted by Bill and Melinda Gates in 2007, and supported by the current Director-General of the WHO, [Dr] Margaret Chan. And with this growing commitment, global health experts and international funders are determined that this time sub-Saharan Africa will not be excluded.

There are four main intervention strategies for malaria

prevention and treatment: long-lasting insecticide-treated nets (LLINs); indoor residual spraying (IRS) with approved insecticides; artemisinin-based combination therapies (ACTs); and intermittent preventive treatment in pregnancy (IPTp). To this 'package' has been added the prospect of a future malaria vaccine.

Bed nets, as well as other forms of personal and domestic anti-mosquito measures such as screening doors and windows, head nets and mosquito-proof tents and boots, have long been used to prevent mosquito bites. Since the mid-1990s, there has been a huge push to distribute and make accessible to all those who need them (often free of charge or at a low cost) insecticide-treated bed nets (ITNs) as well as long-lasting insecticide-treated bed nets (LLINs), which retain activity for the natural life of the net without re-treatment. Around 136 million LLINs were delivered to malaria-endemic countries in 2013. They are particularly effective in regions where the mosquito bites after dusk, and can have a massive impact on preventing children from being bitten by malaria-infected mosquitoes. In addition to protecting the user, these nets protect the community by killing anopheline mosquitoes that come into contact with the treated net.

Indoor residual spraying remains a powerful vector control tool for reducing and interrupting malaria transmission, though only about 4 per cent of the population at risk are currently protected by IRS. Non-immune travellers to malarial areas are advised to take anti-malarial chemoprophylactics, as well as to sleep under bed nets and use mosquito repellents such as those based on DEET (diethyltoluamide). Mosquitoes have an uncanny knack of being attracted to or repelled by certain smells, which may explain why some people are bitten more frequently than others. The search is now on to find which chemical components of body odour have a repellent effect on the blood-sucking mosquitoes.

A remarkable 'rediscovery'

'Artemisinin . . . is a true gift from old Chinese medicine.'
Tu Youyou, *Nature Medicine*, 2011

In terms of treatment, one of the most remarkable stories in the history of malaria has been the 'rediscovery' of an ancient Chinese herbal remedy. This is sweet wormwood, *Artemisia annua*, known in Chinese as *Qing Hao* ('green herb'), which has been used for chills and fevers for over 2,000 years. In 1967, a research programme was set up by the People's Republic of China to find a treatment for malaria, especially given the urgent need to replace chloroquine, which was, increasingly, becoming ineffective. A Chinese scientist, Dr Tu Youyou (b.1930), and her team in Beijing combed numerous ancient texts and folk remedies and in the early 1970s extracted the active principle of the *Artemisia annua* plant, now known internationally as artemisinin.

ACTs (artemisinin-based combination therapies) which combine artemisinin with a number of other antimalarials (a concept pioneered by British scientist Nick White, based in Bangkok) have over the past few decades been a phenomenal success in treating severe malaria, though signs of resistance on the Cambodia-Thailand border and in the Greater Mekong sub-region (where chloroquine resistance initially emerged in 1957) are worrying and are being closely monitored. If artemisinin drug-resistance spreads to sub-Saharan Africa, this would pose a major threat to further advances in malaria control. Older drugs such as sulfadoxine-pyrimethamine can be given to pregnant women after the first trimester at routine antenatal visits, regardless of whether the recipient is infected with malaria, in a programme known as intermittent preventive treatment in pregnancy (IPTp-SP). It is hoped that this will reduce maternal malaria episodes and associated anaemia and will benefit both mothers and babies. The search for new antimalarials for both falciparum and vivax malaria, the detection of fake or substandard medicines (which contain either none or insufficient amounts of an active antimalarial ingredient), and the development of synthetic arteminisin-based drugs (using a by-product, artemisinic acid) also continues.

While the ACTs were the exciting 'new' news of the late twentieth and early twenty-first centuries and continue to be instrumental in saving many lives, another possible 'breakthrough' received widespread coverage in 2011. This was the publication in the *New England Journal of Medicine* of the preliminary results of a Phase III clinical trial of a new vaccine, RTS,S (or Mosquirix), designed for children in Africa. Scientists have been pursuing the goal or dream of a malaria vaccine for decades. The trial of this first vaccine in the world against a parasite reduced clinical episodes of falciparum malaria by approximately one-half in children in the age group five to seventeen months. For infants aged six to twelve weeks, the vaccine protected around a third against clinical malaria, with about a quarter protected against severe malaria in the twelve months after the last dose.

Eleven African research centres in seven African countries are conducting this trial, together with its creators, the British pharmaceutical company, GlaxoSmithKline, and the Programme for Appropriate Technology (PATH) Malaria Vaccine Initiative (MVI), with grant funding from the Gates Foundation. The results of this Phase III clinical trial look promising (though we still await the final stages and follow-up studies). If recommended for large-scale implementation in 2015, GlaxoSmithKline and MVI will make this vaccine available and affordable to those who need it most. Even a partially effective vaccine for malaria, when used in combination with other preventive and treatment strategies, could greatly reduce the devastating toll on human life.

Many other initiatives are paving the way forward to bolster current anti-malarial strategies. Larval source management – to prevent mosquitoes from breeding in swampy land and standing water – is an old idea which is receiving renewed interest. More attention is being given to vivax malaria – which, while generally known as a 'benign' form of the disease (though evidence from history suggests it was far from benign), has recently been recognized as 'the forgotten malaria' and is currently a threat to many people in some tropical and subtripical countries. The Malaria Atlas Project (MAP), led by Robert Snow, Simon Hay and others at Oxford University and KEMRI, a Wellcome Trust research centre based in Kenya, is generating innovative methods of mapping malaria risk from national, continental and global perspectives to develop a more accurate picture of the geographical distribution and burden posed by both falciparum and vivax malaria parasites and their vectors, which, in turn, can be used to guide more effective planning of control. Such projects remind us of the importance given by an earlier generation of malariologists (and overlooked during the Global Malaria Eradication Programme) to local variations in the epidemiology of malaria, as epitomized by Lewis Hackett in the 1930s.

Better diagnostics and surveillance are part of a WHO 2012 venture known as T3: Test. Treat. Track. Much scientific knowledge has recently been assembled about the mosquito, its parasite and its effects on the human body. The unveiling of the complete genome sequence of *P. falciparum* was announced in 2002, and that of *A. gambiae*, the world's most dangerous mosquito vector, in 2003 – have led to expectations of further advances in understanding and the control of this complex parasitic disease. The creation of genetically modified mosquitoes, unable to spread malaria and capable of competing with, and outliving, natural mosquitoes in the wild, is currently being explored by scientists and is another possible way forward.

Future prospects

'Malaria has been humanity's biggest killer for 200,000 years and for the first time, we are really beating it on the head. It is an amazing success story . . . But if we blink, if we take our foot off the pedal, we will go back very quickly.' Richard Feacham, founding Executive Director of GFATM 2014

Malaria morbidity and mortality rates have decreased significantly in the past decade or so (indeed, some estimates suggest by a quarter or even a half since 2000), though there are still an estimated 207 million cases and 627,000 to 855,000 deaths annually, mostly among African children. From the neglected era of the 1970s when it was said that a child died every twelve seconds from malaria, we continue to be reminded that in the second decade of the twenty-first century, in spite of the huge drive to control the disease, malaria takes the life of an African child every minute. While malaria is no longer described as a Neglected Tropical Disease (NTD) and the malaria map is 'shrinking', there is a long way to go before the vision of 'global eradication' can be realized. The fact that so many people – and especially children – are dying from mosquito bites leaves no room for complacency.

If lessons can be learned from history, absolute commitment and funding for research and control has to be sustained and maintained well into the future. Recognizing malaria as a 'social disease' or 'disease of poverty' (malaria death rates are highest in countries where a majority of people live on less than $1.25 per person per day) must ensure that improvements in the overall health, welfare and standards of living of the poorest and most marginalized communities in the world are addressed. And these messages, too, apply to the control of many other infections, such as TB and HIV/AIDS as well as the parasitic NTDs of the globe's poorest tropical and subtropical countries, which are often co-endemic with malaria and for which integrated measures of prevention and treatment could be both cost-effective and lead to major health gains.

Ultimately, as Peter Hotez envisions in his book, *Forgotten People, Forgotten Diseases: The Neglected Tropical Diseases and Their Impact on Global Health and Development* (2008), we need to achieve the happy position of being able to replace the word 'Neglected' with 'Former', so that potentially fatal diseases will become 'Former Tropical Diseases'.

AFRICAN TRYPANOSOMIASIS

African trypanosomiasis – commonly known as sleeping sickness – is a devastating disease caused by a parasitic protozoan of the genus *Trypanosoma*. It is endemic in the so-called Tsetse Belt, a vast area spanning much of West, Central and East Africa between the Sahara and the Kalahari Desert. The Tsetse Belt is home to the tsetse fly, whose vicious bite injects the trypanosome parasite into both humans and cattle. For centuries the human form of the disease was called 'sleeping sickness' because of its striking symptoms of lethargy and sleepiness, leading eventually to coma and death. Its impact on livestock farming has also generated a cycle of sickness, poverty, hunger and death. Although the number of reported cases has now fallen for the first time in over fifty years, it remains one of several diseases affecting the poorer areas of the world that have been called Neglected Tropical Diseases which deserve and need further international funding.

∾

In the late fourteenth century details of the death of Mari Jata, the ruler of the great West African empire of Mali, were recorded by the Arab historian Ibn Khaldūn:

Sultan Jata had been smitten by the sleeping sickness, a disease that frequently afflicts the inhabitants of that

climate ... Those afflicted are virtually never awake or
alert. This sickness harms the patient and continues until
he perishes ... The illness persisted in Jata's humour
for a duration of two years after which he died in the
year 775 AH.

When Europeans began to explore and trade along the coast of
West Africa over the next few centuries, they too discovered a
disease amongst the Africans that led to extreme sleepiness and
lethargy. They called it the 'sleepy distemper' or, in French, *la
maladie du sommeil*. The peculiarities of the disease and its
striking symptoms led to all sorts of speculations as to its cause.
Some associated it with drinking too much palm wine, others
with smoking hemp or eating rotten food. At the time of the
slave trade, a number of physicians examining the disease suggested that the psychological trauma of being uprooted and
taken away from their families triggered a mental 'disposition'
amongst the slaves that gave rise to the 'African lethargy'.

Thomas M. Winterbottom (1766–1859) a physician in the
colony of Sierra Leone wrote *An account of the native Africans in
the neighbourhood of Sierra Leone, to which is added an account
of the present state of medicine among them* (1803) and described
the enlarged glands in the neck, characteristic of the early stages
of trypanosomiasis, which became known as 'Winterbottom's
sign': 'Small glandular tumours are sometimes observed in the
neck a little before the commencement of this complaint ...
slave traders ... appear to consider these tumours as a symptom
indicating a disposition to lethargy, and they either never buy
such slaves, or get quit of them as soon as they observe any such
appearance.'

Stallion sickness, nagana and the fly disease

While many of the early European explorers sent back reports of the 'new' and deadly human diseases they encountered in the African rainforests and grasslands, some also described sickness amongst the animals. David Livingstone, the Scottish missionary doctor and explorer of the African interior, was struck by the frequent deaths of horses and oxen on his travels in the 1850s, noting that the bite of the tsetse fly was 'certain death to the ox, horse, and dog.' The word 'tsetse' means fly in Tswana, a language of southern Africa, and came into the English language in the mid-nineteenth century.

The effect of the tsetse fly on the horses was especially troublesome, as it meant that throughout equatorial Africa it was difficult to use them for transport. Livingstone treated horses suffering from 'stallion sickness' with arsenic. He and his luggage bearers were incessantly bothered by humming, buzzing and biting insects like the tsetse fly, and were warned by the locals to travel during the night when the flies were less active. Livingstone, however, was certain that it was only the animals, and not the people, who suffered as a result of the tsetse bites.

In the era of European colonization that followed, farmers began to report on a fatal disease that was decimating their cattle. The disease was known in Zululand (now northern KwaZulu-Natal in South Africa) as nagana, meaning 'the wasting disease'. The effect on livestock production was dramatic. By the late nineteenth century both European farmers raising cattle for profit and African pastoralists dependent on the meat and milk of their cattle for subsistence were facing disaster.

Game hunters were also struggling, as their horses died from a wasting sickness. The local Zulus thought that cattle with nagana were being poisoned by food contaminated by game animals. The game hunters, meanwhile, began to suspect, like Livingstone, that their horses were being made ill by the ever-present tsetse fly. They called it the 'fly disease'. It took over half a century, but in the end scientists worked out the connection between the sleeping sickness of humans, the nagana suffered by cattle, and the stallion sickness of horses.

The first clues and the missed connections

Between the 1840s and 1880s, an unusual 'new' organism was observed in fish, frogs, rats, camels and horses. In Paris in the early 1840s David Gruby (1810–98) saw the parasite in the blood of a frog, and called it *le tire bouchon* – French for 'cork-screw' – after the way it swam through its host, curling and spinning. The scientific name for the genus, adopted shortly thereafter, was *Trypanosoma*, from the Greek words *trypanon*, meaning 'borer' (as in trepanation, the ancient operation of drilling holes into the skull), and *sōma*, 'body'. In 1880, Welsh veterinary surgeon Griffith Evans (1835–1935) found trypanosomes in the blood of horses and camels in India with a wasting disease called 'surra' and suggested that the parasites might be the cause of this disease. In Algeria in 1891 Gustave Nepveu (1841–1903) saw and described 'a flagellated parasite' in a patient with malaria. It was undoubtedly a trypanosome, but the significance of his observation was missed at the time.

The next breakthrough came in 1894 in Zululand – but at this point the focus was on the animal, and not the human form of the disease. David Bruce (1855–1931), a British army surgeon, and his wife Mary (1849–1931) were dispatched to Ubombo by the governor of Zululand, Walter Hely-Hutchinson (1849–1913), to investigate an epidemic of nagana in cattle which were, so to speak, dying like flies. It took the couple several weeks to reach their destination.

It was in the makeshift laboratory that he set up on the veranda of their hut that Bruce, assisted by his wife, observed trypanosomes in blood slides taken from the sick cattle, describing the micro-organism as 'a curious little beast ... a creature with a blunt rear-end and a long slim lashing whip'. Bruce then sent dogs and oxen into the 'fly belt', and when they returned and were examined, they too were infected with trypanosomes. His next step was to collect hundreds of tsetse flies from the 'fly belt' and bring them back to Ubombo. The flies were put in a cage made of muslin and left to feed on horses – which, after a month, sickened and died. There was compelling evidence that the tsetse fly might be responsible for the disease in cattle and horses, and that some wild game animals might be the reservoir for the parasite. In 1899 the parasite found by Bruce in the nagana cattle was named *Trypanosoma brucei*, but still no connection was made with sleeping sickness in humans.

Over the next decade, the pieces of the puzzle fell – somewhat haltingly – into place.

The cases of Mr Kelly and Mrs S.

In May 1901, Mr Kelly, the forty-two-year-old master of the government steamer on the River Gambia in West Africa, began to feel vaguely unwell, with a slight fever. He consulted Robert Michael Forde (1861–1948), the colonial surgeon, who suspected malaria and admitted him to hospital. Malaria was, however, quickly ruled out – Kelly didn't respond to quinine, and there were no malarial parasites in his blood. Forde did, however, notice in some of the blood slides some strange 'wriggly worms', which he had never seen before. These parasites seemed to be more noticeable in the slides taken when Kelly's temperature rose. Forde thought there must be a connection between the 'worms' and the illness. But what?

In December of that year, Joseph Everett Dutton (1874–1905), a young parasitologist from the newly founded Liverpool School of Tropical Medicine, visited the Gambia to do a malaria survey. When asked by Forde to look at Kelly's perplexing blood slides, Dutton immediately recognized the 'worms' as trypanosomes – which until then had only been associated with the nagana disease of cattle. Dutton sent a telegram to the Liverpool School: TRYPANOSOMA EUROPEAN, PECULIAR SYMPTOMS. DUTTON.

Kelly's condition showed no signs of improvement, and in 1902 he was sent home to England. His case was presented to the British Medical Association meeting in Liverpool. For some time Kelly continued to get more and more feverish – displaying the characteristic 'moon face' (oedema) of sleeping sickness, caused by the leaking of small blood vessels. Eventually Kelly's heart gave up, and on 1 January 1903 he died.

In the meantime, in London, Patrick Manson was investigating a case of sleeping sickness in a Mrs S., a missionary's wife from the Congo. She had first consulted him in 1902 with a fever. The following year Mrs S. became very sick, and her illness was beginning to affect her central nervous system – one of the classic signs of the last stages of sleeping sickness. Mrs S. died in November 1903.

Mr Kelly and Mrs S. were the first two human cases of sleeping sickness to attract the attention of experts in tropical medicine in the early twentieth century. The search was now on to find the cause and means of transmission of sleeping sickness in humans and nagana in cattle . . .

The final links

Around this time, a major epidemic of sleeping sickness was sweeping through the new British protectorate of Uganda. The urgency of the situation was highlighted by Albert Ruskin Cook (1870–1951) and his brother John Howard Cook (1871–1946), who were based at the Mengo Missionary Hospital in Uganda. In 1902 three researchers – Count Aldo Castellani (1874–1971), George Carmichael Low (1872–1952) and Cuthbert Christy (1863–1932) – were sent out to Entebbe, Uganda, by the Foreign Office and the Royal Society of London to solve the puzzle of the human form of the disease. All three were looking for a bacterial cause of sleeping sickness – and so missed the real culprit, the parasitic protozoan.

Exasperated by their lack of results, David Bruce, with his assistant David Nabarro (1874–1958), went to Entebbe 'to take control' of the investigation. In 1903 it was confirmed that the trypanosome parasites which caused the wasting disease in cattle were also responsible for human sleeping sickness. The question as to who found what, and who found it first, caused bitter controversy.

The next step was to find how the parasites were transmitted. In 1903 the tsetse fly, *Glossina palpalis*, was identified in Uganda as a vector, and in 1912 another species of tsetse fly in Northern Rhodesia (now Zambia), *Glossina morsitans*, was also found to be a vector. *Glossina palpalis*, the principal vector in West and Central Africa, is mostly found in humid forests bordering lakes and rivers. *Glossina morsitans* is found in the dry savannah woodlands and open scrub country in East Africa. Friedrich Kleine (1869–1951), a colleague of Robert Koch, and Muriel Robertson (1883–1973) from the Lister Institute in London made key discoveries about the life cycle of trypanosomes in the early twentieth century.

Moreover, it was realized that there were two sub-species of *Trypanosoma brucei*: *T. brucei gambiense* and *T. brucei rhodesiense*. The former is endemic in West and Central Africa and causes a chronic form of the disease which takes a slow course, with bouts of fever and lymph node enlargement, progressing over months and years to cross the blood-brain barrier and affect the central nervous system. It leads to sleep disturbances, severe lassitude, coma and eventual death. The latter is endemic in East Africa. It is more virulent and acts and kills quickly, often in a matter of weeks or months. Both are spread by the blood-sucking tsetse fly, but the *gambiense* form is exclusively a human disease (i.e. there is no significant animal reservoir involved in disease transmission) while the *rhodesiense* form is a zoonotic disease involving cattle and game in the transmission cycle. A third sub-species, *T. brucei brucei* (bovine trypanosomiasis), does not infect humans, but causes nagana in animals. David Bruce's contribution to their discovery is remembered in the names of these sub-species (as well as in his pioneering investigations of the disease brucellosis), and Bruce himself was honoured with a knighthood.

By the early decades of the twentieth century, the tsetse fly and the trypanosome parasite had finally been established as the links between the sleeping sickness of humans, the nagana of cattle and the stallion sickness or fly disease of horses. It was also discovered that game animals such as waterbuck,

hartebeest and antelope could act as reservoirs for the trypanosomes but remain healthy. The trypanosome, adapted to
mammalian and non-mammalian hosts, had found its perfect
partner in the tsetse fly and, by doing little harm to some of its
animal hosts, had evolved to allow the cycle to keep
perpetuating.

Sleeping sickness – the 'colonial disease'

'Black shapes crouched, lay, sat between the trees, leaning
against the trunk, clinging to the earth, half coming out,
half effaced within the dim light, in all the attitudes of
pain, abandonment, and despair . . . They were dying
slowly . . . nothing but black shadows of disease and starvation, lying confusedly in the greenish gloom.' Joseph
Conrad (1857–1924), *Heart of Darkness*, 1899

While the scientists were elucidating the cause of the disease,
devastating epidemics of sleeping sickness erupted in the British,
Belgian, French, Portuguese and German colonies of Africa in
the late nineteenth and early twentieth centuries. Between 1896
and 1906, in the British protectorate of Uganda, 250,000 Africans
died of sleeping sickness and, in the Congo basin, half a million
were killed by the disease. Epidemics from the 1920s through to
the 1950s continued to claim many more thousands of lives in
Africa. Sleeping sickness – which, if left untreated, is invariably
fatal – attracted huge attention from the colonial authorities.
The horrors of the disease appalled the public back in Europe,
persuading the colonial powers to send scientists out to Africa
to find a solution.

Intensive campaigns were launched in an attempt to control

sleeping sickness. Many different methods were employed by the various colonial governments, including forced resettlement away from tsetse-infested areas, systematic surveillance and isolation of patients in lazarettos (quarantine stations), treatments using Atoxyl, an arsenic derivative (which could have serious side effects, including blindness), bush clearance and various attempts to break the cycle of transmission, such as the use of fly traps. Some of these measures conflicted with age-old traditional practices, and were often deeply unpopular with the indigenous populations.

One large-scale campaign was conducted by the French physician Eugène Jamot (1879–1937) in French Equatorial Africa between 1917 and 1931. Tens of millions of people were screened by mobile field teams. Those found positive were treated with injections of Atoxyl and another arsenical drug, tryparsamide. The treatment entailed numerous injections over three years but led to a dramatic fall in the number of cases of sleeping sickness and helped to interrupt transmission of the *gambiense* form of the disease. These and other medical campaigns in equatorial Africa were based on reusing a small number of syringes for the intravenous injections, and although successful in controlling sleeping sickness in parts of West Africa, it has recently been suggested that the frequent use of unsterilized syringes for these intravenous injections may have helped the early (and 'silent') spread of HIV as a blood-borne virus in the human population before the epidemic of HIV/AIDS became known to the world.

Historians looking back over the last hundred years or so have emphasized the inextricable links between sleeping sickness and the ecological disturbances and upheavals brought on by colonization. The opening up of new areas and population centres, the extension of trade routes into the Tsetse Belt, the modification of the environment, the movement of people to work in tsetse-infested areas, and the destruction of local practices that had for centuries enabled many small scattered groups to coexist with the tsetse fly and the trypanosomes, have all been cited as possible factors facilitating the spread of the disease. Concern for animal and human trypanosomiasis in the first half of the twentieth century, it has been argued, was as much to do with its threat to the colonizers and the preservation of their health and economic activities as it was to do with the impact on the indigenous populations.

Sleeping sickness bites back

By the 1960s some progress had been made in the battle against sleeping sickness, and in the 1970s human cases of the disease had dropped to encouragingly low levels. But in the 1980s and 1990s – following widespread political instability, civil wars, large-scale displacements of populations, economic decline, the breakdown of health services and the dismantling of disease-control programmes in many newly independent African countries – the disease resurfaced. There have been devastating epidemics in Uganda, the Democratic Republic of the Congo, Sudan, the Central African Republic and Angola, killing and disabling many, especially in war-torn areas and amongst refugees. In some areas, the disease appeared for the first time, with some villages reporting levels as high as 50 per cent of the entire village population. The relationship between 'conflict and contagion' became a major theme of the re-emergence of human African trypanosomiasis in sub-Saharan Africa.

By the first decade of the twenty-first century it was estimated that there were 60 million people at risk in thirty-six endemic countries, with about half a million new cases and possibly as many as 60,000 deaths every year. The drugs used to treat the human form of the disease, such as melarsoprol (for the treatment of central nervous system human African trypanosomiasis), and pentamidine and suramin (for use in the earlier stages of the disease) were more than fifty years old, and those based on arsenic derivatives had nasty side effects. Only one new drug, eflornithine (initially developed as a cancer treatment), was registered in the 1990s for the treatment of sleeping sickness. It is effective in the later stages of *T. brucei gambiense* – hence its nickname, the 'resurrection drug' – but it is difficult to administer, requiring intravenous infusions four times a day (for one to two weeks). More recently the combination of eflornithine and another drug, nifurtimox, have been placed on the WHO Essential List of Medicines for the treatment of human African trypanosomiasis. The tsetse fly bites during the day, so bed nets are not useful. Many puzzles about the epidemiology and immunology of the disease persisted.

Moreover, 3 million cattle were dying each year and over 6 million square miles (15.5 million sq. km) of land was precluded from stock production because of the presence of tsetse flies, adding to the misery, hunger and despair of many. John Playfair, in his book *Living with Germs* (2004), highlighted the impact on the animal population and, in turn, the human population:

I used to visit a beautifully equipped research institute outside Nairobi, in Kenya, which specialized mainly in trypanosomiasis, but I was surprised to find, on my first visit, that it was cattle trypanosomiasis that mattered most to them, since it was a major cause of meat shortages and mass under-nutrition. I was assured that far more human lives would be saved by a cure of that than of human sleeping sickness, which was an eye-opener to someone in the habit of thinking only of sick *people*.

A number of initiatives were launched to try to reinforce disease control and surveillance, including the Pan African Tsetse and Trypanosomiasis Eradication Campaign in 2000 to 'tackle the huge impact of African trypanosomiasis'. Geographical information systems were developed to identify grazing areas at most risk and to predict tsetse fly environments, allowing more precise monitoring, and in 2008 the WHO launched the Atlas of Human African Trypanosomiasis (HAT) initiative to map all reported cases at the village level. But given the economic and public health impact of sleeping sickness, the funding for research into this important disease had fallen badly behind in recent decades. Like other 'diseases of poverty' more international attention was needed.

African Trypanosomiasis and other Neglected Tropical Diseases (NTDs)

In 2005 a group of specialists coined the phrase Neglected Tropical Diseases (NTDs) to highlight the very real neglect of a number of diseases, mostly those of the tropics and subtropics, that collectively affect over 1.4 billion people, including some 800 million children. Such diseases include African trypanosomiasis, as well as leprosy, dengue, rabies, Chagas' disease, lymphatic filariasis, schistosomiasis, hookworm and onchocerciasis. The NTDs are a diverse group of diseases with distinct characteristics, but they share a common stranglehold by thriving in the poorest and most marginalized communities, causing severe pain, permanent disability, stigma and death to millions of people. Individuals are frequently infected, simultaneously, with multiple NTDs which exhibit a high degree of geographic overlap and co-endemicity, especially in sub-Saharan Africa. These diseases have been 'neglected' because they have failed to attract sufficient attention in terms of funding and research, and because their huge impact on the globe, especially amongst the poorer and most vulnerable populations of the tropics and subtropics, is often overlooked.

Since the term NTDs was coined there has been considerable collaborative activity from the WHO, philanthropic donors, academic researchers, governments, NGOs and product development partnerships, as well as from pharmaceutical companies. At an influential meeting in January 2012 at the Royal College of Physicians in London, participants from many organizations from around the world, including the WHO, the World Bank and the Gates Foundation, met with representatives of the world's top thirteen pharmaceutical companies and government representatives from different countries in a new, united effort to control, eliminate, or eradicate ten NTDs by 2020 – committing to what is now known as the 2012 London Declaration. Significant advances have already been made by the global health partnerships, both in supplying treatments and integrating mass drug administration (MDA) programmes into broader development strategies, such as improving sanitation, nutrition and health education – with the long-term aim of eliminating these ancient diseases of poverty. 'Our vision', writes

Peter Hotez, one of the major leaders in the field, 'is a world free of NTDs in which healthy people can develop fully, learn effectively, raise families, and be productive members of their communities.'

Fly traps, trypano-tolerant cows and the future

There have been a few glimmers of hope in the flight to control or even eliminate African trypanosomiasis and, indeed, the disease has declined dramatically, such that the reported number of annual cases is now below 8,000 – the lowest for fifty years – although the actual number may be higher because of incomplete surveillance.

The genome sequence of the trypanosome was decoded in July 2005 – offering the possibility of finding new ways of treating and preventing the disease. A new orally administered drug, fexinidazole, is currently under development, and other drugs used for the treatment of African trypanosomiasis are now donated to the WHO for free distribution by the manufacturers Sanofi and Bayer. Two field-adapted rapid diagnostic tests became commercially available in 2013 and are helping to improve screening and detect cases before the parasites start to destroy the central nervous system. The latest fly traps impregnated with insecticides are proving successful in vector control. On the island of Zanzibar the tsetse fly has been eliminated by releasing sterile males into the wild fly population. Scientists have found one breed of African cattle, the N'Dama, which, though not as high-yielding as the traditional zebu, is less susceptible to the disease. Researchers are now aiming to breed 'trypano-tolerant' cattle.

All these positive gains are cause for optimism, but there is still some way to go. Elimination of this complex disease – which has had, and continues to have, such an adverse effect on the world's poorest continent – must remain a global health priority.

CHAGAS' DISEASE

Chagas' disease – also called American trypanosomiasis – is a potentially life-threatening parasitic infection. It may involve a range of symptoms, including irregularities in the heartbeat and digestive disturbances. The disease is confined to the Western hemisphere, and is endemic in many regions of South and Central America and Mexico. Its causative agent, the protozoan parasite *Trypanosoma cruzi*, is transmitted by the triatomine bug – often known as the kissing or assassin bug. The disease is named after the Brazilian scientist Carlos Chagas (1879–1934) who began to unravel its causes in the first decade of the twentieth century, though it was not until the mid-1930s that scientists were clearly able to identify the acute stage of the disease, based on a key feature known as Romaña's sign. Today, some 7 to 8 million people are infected, and Chagas' disease is not only the most debilitating infectious disease in South and Central America, but also the leading cause of heart disease in young adults.

∾

Spanish and Portuguese missionaries and travellers in South America in the sixteenth, seventeenth and eighteenth centuries have left a number of accounts of the blood-sucking insect, often called the 'kissing' bug, which we now know as the triatomine bug that transmits Chagas' disease. These writers noted that by day the bug is 'afraid of the light' and hides away in the thatched roofs and mud walls of huts. But at night, 'guided by the smell of people asleep', it drops down onto the face or head of those below. With a bite as 'delicate and sweet' as a kiss, it gorges itself on the blood of its sleeping victim. As it withdraws, it 'leaves an intolerable pain and an itch that can hardly be borne'. By the time it has had its blood meal, the bug resembles 'a fat grape . . . as big as the tip of the little finger'. One writer goes on to describe how 'as soon as it has digested, it defecates and this taint makes an indelible spot on the white linen . . . and when crushed gives out a strong stench of bedbugs'.

Bernabé Cobo (c.1582–1657) described the triatomine bug at work in Peru:

> They are as big as tip of the little finger, longer, brownish and in the shape of beetles. They live in the ceiling of the houses and get out at night guided by the smell of people asleep, and getting down on the beds, bite cruelly, making a big wheal and sucking up to half a thimble full of blood.

The name '*vinchuca*' is used for the bug in Andean countries. It is derived from the Quechua language of the Incas and literally means 'that which falls to the ground'.

Did Darwin have Chagas' disease?

In 1835, while travelling around South America, the young naturalist Charles Darwin (1809–82) wrote a fascinating account of the triatomine bug, which he called the 'Benchuca':

We slept in the village of Luxan, which is a small place surrounded by gardens, and forms the most southern cultivated district in the province of Mendoza [Argentina]; it is five leagues south of the capital. At night, I experienced an attack (for it deserves no less a name) of the *Benchuca*, a species of Reduvius, the great black bug of the Pampas. It is most disgusting to feel soft wingless insects, about an inch long, crawling over one's body. Before sucking they are quite thin, but afterwards they become round and bloated with blood, and in this state are easily crushed. One which I caught at Iquique (for they are found in Chile and Peru) was very empty. When placed on a table, and though surrounded by people, if a finger was presented, the bold insect would immediately protrude its sucker, make a charge, and, if allowed, draw blood. No pain was caused by the wound. It was curious to watch its body during the act of sucking, as in less than ten minutes it changed from being as flat as a wafer to a globular form. This one feast for which the benchuca was indebted to one of the officers, kept it fat during four whole months; but after the first fortnight, it was quite ready to have another suck.

When Darwin returned to England, as a twenty-seven-year-old from his five-year voyage around the world on the HMS *Beagle*, he began to suffer from a bizarre range of symptoms, including flatulence, heart palpitations, insomnia and hysterical crying, which throughout the rest of his life often frustrated and incapacitated him. There has been much speculation about the cause of Darwin's illness, including the suggestion that he suffered from Chagas' disease after being bitten by the bug. Retrospective diagnosis is, however, very hard to make and it is possible we may never know with what illness, or combination of illnesses, Darwin was afflicted. (He died from heart failure at the ripe old age – for the nineteenth century – of seventy-three.)

The triatomine bug and infected faeces

We now know that the parasitic protozoan that causes Chagas' disease is transmitted via the bug's faeces when they are rubbed inadvertently into a person's eyes, mucous membranes or abrasions, or when he or she scratches the wound of the bite. The parasite then works its way into the bloodstream and ends up in the tissues of its unsuspecting victim, where it multiplies by binary fission. Infection results in clinical symptoms in a short, acute phase followed by long-term chronic ill health. To complete the life cycle, the bugs can also suck up the parasite from the blood of an infected person or other vertebrate hosts when they feed. The parasite multiplies and develops in the bug's midgut and then moves down into its hindgut, ready to 'assassinate' another sufferer. Gut infection in the insect persists for its whole life – which can be as long as two years.

An ancient disease

Archaeological and DNA evidence from mummies in northern Chile and southern Peru suggest that the disease has been around for millennia – possibly even dating as far back as 4,000 years ago. There are two distinct forms of trypanosomiasis – Chagas' disease in the New World and African trypanosomiasis (sleeping sickness) in the Old World. The parasites responsible are single-celled organisms called trypanosomes but the diseases are transmitted in quite different ways, with very different pathologies and geographies. Some historians have suggested that the trypanosomes reached the New World during the slave trade, but the antiquity of Chagas' disease, as evident from *Trypanosoma cruzi* DNA detected in the heart and oesophagus of mummified bodies from Peru and Chile dating from 2000 BC to AD 1400, suggests that the diseases evolved independently. Another medical mystery!

The discoveries of Carlos Chagas

The credit for unravelling the cause of the disease has been attributed to Carlos Chagas. Chagas was a young Brazilian doctor appointed in the early twentieth century to work at a new medical institute in Rio de Janeiro (then the capital of the country), under the directorship of Oswaldo Cruz (1872–1917). From here, Chagas was sent in 1907 to Minas Gerais, in the interior of Brazil, to investigate and control a severe epidemic of malaria. Chagas was deeply concerned about the social and economic costs of the disease – to him the Brazilian interior was like a 'huge hospital'.

While there, he became intrigued by frequent complaints about an insect which, he was informed, 'inhabits human dwellings, attacking man at night, after the lights are out, and hiding during the day in cracks of the walls'. The locals, he said, called it *barbeiro* (the 'barber' bug) because of it tendency to bite people's faces. Chagas visited many infested homes, curious to find out more about this bug. Chagas identified an unusual parasite in the contents of the bug's hindgut. The parasites seemed to be similar to – and yet subtly different from – the trypanosomes that had recently been implicated as a cause of African trypanosomiasis or sleeping sickness. Some of the bugs were sent back to the Oswaldo Cruz Institute, and their parasites were found to cause disease in monkeys. It appeared to be a new species of trypanosome, and back in the Institute in Rio de Janeiro, Chagas named the parasite, *Trypanosoma cruzi*, in honour of his mentor, Oswaldo Cruz. Shortly thereafter, returning to Minas Gerais, he discovered the same parasite in the blood of a sick young girl called Berenice. In April 1909 he announced the discovery of a new human trypanosomiasis. A disease associated with *T. cruzi* was named 'Brazilian trypanosomiasis' and became more generally known as Chagas' disease (or Chagas disease).

What is Chagas' disease?

But many puzzles and details were still to be resolved. For example, Émile Brumpt (1877–1951), a Parisian working in Brazil, showed in 1912 that the parasite was transmitted not by the bite of the triatomine bug, but through its infected faeces.

Moreover, one of the difficulties faced by Chagas and his contemporaries was how to embrace a multitude of diverse and seemingly unrelated symptoms under the heading of 'Chagas' disease'. In the early decades of the twentieth century, scientists investigating the disease in the bug-infested houses of South America came across people with all sorts of clinical problems, both acute and chronic. Chagas believed that *T. cruzi* infection caused neurological, cardiac and endocrine (mainly thyroid) problems. He thought that endemic goitre, which was common in regions where he found *T. cruzi* infection, was caused by this parasite. From the mid-1910s and through to the 1920s, several scientists contested Chagas' claims about the endocrine and neurological forms of the disease. But his ideas about the role of

T. cruzi in causing cardiac problems in young people were largely confirmed and extended, as was his hypothesis about digestive problems, such as difficulties in swallowing, known as *mal de engasgo*.

However, in many ways Chagas' disease remained an enigma until the mid-1930s when the Argentinian physician, Cecilio Romaña (1899–1997), recognised a key sign by which to identify patients suffering from the acute phase of Chagas' disease. He noticed that the infected had a swelling of the eyelids on the side of the face near the site of the bite or where the bug's faeces had been deposited or accidentally rubbed into the eye. This sore at the point of infection was known as a 'chagoma' and is now called Romaña's sign. This became the defining clinical manifestation of acute Chagas' disease, and the true dimensions of the disease as a distinct clinical entity could be seen for the first time.

By the 1950s and 1960s, it became clear that the disease was indeed widespread in South America and that it manifests itself in diverse and puzzling ways. In general, people experience an initial acute phase of fever and swollen lymph nodes, which may in a few cases prove fatal, especially in children. Some of the infected may notice the lesion (Romaña's sign) where the bug has bitten and defecated. However, in the majority of cases, it is only after perhaps ten to twelve years that the parasite's cruel attack on its human host becomes visible, when the chronic problems manifest themselves. By then the parasites have invaded some organs of the body, causing damage and swelling of the heart, damage to the intestines and oesophagus, and premature death, mainly by heart failure. The long period of latency makes early diagnosis and treatment difficult.

How to beat the bugs?

Most attempts to control Chagas' disease have been directed against the triatomine bug. In the 1940s the insecticide DDT proved ineffective, but other organochlorine insecticides, such as BHC and dieldrin seemed to be much more potent. In the late 1940s two Brazilian researchers, Emmanuel Dias (1908–62) and José Pellegrino (1922–77), who had at that time concluded their experiments proving the efficacy of BHC, expressed to the Brazilian ministry of health in Rio de Janeiro their optimism that Chagas' disease would be soon eliminated. The first campaign against the triatomine bug was launched in the 1950s.

Their early optimism proved unrealistic, although several programmes have been initiated in recent years with some success. There are two drugs (benznidazole and nifurtimox) that are highly effective if given soon after infection at the onset of the acute phase, but control primarily relies on killing the bugs in people's dwellings with insecticides, and substituting plastered walls and metal roofs for adobe-walled, thatch-roofed dwellings, so making them less appealing to the bugs. In the early 1990s, the Southern Cone Initiative was established, followed by the Andean Countries Initiative (ACI) and the Central America Countries Initiative (CACI). These cooperative public health programmes were designed to rid the countries of Latin America of the triatomine bug and stop transmission via the application of insecticides. An expanded Global Network for Chagas Elimination programme, with support from Bayer HealthCare, was launched by the WHO in 2007 with the aim of eliminating the disease entirely by the year 2010. So far, this has not been achieved.

There are many complex and mysterious aspects of the disease, however, and these create major obstacles to control. Although transmission is primarily via the bug, the infection can also be passed on through blood transfusions or organ transplants from infected donors, by mothers to their unborn or breast-fed children, or by eating meat contaminated with the faeces of the bug. Some cases infected by blood or organ transplants have been identified in non-endemic countries in Europe, and in Canada and the USA. In Spain, for example, it is estimated that between 40,000 and 80,000 Latin Americans – mainly from Bolivia – either have the disease or the parasite, and efforts are underway to prevent transmission, including from mother to child. Humans, as a source of parasites for the blood-sucking bugs, may remain infectious for years, and there is also a vast reservoir of the parasite in wild and domestic animals. In parts of South America the bug infests not only houses but also lives in palm trees. Breaking the chain of infection in some of the poorest areas of the world has been fraught with difficulties.

There have been signs of hope and signs of concern. In the 1980s over 20 million people were thought to be infected in Latin America. By 2006, with the enormous efforts in the region to control the infection, there were fewer than 9 million cases. Transmission of the disease had been interrupted in Chile, Uruguay, a large part of Brazil and vast areas of Central America, Argentina, Bolivia and Paraguay. However, the latest data suggests that there are still about 7 million to 8 million people infected worldwide, mostly in Latin America. Chagas' disease has recently emerged in regions previously considered to be free of the disease, such as the Amazon Basin, and it has re-emerged in regions where control had been in progress, such as the Chaco region of Bolivia.

In 2005 the genome sequence of the parasite causing Chagas' disease (along with those leading to African trypanosomiasis and leishmaniasis – known collectively as the 'tritryps') was announced. Researchers hoped that this would lead to new methods of prevention and treatment. But like many of the other parasitic diseases, there is still no vaccine for Chagas' disease and, as yet, no miracle drugs for the chronic stage of the disease. Fighting the bugs with the latest insecticides, raising public awareness of the disease, the use of bed nets, and improvements to housing to make them less attractive to bug infestation, continue to remain the main focus of control efforts. The challenge is not just to keep up surveillance and control and to find new tools, but also to prevent transmission by blood transfusion and to provide care to the many people who have been infected in the past and continue to bear the burden of the chronic condition. A poignant reminder is that Chagas' disease is a leading cause of heart disease among people living in extreme poverty in Latin America.

A century after Chagas' discovery, Chagas' disease, like its Old World counterpart, African trypanosomiasis, is now considered as one of the Neglected Tropical Diseases of the twenty-first century. With a commitment by the WHO and other agencies to give more funding and attention to diseases of the poverty-stricken regions of the world, we can only hope that the target of eliminating Chagas' disease in the coming years will be achieved.

LYMPHATIC FILARIASIS

Lymphatic filariasis – or elephantiasis – belongs to a group of tropical diseases caused by thread-like parasitic roundworms (filariae) and their larvae (microfilariae) and transmitted to humans by mosquito bites. Lymphatic filariasis is caused by three types of worms, the most common of which is *Wuchereria bancrofti*. In its advanced stages the disease may cause damage to the kidneys and lymphatic system, as well gross deformities (such as massive swelling of the limbs, breasts and genitals). With the discovery of the life cycle of the filarial worm and its transmission by mosquitoes in the late nineteenth century, scientists were optimistic that the vector and its disease could be eradicated. Today, however, although drug treatments are available, millions continue to suffer from the chronic and disfiguring symptoms of lymphatic filariasis.

∾

Lymphatic filariasis was probably known in parts of the ancient world, especially in the Nile Delta. The swollen limbs of a statue of the Egyptian Pharaoh Mentuhotep II (*c.*2000 BC) suggest elephantiasis. A recent autopsy on the mummified body of Natsef-Amun, a priest during the time of Ramses XI (*c.*1100 BC), has revealed the presence of filarial worms.

Greek and Roman writers mention *elephantiasis arabum*, and

the Persian physician Ibn Sina (or Avicenna) (AD 980–1037) described the differences between leprosy and elephantiasis. The clearest early descriptions date from the sixteenth century, when European explorers in the tropics and subtropics witnessed numerous cases of the bizarre 'elephant leg' (the elephantine association derives both from the swelling of legs and genitalia and the rough texture of the skin). Around 1515 Tomé Pires, a Portuguese envoy in India, wrote: 'Many people in Malabar, Nayars as well as Brahmans and their wives – in fact about a quarter or a fifth of the total population, including the people of the lowest castes – have very large legs, swollen to a great size; and they die of this, and it is an ugly thing to see'. In the same era, Ralph Fitch, an Englishman in India, also noted: 'This bad water causeth many of the people to be like lepers, and many of them have their legs swollen as big as a man in the waste, & many of them are scant able to go.'

French scientists accompanying Napoleon in 1798 add another poignant account of the disease in a *Description de l'Égypte*: 'This unfortunate, sightless boy was affected in both legs with elephantiasis that he had sustained for a number of years. His ankles were thicker than the thighs; the feet were monstrous . . . covered with thick, yellowish crusts disposed in scales separated at intervals by deep ulcerated furrows from which oozed foetid, aqueous pus.' Although the disease was chiefly prevalent amongst the local populations, Europeans could also contract it. In the West Indies it was not unknown for plantation owners to suffer from what was known as 'Barbados leg'.

Something in the water?

Prior to the late nineteenth century, all sorts of ideas were postulated to explain what caused the disease. When the Dutch explorer Jan Huygen van Linschoten (1563–1611) visited the Portuguese colony of Goa on the west coast of India between 1588 and 1592, he reported on the belief that those suffering from elephantiasis were the descendants of the murderers of St Thomas the Apostle, who was said to have travelled to India:

> and they say that the progeny of those that slew him, are accursed by God, which is that they are all borne with one of their legges and one foote from the knee downewardes as thick as an Elephantes legge . . . there are whole villages and kyndreds of them that are borne in the said land of S. Thomas.

For some time afterwards, elephantiasis in the region became known as the 'curse of St Thomas'.

Several writers noted the close association with 'bad water', even incriminating water in coconuts. Others implicated 'bad airs' or 'consumption of rotting fish'. Some blamed snake venom. One commentator mentioned 'the Knats which never ceas'd tormenting us' in regions of elephantiasis, but it was not until the endeavours of Patrick Manson in 1877 that the pieces of the epidemiological puzzle began to fall into place.

Seeing the worm – the first clues

In 1863 larval stages (microfilariae) were first seen in hydrocele fluid by the French surgeon Jean-Nicolas Demarquay (1814–75). Three years later they were also seen, independently, in urine by Otto Henry Wucherer (1820–73) in Brazil. Wucherer's name is remembered in the scientific designation for one of the most common of the filarial worms, *Wuchereria bancrofti*. Timothy Lewis (1841–86), a British medical officer in India, discovered in 1871 the presence of microfilariae in blood and urine. His announcement in 1872 of the vast number of worms circulating in the blood caused a great deal of scientific interest. In 1877 Lewis named the adult male worm *Filaria sanguinis hominis*. He also recognized a link with elephantiasis. In the same year, the English parasitologist Thomas Spencer Cobbold (1828–86) identified a female adult worm that had been sent to him from Australia by Joseph Bancroft (1836–94) who had found it in the abscess of a patient. Cobbold gave it the name *Filaria bancrofti*. (This is the worm now known as *Wuchereria bancrofti*.)

But how did the worms enter the body and give rise to such distressing and disfiguring symptoms? The credit for the first critical discoveries goes to Patrick Manson, ('Mosquito Manson'), known also as the 'Father of Tropical Medicine'.

'Mosquito Manson'

'I live in an out-of-the world place, away from libraries, and out of the run of what is going on, so I do not know very well the value of my work, or if it has been done

233

before, or better.' Patrick Manson, letter from Amoy to
T. Spencer Cobbold, 17 November 1877

Patrick Manson was born in Aberdeenshire, Scotland. While a
medical officer in the Imperial Maritime Customs Service in
Amoy (now Xiamen) on the south-east coast of China, Manson
operated on many elephantiasis patients. One of his patients was
a street vendor 'who spread a cloth over his gross deformity and
used it as a table to sell his goods'. He was successfully treated,
but, as Manson's son-in-law later recalled, 'instead of showing
gratitude to his benefactor he tried to sue him for compensation
for loss of his livelihood'.

Manson followed up ideas already put forward by others,
especially those who had seen under the microscope 'threadlike
worms' (larval microfilariae) in the blood and urine of patients.
In 1877 he found microfilariae in the blood of dogs and humans,
and had a hunch that perhaps some bloodsucking insect was
responsible for transmitting the parasites. He ruled out fleas,
lice, bugs and leeches, because they were all distributed far more
widely than elephantiasis, but his suspicions fell on a species of
mosquito common in Amoy.

Manson had also found microfilariae in the blood of his gardener Hin Lo, and to test his hypothesis he kept Hin Lo in a
'mosquito house' into which Manson released mosquitoes to
feed on his blood. The mosquitoes were then recaptured with a
wine glass and paralysed with tobacco smoke. When Manson
subsequently dissected them, he found larval stages of the filarial
worm. This remarkable discovery suggested that the mosquito
was the 'nurse' of the filarial embryo. Moreover, the experiment
was the first to demonstrate conclusively the insect-borne transmission of any human disease.

While being the first to discover the full life cycle of the worm that causes lymphatic filariasis, Manson did not quite get the whole picture. He thought that the mosquito sucked up microfilariae from a patient in its blood meal, then when it died a few days later in stagnant water it released the parasite into the water. The next victim, Manson assumed, acquired the disease by drinking the contaminated water or via penetration of the skin.

The final pieces of the puzzle were, however, put in place some twenty years later by the Australian parasitologist Thomas Lane Bancroft (1860–1933) (son of Joseph Bancroft) and the Scottish physician George Carmichael Low (1872–1952), who were able to prove that the infective filarial larvae were transmitted not by ingestion but through the bite of the mosquito. By the early 1900s the full life cycle of lymphatic filariasis had for the most part been established, though it was shown some time later that there are three different filarial worms (*Wuchereria bancrofti, Brugia malayi* and *Brugia timori*) capable of causing lymphatic filariasis, with different biological patterns and geographical distributions. The disease is also transmitted by different species of mosquito – *Culex* (widespread across urban and semi-urban areas), *Anopheles* (mainly in rural areas) and *Aedes* (mainly in endemic islands in the Pacific).

The most common filarial worm is *Wuchereria bancrofti*, which is responsible for 90 per cent of the cases. Once in the human system its larvae make their way to the lymphatic vessels where they develop into adult worms and mate. The adult females release millions of immature microfilariae (tiny larvae), which circulate in the blood, often for several years, and can be taken up by female mosquitoes when they suck blood from the infected human. After repeated infections, the worms lodged in the person's lymph nodes and vessels eventually cause extreme swelling – elephantiasis – of the limbs, breast or scrotum, as well as internal damage to the kidneys and lymphatic system. The disease is usually first contracted in childhood, but its devastating symptoms do not appear until some years later. There are still a number of mysteries about the life history of *W. bancrofti* and the disease that it causes.

A way forward?

'And it's not just the story about one billion people who are afflicted with disabling, often-times stigmatizing, neglected tropical diseases, such as human hookworm infection and elephantiasis . . . it's all about the faces of dying children and sick mothers who haunt those who have seen them.' Former US President Bill Clinton

Manson paved the way for scientists to unravel the life cycles of other vector-borne diseases, such as malaria and yellow fever. Manson himself hoped that his discovery would lead to the elimination of lymphatic filariasis.

Sadly this has not yet come about and, although the disease is no longer endemic in some former regions such as parts of North America (especially Charleston and the 'low country' of South Carolina), southern Europe and Australia, it remains a leading cause of chronic disability in the tropical and subtropical regions of Africa, Asia and Latin America, with remaining foci on islands of the Caribbean and Pacific.

There has in recent years been a push by the WHO and other agencies to interrupt the cycle of transmission and to alleviate the suffering and disabilities caused by the disease. Early efforts to control the mosquito vector using insecticides did not prove entirely successful, but there are a number of microfilaricidal drugs that can kill the parasite in its larval stage and so block further transmission, including diethylcarbamazine citrate (DEC), discovered in the 1940s, and the first drug effective against filariasis. The British parasitologist Frank Hawking (1905–86) – father of Stephen Hawking, the great cosmologist – made important contributions to the development and testing of DEC, and pioneered the concept of adding DEC to common table salt. DEC is still used, in combination with more recently developed drugs, such as albendazole and ivermectin.

In 1997 the World Health Assembly passed a resolution to launch a Global Programme to Eliminate Lymphatic Filariasis (GPELF). GPELF began in 2000 with the aim of eliminating lymphatic filariasis by the year 2020. In 2000 the Global Alliance to Eliminate Lymphatic Filariasis (GAELF) was also set up as a joint partnership between the public and private sectors. The pharmaceutical companies, SmithKline Beecham, (now GlaxoSmithKline) and Merck pledged to provide free all the albendazole and ivermectin drugs necessary to eliminate the disease – the largest drug donations, at that time, in history. From 2000 to 2012, more than 4.4 billion treatments were delivered to a targeted population of about 984 million individuals in fifty-six countries, considerably reducing transmission in many places. Lymphatic filariasis was successfully eliminated as a public health problem in the People's Republic of China in 2007, though there is still need to care for those previously infected. While, many endemic areas (mostly in Africa) still remain to be covered by mass drug administration (MDA), the global pharmaceutical industry is continuing to donate some 5.5 billion treatments to help control lymphatic filariasis until 2020. The microfilaricidal drugs do not, however, kill the adult worm, so that annual treatment is necessary for at least four to six years – the average lifespan of the adult worm in the human body. Measures such as insecticide-treated nets or indoor residual spraying may help protect people from infection. Medical care of sufferers also involves dealing with secondary bacterial and fungal infections of the limbs and genitals, which, with treatment and better hygiene, can dramatically improve the condition.

Lymphatic filariasis, which affects millions of people in seventy-three countries, remains one of the leading causes of long-term disability in Africa, Asia, and Latin America. Over 120 million people are currently infected, with about 40 million disfigured and incapacitated by the disease, and it is one of the most disabling of the so-called Neglected Tropical Diseases. The deformities associated with the disease lead to social stigma, as well as financial hardship from loss of income and increased medical expenses. The socio-economic burdens of isolation and poverty are immense.

For those who suffer from this disfiguring condition – which often affects prospects of marriage for young adults and prevents many sufferers from leading a normal life – there is still much to hope for. Integrating diagnostic testing, mass drug administration, vector control and morbidity management for lymphatic filariasis with other disease programmes (such as those for malaria and onchocerciasis) will be an important future strategy for the neglected populations who often suffer concurrently from several overlapping diseases linked to poverty.

SCHISTOSOMIASIS

Schistosomiasis – also known as bilharzia – is a disease caused by a parasitic worm belonging to the genus *Schistosoma*, which spends its complex life cycle in both humans and aquatic snails. It is a disease that has been prevalent in China and the Nile Delta of Egypt since ancient times and has had a profound impact on the health and development of populations in endemic countries. The disease is found in areas of poor sanitation where people are in close contact with the freshwater habitats of the snail vector. Schistosomiasis can be horribly debilitating, and while it has a low fatality rate it can, in severe cases, lead to chronic bladder, gastrointestinal or liver disease. Although there have been control programmes to eliminate the snail and there is an effective drug, schistosomiasis continues to infect over 200 million people worldwide, with around 90 per cent of the burden occurring in sub-Saharan Africa. Like other Neglected Tropical Diseases it is a disease of poverty and one that also perpetuates poverty.

∽

'A most stubborn haematuria manifested itself among the soldiers of the French Army . . . continual and very abundant sweats diminished the quantity of urine, the latter becoming thick and bloody. The sickness gives sharp pains in the region of the bladder . . . the last contractions of the bladder are accompanied by the most lively and piercing pains.' A.J. Renoult, a French army surgeon, describing a disease – probably schistosomiasis – affecting Napoleon's troops at Aboukir Bay, Egypt, 1798

In 1851 a young German doctor called Theodor Bilharz (1825–62) was working in the Kasr El Aini Hospital in Cairo as an assistant to Wilhelm Griesinger (1817–68), the personal physician of the Khedive of Egypt. In Egypt at this time many people were afflicted with this strange disease characterized by 'bloody urine'. Bilharz was fascinated by the newly emerging field of helminthology – the study of worms – and while conducting an autopsy on a young man he saw in his portal vein (the great vein that carries blood from the stomach, intestines and spleen to the liver) a number of long white worms. As he peered down the microscope at one 'splendid' worm, he noticed that it had a flat body and a spiral tail. In a letter to his German professor, Carl von Siebold (1804–85), he described his exciting findings, and asked 'What then is this animal?'

The first worm Bilharz observed was a male. On examining another specimen he saw, living and moving 'back and forth' within a groove of the male, a slender female worm complete with internal organs and eggs – 'similar to a sword in a scabbard'. When Bilharz discovered eggs in the bladder wall of a patient, he and his fellow German scientists, including Wilhelm Griesinger, were quick to recognize that this parasitic worm, or blood fluke, was the likely cause of the 'bloody urine' infection that had plagued humans in the Nile Delta since the dawn of civilization. The disease became known in 1859 as 'bilharzia' or 'bilharziasis' in honour of its first discoverer.

Opening up a can of worms – and finding the answers at a snail's pace

Bilharz's discovery left many questions unanswered. How did the worm get inside the human body? Was it ingested through drinking water? Was there an intermediate host for the worm before it entered the human? Some fifty years after Bilharz's discovery, the Scottish physician Patrick Manson examined eggs that were rather different in shape from those Bilharz had observed in the bladder – the eggs Manson studied were in the faeces. Were there two forms of the disease – one of the urinary tract, the other the bowel – or did the eggs pass out of the body by either route?

A number of scientists were convinced there were two separate species of the worm affecting the bladder and the bowel, naming them, respectively, *Schistosoma haematobium* and *Schistosoma mansoni*. The word *schistosoma* comes from the Greek *skhizein* or *schisto*, 'to split or cleave', and *sōma*, 'body', referring to the way the female worm is enclosed in the deep cleft of the male during copulation. *S. haematobium* (from the Greek word for blood, *haema*) was the disease first seen by Bilharz in Egypt. The worms live in the veins of the bladder and give rise to the blood in the urine. *S. mansoni* was named after Patrick Manson, who had speculated that a different species affects the intestines. However, not everyone agreed on this dichotomy of species. Arthur Looss (1861–1923), the German authority on parasitology in Egypt, refused to believe there was more than one species, so beginning a series of fierce quarrels with the British parasitologists.

In the meanwhile, Japanese scientists were pursuing their

own line of investigation. A few years before Bilharz's observation, a Japanese physician Daijiro Fujii had travelled to Katayama Mountain, near Hiroshima, in 1847 and had described the symptoms of 'Katayama disease'. According to local legend, this was caused by the shipwreck of a cargo of lacquer, which poisoned the rice paddies. Fujii's description of the disease is now known to be the first written scientific account of schistosomiasis, although it did not come to light until 1909. But in 1904 two Japanese physicians, Fujiro Katsurada (1867–1946) and Akira Fujinami (1870–1934), found eggs and adult worms in patients with Katayama disease, naming it *Schistosoma japonicum* (after the country of its discovery). This form, affecting the intestines, was suggested to be a third species of the disease.

The puzzle was to ascertain how and why people were infected with the worm. Between 1909 and 1913 Japanese scientists set up experiments using cattle from Hiroshima City to prove that the infection occurs through the skin. The experimental cows were all free from infection. One group of cows was allowed to stand or roam in the rice paddies. Another group had their legs oiled and protected with water-proofed bags before going into the water. The cattle exposed to water became infected – those in 'water-proof boots' remained free of the disease. The Japanese scientists suspected that the freshwater snail was the immediate host, and a description of the whole life cycle of the infection in humans and its intermediate host, the snail, was published (first in Japanese in 1913 by Keinosuke Miyairi and Masatsugu Suzuki, and then in German with an English summary in 1914), describing for the first time the fork-tailed schistosome cercariae (larvae) emerging after a few weeks from the snails.

Around the same time, British scientists Robert Leiper (1881–1969) and Edward Atkinson (1881–1929) went to

Shanghai in China and Fujinami in Japan. They obtained snails from Katayama to explore the possibility of a snail host. Leiper then led a British Royal Army Medical Corps mission to Egypt and, independently, unravelled the life cycle of schistosomiasis with the snail as intermediate host. He also showed that there are two species of worm attracted to two different species of snail. His results were published with little acknowledgement to the earlier Japanese discoveries. Arthur Looss, still objecting to the new findings, remained adamant that there was no intermediate snail host.

Eventually, following many bitter arguments, by 1915 British and Japanese scientists working independently had agreed on the central key to the puzzle – the worm spends part of its life cycle in freshwater snails. And its larvae (or cercariae), emerging from the snail into the water, can penetrate through the unbroken skin of anyone entering, wading, working or swimming in snail-infested rivers and lakes. Once in the human body, larvae enter the bloodstream and are carried to the blood vessels of the lungs. From the lungs they migrate to the liver, where they mature and then move to the veins of the bladder or the abdominal cavity. The three main forms of the disease (*S. haematobium*, *S. mansoni* and *S. japonicum*) have different pathologies, different passages through the human body, different snail hosts, and different geographical distributions.

Several new species have been discovered more recently: *S. mekongi* (in the Mekong basin of Laos and Cambodia); *S. malayensis* (in the Malaysian peninsula); and *S. guineensis* and *S. intercalatum* (in the rainforest belt of Central Africa). Other species infect mammals and birds, and there are strains of the different species that are quite particular about which of any type of snail host they inhabit.

The clinical manifestations and severity of symptoms are extensive, ranging from minor irritation at the point where some cercariae penetrate the skin but do not mature into adults (often known as 'swimmer's itch', which is found among bathers in lakes in many parts of the world, including the USA and UK), to cases where the life cycle of the worm in the human causes anaemia, diarrhoea and fatigue which can sap the energy of the infected, and, in serious cases, lead to debilitating and chronic ill health or, occasionally, life-threatening heart disease, kidney failure and bladder cancer. Much depends on the quirky behaviour of the various worms and their offspring inside and outside the human body.

The disease, originally known in 1859 as 'bilharzia' or 'bilharziasis', also has varied local names, including 'big belly', 'snail fever' and 'red-water fever'. Since the 1950s in scientific and medical circles, it has more commonly been called schistosomiasis – after its causative agent, the trematode flatworm, belonging to the genus *Schistosoma*.

Mummies and eggs

In 1910 Marc Armand Ruffer (1859–1917), British professor of bacteriology at the Cairo Medical School and a pioneer of palaeopathology, made a remarkable discovery: in the kidneys of two Egyptian mummies he found the calcified eggs of *S. haematobium*. The mummies were about 3,000 years old – from the Twentieth Dynasty of the New Kingdom (c.1190 –1077 BC). At Manchester University Museum, an International Ancient Egyptian Tissue Bank was set up in the 1990s, with the prime aim of examining mummies and ancient tissues to trace the history and evolution of diseases over the past 5,000 years. Using a variety of techniques including the latest non-invasive technology to look inside mummies without removing their outer wrappings, scientists are revealing a wealth of information – and, in particular, confirmation that schistosomiasis was undoubtedly prevalent in ancient Egypt at the time of the Pharaohs.

Eggs of the schistosome worm have also been found in a corpse buried in the province of Hunan in China more than 2,000 years ago and, in a recent remarkable excavation, schistosome eggs have been recovered from the pelvic sediment of an individual buried in a 6,200-year-old grave in one of the earliest farming settlements in the Euphrates river valley of northern Syria. Schistosomiasis presumably became a significant human infection in river valleys such as the Euphrates, the Nile in Egypt and the Yellow (Huang He) River in China, when people began to settle, farm and irrigate their land. Snails like to lie on the surface of freshwater plants or hide in reed beds along the banks of rivers and lakes. How, when and why the schistosome worm first appeared on the scene is a puzzling question, but it seems likely that when humans started to use snail-infested waters and man-made irrigation systems for domestic and agricultural purposes the cycle of disease began.

The finding of eggs in mummies and corpses is not simply a reminder of the antiquity of this disease – it is also a key to one of the many peculiarities of schistosomiasis. Unlike many other worm infections, it is not the adult or larval worms that cause the disease, but the eggs. The female worm lays hundreds of eggs each day, and can keep reproducing for several years. About half the eggs pass out in the urine or faeces, and then hatch in fresh water, after which the larvae enter and live in freshwater snails, thus perpetuating the cycle. The rest of the eggs lodge in the tissues of the liver, bladder or intestine, depending on the variety of the parasite, resulting in the formation of obstructive nodules called granulomas, causing immune reactions and progressive damage to organs.

The toll of schistosomiasis

Schistosomiasis has, over the past centuries, taken a huge toll on populations living in areas where the disease is endemic – costing lives, stunting the growth of children, impeding development and seriously affecting productivity through its debilitating effects on the human body.

The effect on communities living and working in the Nile Delta in Egypt has probably been one of the most dramatic examples of the insidious and destructive nature of schistosomiasis. As irrigation schemes were changed or expanded to improve productivity of crops, so people wading and working in the snail-infested waters became more and more at risk from the disease, and, in turn, by urinating or defecating in or near the water, they perpetuated the cycle – from humans to snails and back to humans.

'Defeating the snail' – twentieth-century campaigns to control schistosomiasis

'Welcome the sunrise, come under the stars, work from dusk to daybreak

Our strength is boundless, our enthusiasm is redder than fire . . .

Be the river like a sea, drained clean it shall be . . .

Empty the rivers to wipe out the snails, resolutely to fight the big-belly disease.' Wei Pen-po, 1958

There have been a number of campaigns to control the disease, including that mounted by the Rockefeller Foundation against schistosomiasis and hookworm in Egypt in the 1930s. The Second World War brought schistosomiasis to international attention when Allied soldiers were affected during military operations in China, the Philippines and other Pacific islands. An extensive campaign was initiated, using posters and cartoons to teach the soldiers how to prevent the infection. Other programmes in the Philippines, Japan, China, Venezuela, Puerto Rico and Israel during or shortly after the Second World War were also set up to 'defeat' the snail. At a time when the disease was believed to affect up to 150 million people, campaigns were primarily directed against the snail, using molluscicides (initially copper sulphate, and later a range of chemicals including niclosamide). These campaigns also involved treatment of infected populations using tartar emetic and other highly toxic drugs. The provision of latrines and improved sanitation was, additionally, seen to be vital in breaking the cycle, but the effectiveness of efforts to link control with health education and improvements in social and economic conditions was variable.

One of the many formidable campaigns to eradicate schistosomiasis was launched in the 1950s by the newly founded People's Republic of China. At the start of the campaign, some 10 million Chinese were heavily infected with worms of the *S. japonicum* form of the disease. The Chinese used many different approaches to target the disease and employed millions of farmers, barefoot doctors and others in the 'People's War against the Snail'. It is even said that peasants walked through irrigation ditches plucking out the 'devil snails' one by one – using chopsticks. Mao Zedong (1893–1976, commonly referred to as Chairman Mao) wrote a poem about the success of the campaign entitled 'Farewell to the God of Plague'. Today, schistosomiasis has been successfully eliminated from many, though not all, parts of China.

In other areas of the world, the construction of dams, reservoirs and irrigation canals for hydroelectric power and agriculture allowed the snail population to explode massively. In the 1960s the Aswan High Dam scheme in Egypt and the Volta project in Ghana, designed to provide hydroelectricity and irrigation, created vast artificial lakes, such as Lake Nasser in Egypt, which are ideal breeding sites for the snail. In some villages many of the children subsequently became burdened with worms.

'Treating the children' – twenty-first century campaigns to eliminate schistosomiasis

For the first sixty years of large-scale efforts to control schistosomiasis, snail control was the primary method used to prevent infection (and this strategy, using molluscicides, still continues). The earliest injectable drugs to be developed for schistosomiasis, such as antimony potassium tartrate, were highly toxic and nearly as bad as the disease itself. Indeed, it has recently been speculated that the current massive epidemic of hepatitis C (a blood-borne viral disease) in Egypt – dubbed the 'eleventh plague of Egypt' – might be related to the well-intended schistosomiasis campaigns of the 1950s to the 1970s when unsterilized needles were used for intravenous injections time and again.

Since the 1970s three new drugs have come on the market. One – praziquantel – was hailed as a 'wonder drug'. This oral drug is safe and effective against all schistosome species; it acts against adult schistosome worms, though it has poor activity against immature schistosome larvae and does not prevent rein-fection. The cost and logistical difficulties of treating people in the poorest parts of the world have remained huge. However, there have been a number of recent initiatives, based on the mass distribution of praziquantel, in an attempt to control mor-bidity for millions of schoolchildren and adults at high risk.

The Schistosomiasis Control Initiative (SCI), for example, was launched by Imperial College, London, at the turn of the twenty-first century. In 2002, it received substantial grants from the Gates Foundation to enable it to help governments in African countries to bring treatment for schistosomiasis to the poorest populations of the continent. Under the directorship of Alan Fenwick, professor of tropical parasitology, this charitable insti-tution is now also supported by the United States Agency for International Development (USAID) and Geneva Global (an international philanthropic company). By 2013, the SCI had facilitated delivery of its 100 millionth treatment. The SCI is also assisting the WHO to distribute praziquantel, donated by Merck, primarily to African schoolchildren. This pharmaceutical com-pany has been freely donating the drug since 2007 and has now pledged to increase its annual donation over the next few years to 250 million tablets – enough to treat 100 million children every year from 2016. The WHO in 2012 has now also recom-mended the inclusion of preschool children in preventive chemotherapy efforts.

There is, nevertheless, still a long way to go before the goal of global schistosomiasis elimination can be realized. While there have been effective and encouraging campaigns to eliminate the disease in some of the middle-income countries previously afflicted, the burden rests on sub-Saharan Africa. It is estimated that there are around 240 million people, especially school-age children and young adults, infected with the disease in fifty-two endemic countries in Africa, parts of the Caribbean and South America, the Middle East, China and South-east Asia. Some ninety per cent of all people requiring treatment live in sub-Saharan Africa. Schistosomiasis remains, after malaria, the second most serious parasitic disease in the world and one of the most devastating of the group of Neglected Tropical Diseases (NTDs).

Schistosomiasis and a host of worm diseases

Schistosomiasis is not only one of the NTDs but also one of a number of diseases caused by 'worms'. Worms – or, to give them their scientific name, 'helminths' – come in all shapes and sizes: roundworms, hookworms, pinworms, flatworms, whipworms, threadworms and tapeworms. (Despite its name, ringworm doesn't have anything to do with worms and is a fungal infection.) Parasitic worms, transmitted in any number of complex ways, can be microscopic or reach several metres in length. Humans are host to at least 300 parasitic worms, and many have been around for thousands of years. Worms have been found in desiccated or fossilized human faeces dating back to the earliest civilizations.

Millions of people in the world today carry some sort of intestinal worm. The thought of worms penetrating and wriggling through the skin, invading the gut, living, mating and laying eggs in our bodies, exiting through urine or stools, being coughed up or crawling out of legs is enough to make anyone feel squeamish. Over the centuries, people have sought all sorts of ways to kill or get rid of worms. Various concoctions such as pomegranate bark, turpentine or wormwood have been used to poison the worms. Castor oil, jalap, senna, liquorice and other plant extracts have been given to people as purgatives. The Guinea worm (*Dracunculus medinensis*), which breaks out of blisters in the skin when immersed in water, has traditionally been extracted by winding it round a stick.

Increasingly, with the availability of effective of anthelminthic drugs, various control programmes for helminth-related diseases are being coordinated. In many regions of the developing world, especially sub-Saharan Africa, it is common for children to be polyparasitized with both soil-transmitted helminths (such as hookworm) and schistosomes. In 2001, the Partners for Parasite Control (PPC) programme was launched to tackle the co-morbidity of these diseases – with the aim of treating ('de-worming') at least 75 per cent of all school-age children at risk by the year 2010. There is also a need for further research to understand the synergistic relationship between these diseases and HIV/AIDS, tuberculosis and malaria, which, especially in sub-Saharan Africa, are also often co-endemic.

Another key strategy is to break the cycle of contact between worms and humans – ideally through improvements in sanitation, hygiene and public health. This is an important component in the fight against schistosomiasis, with the aim of preventing infected people urinating or defecating in snail-infested water sources and exposing their bare skin to these waters. One of the most remarkable recent success stories is the near eradication of Guinea-worm disease (dracunculiasis). There has never been a vaccine or cure for this painful disease which is transmitted through drinking water contaminated with parasite-infected water fleas (*Cyclops*). Eradication efforts have been based on health education and behaviour change, such as teaching people to filter all drinking water and to avoid contaminating water sources with worms emerging from the skin. From an estimated

3.5 million cases in the mid-1980s, only 148 cases in four remaining endemic countries (Chad, Ethiopia, Mali and South Sudan) were reported in 2013.

We can only hope that for other worm diseases, like schisto-somiasis, the combination of diagnostic, curative, environmental, behavioural and preventive strategies, and perhaps, eventually, prophylactic or transmission-blocking vaccines, will lift millions from the burden of these diseases of poverty in the coming decades.

HOOKWORM

Hookworm is a parasitic infection caused by a bloodsucking roundworm that clamps its mouth parts onto the small intestine and feeds on the host's blood. It is a disease that has probably affected humans since ancient times. Its chief symptom is severe anaemia, which leaves the sufferer physically weak, lethargic and incapacitated. Hookworm is one of several soil-transmitted helminth infections in which parasitic eggs in human faeces can contaminate soil in areas of poor sanitation. One of the first major campaigns to control hookworm was that launched by the Rockefeller Sanitary Commission in the early twentieth century in an attempt to eradicate the disease from the southern states of the USA. This was succeeded by a number of international anti-hookworm programmes. Today, in the developing nations of the tropics and subtropics, more than 1.5 billion people, the majority of whom are children, are infected with hookworm and other soil-transmitted helminth infections, and ongoing efforts are needed to rid the world of these intestinal worms.

ᲒᲮ

The lethargy resulting from the anaemia caused by hookworm led the Chinese in the third century BC to call it the 'able-to-eat-but-lazy-to-work yellow disease'. In Egypt in the nineteenth century it became known as 'tropical chlorosis', reflecting the pallor and greenish-yellow skin of those afflicted (rather like the anaemic Victorian girls in England who were diagnosed with 'chlorosis' or 'green sickness'). A journalist in the early twentieth century in the southern states of the USA dubbed it 'the germ of laziness'. It has also been called 'angel wings' or 'pot belly' because it can lead to misshapen shoulder blades and a distended abdomen. Other names, such as 'ground itch' or 'dew poison' in the southern USA, and 'water itch' or 'coolie itch' in India, have been used to describe the initial dermatological symptoms, when the larval hookworms penetrate the skin of the feet. Its scientific name, ancylostomiasis (a combination of the Greek names *ankylos* and *stoma* meaning 'hook' and 'mouth'), was coined in the mid-nineteenth century.

An ancient infection

The many colloquial names (there are over 150) reflect the breadth of symptoms, characteristics and outcomes of this insidious disease. Although only a small proportion of those infected eventually die from the disease, it can lead to severe iron-deficiency anaemia, protein malnutrition and chronic ill health, which, in turn, can have serious consequences for daily life and intellectual and physical development. If left untreated, those with a heavy worm load – maybe with some hundreds or thousands of worms drinking blood from their gut – are barely able to carry out even the most basic everyday activities. Its threat to pregnant women is especially serious, with an increased risk of death and complications for both mother and infant.

There are a number of descriptions of a hookworm-like anaemia in early written records, including hieroglyphic entries in the Egyptian Ebers Papyrus (*c.*1550 BC) and descriptions in the Hippocratic corpus (fifth century BC) – suggesting that humans may have long been plagued by this debilitating scourge. Eggs and larvae, possibly of hookworms or some other intestinal worm, have been found in human coprolites (fossilized faeces) from Brazil dating from 430 to 340 BC, while the remains of adult worms have been discovered in the intestines of an ancient Peruvian mummy dating from about AD 900. However, there is some debate as to whether hookworm was endemic in pre-Columbian America or introduced following the opening up of the New World by infected slaves from sub-Saharan Africa. It has also been observed since ancient times that some people would eat clay or dirt. This condition, known as 'pica' (from the Latin word for magpie, a bird which is reputed to eat almost anything), causes the person to crave all sorts of bizarre substances, and may be related to iron deficiency – such as that caused by hookworm.

A year in the life of a hookworm

Like many worm infections, the life cycle of the hookworm – inside and outside the human – is quite extraordinary. The adult worm, which is about one centimetre (0.4 inches) long, lives in the small intestine, where it attaches itself to the lining and feeds on blood. One species of human hookworm, *Ancylostoma duodenale*, locks itself on with its sharp teeth, while the other species, *Necator americanus*, uses cutting blades. The female lays her eggs – up to several thousand a day – in the host's intestine, from where they are passed out in the faeces.

In areas of the world where human faeces are left untreated in backyards or spread onto the fields to be used as fertilizer, the eggs hatch in the warm, moist soil and grow through three larval stages. The third stage, known as 'wriggling larvae', can then penetrate through the skin of anyone living or working barefoot in contaminated areas.

In the next phase, the larvae that have burrowed through the skin, most usually through the feet, make their way via the bloodstream to the lungs. But rather than settle here, they continue to migrate through the respiratory tract to the back of the mouth, where they are swallowed. And so the larvae return back to the gut, where they become adults, mate, lay eggs and live for up to a year or more on human blood. Somehow, throughout its life, the adult parasite has a way of keeping its host alive and the blood flowing.

The main stages of this intricate life cycle were unravelled by a number of scientists from the mid-nineteenth to the early twentieth century. These researchers painstakingly looked at the intestines of cadavers and endless stool samples, examined the worms under the microscope, measured 'worm burdens', and watched as larvae placed on skin burrowed and disappeared, leaving only their 'abandoned cuticles' on the surface.

Wormy tales

The first key scientist to report on the discovery of a hookworm in a human was the Italian physician Angelo Dubini (1813–1902), when in 1838, during an autopsy, he saw the worms in the bowel of a peasant. Over the following years he found other examples of the peculiar worm in the small intestines of a number of patients. Because the worms had a mouth with four hooks and the tail was slightly curved, he called them hookworms and gave the species a scientific name, *Agchylostoma* (later *Ancylostoma*) *duodenale*. In 1854 Wilhelm Griesinger

(1817–68), a German physician working in Egypt, suggested there was a connection between the worm and the disease known as 'tropical chlorosis'. In Brazil, Otto Wucherer (1820–73) published a paper in 1866 'about a disease vulgarly denominated tiredness', confirming that it was caused by hookworms.

Further evidence came during an epidemic of anaemia and diarrhoea among Italian workmen digging the St Gotthard rail tunnel in the Alps in the 1880s. Hundreds of miners were examined and found to be infected with hookworm; one post-mortem examination in Turin found 1,500 worms in a single miner. The Italian scientists Camillo Bozzolo (1845–1920), Edoardo Perroncito (1847–1936) and Luigi Pagliani (1847–1932) linked the hookworm to anaemia and the insanitary conditions in the tunnel. Scientists also noted that the men had to defecate in the 9-mile (15-km) tunnel, and often wore worn-out shoes. But just how did the worm get into the human body?

When the German scientist Arthur Looss was working in Cairo in the late nineteenth century, he accidentally spilled a culture containing hookworm larvae on his hand. His hand began to turn red and burn – and two months later, examining his stools, he found the eggs of the hookworm. After several experiments – including one in which he put larvae on the leg of a boy who was to have it amputated – Looss was able to confirm by 1901 that the hookworm larvae entered the body through the skin.

Looss is not the only scientist to have discovered the pathway of worms – albeit, in his case, accidentally. The Italian scientist Giovanni Battista Grassi infected himself with the eggs of *Ascaris lumbricoides* (the giant roundworm) and subsequently found eggs in his faeces. In the mid-nineteenth century Friedrich Küchenmeister (1821–90), in much-criticized experiments to understand the life cycle of tapeworms (*Taenia solium*), fed pig meat containing some worm larvae to two criminals who had been condemned to death, and subsequently recovered adult tapeworms – one of them 1.5 metres (5 ft) long – from their intestines after they had been executed.

In the twenty-first century, scholars are curious about our evolutionary history with parasitic worms. At Nottingham University in 2006 scientists infected themselves with hookworm larvae – deliberately. They had speculated that hookworms produce chemical compounds that can calm the human immune system, possibly reducing the symptoms of allergies such as hay fever, asthma and food intolerance. But before testing out the worms on patients they needed to find out just how safe worm infestation is. So they volunteered themselves. Meanwhile, at the London School of Hygiene and Tropical Medicine, another scientist recently infected himself with hookworm and then swallowed a 'pill camera' to get a worm's eye view of the life cycle of this bloodsucking parasite. These self-experimenters (who can now rid themselves of the hookworm with an anti-helminthic drug) are hoping to understand more about the balance and link between the pathological effects of hookworm infections on the gut mucosa and the potentially beneficial effects of the modulated immune response induced. The worm's potential (in safe doses) as a biotherapy is still in the early stages of being tested.

'The germ of laziness'

'Mr Rockefeller your fortune is rolling up, rolling up like an avalanche! You must keep up with it! You must distribute it faster than it grows! If you do not, it will crush

you and your children and your children's children.'
Reverend Frederick Gates, 1906

In 1909 Frederick T. Gates (1853–1929) and Wallace Buttrick (1853–1926), both Baptist pastors, were on a trip to the southern states of the USA. They were travelling in luxury in the private railroad car of Standard Oil magnate John D. Rockefeller Senior (1839–1937) to investigate the prevalence and consequences of hookworm. As they looked out of the windows they saw scenes of unimaginable poverty and despair – pallid, listless children with pot bellies and matchstick-thin legs, dull-eyed and stunted in growth. Such sights were to have a profound impact on the understanding of the so-called 'germ of laziness' and lead to one of the first major philanthropic public health initiatives.

At that time the 'Hookworm Belt' extended across many parts of the globe, between latitudes 30°S and 36°N, with extensive foci in Latin America and the southern states of the USA, as well as being a common condition amongst miners and construction workers in underground tunnels in temperate countries. One of the earliest anti-hookworm campaigns was begun in 1903 in Costa Rica and Puerto Rico, where the disease was rampant among workers in the sugar cane fields. But more campaigns were needed to combat the 'germ of laziness'. Gates and Buttrick were able to persuade Rockefeller to fund a commission to mount a major anti-hookworm campaign in eleven southern states of the USA.

The Rockefeller Sanitary Commission (RSC) was headed by Wickliffe Rose (1862–1931), and the chief scientist was Charles Wardell Stiles (1867–1941), nicknamed the 'Privy Councillor' (because of his insistence on hygiene and clean privies). Gates,

Stiles and Rose perceived anaemia-provoking hookworm disease to be a key factor that explained both the economic
'backwardness' of the southern states and was an impediment to
industrialization. When the commission surveyed infection
rates they found that some 40 per cent of schoolchildren in the
American South suffered in varying degrees from hookworm
infection. This species of hookworm had been named *Necator
americanus* ('American killer') by Stiles in 1902.

The prime emphasis of the campaign, beginning in 1909–10,
was health education, aimed at over 1 million people. Some
25,000 public meetings were held, more than 2 million handbills
were distributed, stool samples were collected, and people were
taught the importance of wearing shoes, how to build sanitary
privies and about the significance of hookworm as a major factor
in ill health and low productivity. The campaign also dispensed
thousands of treatments – although the first drug used to kill the
worms, thymol, could have toxic side effects.

In the days before radio and TV, this campaign was a massive
public health enterprise. It had some immediate successes in
reducing the burden of hookworm, but it proved hard to eliminate the infection entirely. There was also some public resistance
to the programme – it was rumoured that the shoes being 'ped-
dled' were made in Rockefeller-owned factories. However,
contemporaries noted the improvement in school enrolment,
attendance and literacy rates of children, as a resident in Virginia
commented to the RSC in 1915: 'the treatment of these children
had transformed the school. Children who were listless and dull
are now active and alert; children who could not study a year
ago are not only studying now, but are finding joy in learning.'
And another testimonial from a school board in Louisiana said:
'As a result of your treatment for hookworm in our school . . . we

have here in our schoolrooms today about 120 bright, rosy-faced children, whereas had you not been sent here to treat them we would have had that many pale-faced, stupid children.'

The Rockefeller Sanitary Commission for the Eradication of Hookworm Disease initially focused on the southern states of the USA but was later extended to other parts of the 'Hookworm Belt' and, in the first two decades of the twentieth century, many other anti-hookworm programmes were set up around the world, or were added to pre-existing efforts.

But in spite of the intensive efforts of the Rockefeller Sanitary Commission and its optimistic concept of disease 'eradication', by the mid-1920s disillusionment had set in and the RSC was wound down. In the early twentieth century, attempting to 'eradicate' a disease like hookworm that was so entangled in multiple social and economic determinants proved far more complex than envisaged. The campaign, nevertheless, had brought about large reductions in hookworm disease to entire areas, and these gains were further consolidated through improvements in sanitation, though it was not until the 1930s onwards – with rural depopulation, reductions in poverty and a shift to a more urbanized economy – that hookworm began to recede from the USA. The RSC, however, left its legacy in the fields of international health and philanthropy.

Hookworm, international health and philanthropy

The Rockefeller Foundation, based in New York City, was created in 1913, with its central mission being 'to promote the well-being of mankind throughout the world'. With its continued activities in a wide range of scientific, medical, public health and educational spheres, it has recently celebrated its centenary. John D. Rockefeller's enduring legacy also paved the way for the development of other major international health programmes. His commission acted as a model for the League of Nations Health Organization, set up after the First World War, and its successor, the WHO, established in 1948.

And we are reminded of the significant role that Frederick Gates played in persuading Rockefeller to part with his money for a philanthropic public health cause. The International Health Division of the Rockefeller Foundation, developed in 1927 with a mission 'to help bridge the gap between existing medical knowledge and its practical application', bears resonances with another 'Gates' partnership. Inspired by the Rockefeller family's philanthropic focus, Bill Gates (b.1955) of Microsoft fame and fortune, and his wife, Melinda (b.1964), created in the year 2000 the charitable Bill & Melinda Gates Foundation, which has made huge contributions in alleviating the burden of ill health in the poorest parts of the world.

'Children without worms' – a way forward?

'[Hookworm], silent and insidious . . . in my view it out-ranks all other worm infections of man combined . . . in its production, frequently unrealized, of human misery, debility, and inefficiency in the tropics.' Norman Stoll, Rockefeller scientist, 1962

Hookworm has receded or disappeared from some parts of the world over the last century, but has remained a continuous though often neglected problem in many areas of the tropics and subtropics. The USA is now virtually free of the disease, as are Europe and Japan. In part, these successes can be attributed to specific anti-hookworm campaigns, but perhaps more broadly to economic development, as well as improved living conditions, better sanitation and nutrition, greater public health awareness, and the availability of safe and effective anthelminthic ('de-worming') drugs, and of iron supplements to counteract the anaemia.

However, tackling the remaining endemic foci of hookworm and breaking its cycle is still an enormous task in the impoverished rural areas of sub-Saharan Africa, South-east Asia, China and Latin America, where the disease remains entrenched. This chronic and debilitating Neglected Tropical Disease infects between 570 and 740 million people in the world. Children with hookworm are physically, nutritionally and cognitively impaired and account for the major burden of this disease. Up to 44 million pregnant women are also estimated to be infected with hookworm, resulting in severe outcomes for both the mother and her infant. It is the leading cause of anaemia and protein malnutrition in the developing nations of the tropics. Children in areas of poverty and poor sanitation are also likely to be co-infected with the other two major soil-transmitted helminths, *Ascaris* roundworm, and *Trichuris* whipworm, known together with hookworm as 'the unholy trinity'.

There have been some concerted efforts in the twenty-first century to target hookworm and other helminth infections, including the goal of the WHO to 'de-worm' 75 per cent of all at-risk schoolchildren using safe, effective and easy to administer drugs, such as albendazole (donated by GlaxoSmithKline and used also for lymphatic filariasis) and mebendazole (donated by Johnson & Johnson). Frequent and periodic de-worming can have enormous health and educational benefits. The WHO goal has not yet been reached, but since the London Declaration on

Neglected Tropical Diseases in 2012 (see p. 217) there has been progress in reaching more children with de-worming medications.

Other global collaborative partnerships, such as Children Without Worms (CWW), are joining the mission of 'envisioning the world's children to be free of soil-transmitted helminths so they can grow, play, learn normally and enrich their communities'. CWW advocates a four-pronged, comprehensive control strategy – Water, Sanitation, Hygiene Education and De-worming – known as the WASHED Framework. And in April 2014 several organizations, including the Gates Foundation, formed a new partnership to expand current efforts to eliminate hookworm. Efforts to find an effective vaccine are also underway at the Sabin Vaccine Institute in Washington, DC, which could transform future control programmes and reduce the human suffering caused by hookworm.

In the early decades of the twentieth century, the inextricable link between hookworm, poverty and underdevelopment was clearly recognized, or as one officer of the Rockefeller Commission in Mexico wrote in 1925: '[If a person were freed of hookworm, he would have] more money in his pocket with which to buy better food, better clothes, better houses and better schools. With better schools there will come enlightenment. Intelligence will displace ignorance, and with intelligence there will come a true social revolution.'

Let us hope that by 2025, the children of the world will, at last, be free from parasitic worms to take this message forward.

ONCHOCERCIASIS

Onchocerciasis – which is often known as 'river blindness' – is a chronic parasitic disease caused by a filarial worm, *Onchocerca volvulus*, and transmitted from person to person by the bite of an infected female blackfly of the genus *Simulium*. The small, fiercely biting blackfly breeds in fast-flowing rivers in the tropics and subtropics, and for centuries the disease has plagued people living in the vicinity of such rivers. As well as being a leading cause of blindness, especially in Africa, onchocerciasis has had serious social and economic consequences. A successful Onchocerciasis Control Programme in West Africa was initiated in the 1970s aimed at eliminating the blackfly and treating the disease. Other global programmes continue to fight the disease which still infects millions of people living in sub-Saharan Africa, with scattered foci in Latin America and the Yemen.

∾

For people living in many parts of the tropics and subtropics, the river valleys have always been the most productive areas, offering fertile soils, fish and fresh water. But they are also the favoured breeding grounds of the blackfly. In the past, to farm and survive in such areas often became economically impossible. Settlements were frequently abandoned as those tormented by swarming flies, skin lesions, unbearable itching and progressive blindness moved away from the rivers to healthier but less fertile lands. In the drier uplands the pressure on the arid lands led to erosion and poor harvests – and so set up a vicious circle that has been described by one scholar as 'a cyclical pattern of advance and retreat', with farmers 'caught between malnutrition and land shortages on the one hand and the perils of onchocerciasis on the other'.

It took many decades for scientists to unravel the life cycle of the disease, and to recognize its role in mass blindness and the abandonment of riverside settlements.

Craw-craw, worms and blackflies

'Nearness to rivers can eat your eyes.' African proverb

In 1875 Irish naval surgeon John O'Neill (1848–1913), who was working in Addah Fort Hospital in the Gold Coast (now Ghana), examined and described minute filarial larvae measuring about 0.25mm (1/100th of an inch) long. Under the microscope, O'Neill had seen these microfilariae (tiny larval worms) wriggling, twisting, curling and coiling in skin snips cut off with a scalpel from patients suffering from 'craw-craw'. He published a paper, entitled 'On the Presence of a Filaria in "Craw-Craw"', in the British medical journal *The Lancet*, describing the presence of minute filarial larvae in six patients in West Africa:

Among the natives of the West Coast of Africa there is of frequent occurrence a peculiar skin disease called the craw-craw. Its intractability, contagiousness, and irritating nature so aroused my attention that I was induced to bestow much time on its microscopic examination, and

succeeded at length in discovering a filaria which I believe
to be the immediate cause of the complaint.

Craw-craw (or *kru kru*) was the local name for a condition
which gave rise to intense itching which could be so maddening
that sufferers used knives and stones to scratch themselves.
Some were even driven to suicide. We now know that craw-craw
is in fact one of the features of the early stages of onchocerciasis.
O'Neill noted that sulphur, used to treat scabies, was ineffective
against craw-craw, and was intrigued to know how the worms
seen under the microscope entered the human body.

Around this time various scientists – including the Scottish
physician Patrick Manson, – were beginning to suspect that parasitic infections might be transmitted to humans by insect
vectors. A number of culprits were suggested for craw-craw,
including bed bugs, ticks, mosquitoes and the Congo floor
maggot. It was not until the 1920s, following the studies of the
Guatemalan investigator Rodolfo Robles (1878–1939) in the
Americas and the Scottish parasitologist Donald Breadalbane
Blacklock (1879–1955) in Sierra Leone, that the blackfly (sometimes known as the 'coffee fly' or the 'buffalo gnat') was finally
incriminated in the transmission of the disease.

These and later studies revealed that the infectious agent,
the filarial worm *Onchocerca volvulus* (derived from a combination of Greek and Latin words relating to the 'hook' and 'tail'
of the worm and its ability to 'twist about'), is transmitted
through the bite of infected female blackflies of the genus
Simulium. The disease is most common along rich, oxygenated
water in rapidly flowing rivers where the blackflies breed – the
same area where many people congregate for bathing, fishing,
drawing water and defecating. Humans become infected with

onchocerciasis when blackflies inject *O. volvulus* larvae into them while biting and feeding on their blood. Over the course of about a year, the larvae then migrate to different areas under the skin and develop into adult worms which live in nodules, producing over 1,000 eggs per day. The larval worms (microfilariae) migrate from the nodules, mainly to the skin and eyes. When a female blackfly next takes her blood meal from an infected host she ingests any living microfiliariae, which after a period of further development are ready to be passed on through her bite to the next person in the chain. Once infected, people can continue to infect flies as long as the adult worms produce microfilariae, often for ten to fifteen years. The clinical manifestations of onchocerciasis – agonizing itching, visual impairment and eventual blindness – are due to an inflammatory response to dead or dying microfilariae. In a heavily infected person, 100,000 or more microfilariae die daily.

At first, researchers focused their attention on the skin lesions and pigment changes, especially of the lower limbs (known as 'leopard skin'). Loss of skin elasticity and other complications, including 'hanging groin' (or 'lizard skin'), were also striking features, but the fact that the microfilariae could reach the eyes and cause blindness was not fully appreciated by scientists until the 1930s. Jean Hissette (1888–1965), working in the Belgian Congo (now the Democratic Republic of the Congo), first suggested that the eyes of people suffering 'river blindness' might be infected by the microfilariae. In the ensuing years it was realized that onchocercal blindness in Africa was widespread, and by the 1940s the association between the depopulation of river valleys, mass 'river blindness', onchocerciasis and the blackfly vector finally became clear. The close association between areas of blackfly and river blindness, however, must have been well

known to local populations before scientists were able to elucidate the life cycle of onchocerciasis.

Although onchocerciasis is not life-threatening, it probably
reduces life expectancy by up to fifteen years, and its debilitating
and disabling effects can make life intolerable for its sufferers.
People with the disease often have low self-esteem, experience
social isolation and worry that they will never marry. Children
are distracted in school due to constant itching. Those blinded
by the disease suffer on an almost unimaginable scale. Together
with trachoma (a serious and potentially blinding bacterial eye
disease), onchocerciasis is one of the leading and preventable
causes of blindness in the world. The disease has had an enormous economic impact over the centuries, preventing people
from working, harvesting crops, receiving an education or
taking care of children.

Controlling onchocerciasis

'We could hardly pronounce the name of the disease,
much less spell onchocerciasis, but were horrified by what
we heard about it. Literally millions of people were at risk
of a fate that could be worse than death in that society and
time.' Robert McNamara, former President of the World
Bank, 2004, recalling the devastation wrought by onchocerciasis in West Africa in 1972

From the 1930s to the 1960s, various schemes got underway in
endemic areas to reduce the number of blackflies, initially by
clearing vegetation in fast-flowing rivers and streams where they
breed, and from the late 1940s using chemical larvicides,
including DDT.

In 1974 the serious impact of onchocerciasis, especially in Central and West Africa, led the WHO – in partnership with the World Bank, the Food and Agriculture Organization and the UN Development Programme – to initiate a major campaign, the Onchocerciasis Control Programme (OCP) in West Africa, to eliminate the disease. At the start of the programme more than a million people in West Africa were suffering from onchocerciasis. Of these, 100,000 had chronic eye problems and 35,000 were blind. In some West African communities, 50 per cent of men over the age of forty had been blinded by the disease. Many had abandoned the fertile river valleys in fear of contracting the disease. The disease was a major obstacle to socio-economic development and it was estimated that annual economic losses due to river blindness were in the order of $30 million.

The Onchocerciasis Control Programme involved reducing the local blackfly population using aerial spraying of larvicides over the rivers, and moving people away from villages in high-risk areas. Personal protection – avoiding being bitten – is a necessity. Unlike many vector-borne diseases, the blackfly bites during the day, and it takes several bites for a person to become infected. In particularly badly infested areas, some people are bitten up to 20,000 times a year. The greater the number of infective bites, the higher the likelihood of blindness. Interrupting and reducing transmission through vector control was a key component of the first decade of the OCP.

The campaign was transformed in the late 1980s by the discovery of a safe and highly effective microfilaricidal drug, ivermectin. Ivermectin (trade name Mectizan) had originally been developed as a veterinary drug, but early trials by its founder company, Merck, showed that by killing the microfilariae, ivermectin could reduce clinical symptoms, prevent the progression to blindness and lower the chances of further transmission of the disease. Even more significant was the decision by Merck to donate the drug free of charge from 1987 to 'all those who needed it for as long as needed'. This was at a time when few Western pharmaceutical companies were interested in developing drugs for the impoverished parts of the tropical world. The Mectizan Donation Programme has been described as 'one of the milestones of tropical disease treatment' and, to this day, it is the longest ongoing drug donation of its kind. Ivermectin was also found to be safe and effective for lymphatic filariasis and in partnership with GlaxoSmithKline, which in 2000 donated another drug, albendazole, for lymphatic filariasis, these treatments have had a major impact on the control of two of the world's most debilitating and disabling tropical diseases.

The achievements of the OCP are impressive. By the time it ceased operations in 2002, it had relieved 40 million people from infection, prevented blindness in 600,000 people and ensured that 18 million children were born free from the threat of the disease and blindness. In addition, 25 million hectares of abandoned arable land were reclaimed for settlement and agricultural production, capable of feeding 17 million people annually. These efforts were extremely cost-effective; some estimates indicate that OCP achieved its goals for less than $1 per person.

Further programmes, including the African Programme for Onchocerciasis Control (APOC) launched in 1995 and the Onchocerciasis Elimination Programme for the Americas (OEPA) in 1992, have been initiated to try to eliminate onchocerciasis from other remaining endemic areas in Africa and the Americas. Ivermectin, supplemented by vector control, remains the cornerstone of these ongoing programmes. An innovative feature of APOC, building on OCP's successes, is the use of mobile teams to visit infected areas and, with the assistance of local communities, to distribute ivermectin to all those who need it. This strategy is known as community-directed treatment with ivermectin (CDTI) and has brought substantial results for onchocerciasis control in Africa. Approximately 100 million treatments were provided to endemic communities in 2012, and the prevalence of infection has been reduced by about 73 per cent compared with pre-APOC levels.

An additional achievement of this strategy has been to build up a network of trained community volunteers which is helping to supplement and reinforce the traditional primary health care system in remote, rural areas where APOC is working. It has also become a model for distributing other drugs and interventions. Many of the Neglected Tropical Diseases (NTDs) like onchocerciasis and lymphatic filariasis often overlap geographically, so it makes sense to deliver drugs, or even interventions like bed nets for malaria, in one 'rapid-impact package' for a variety of co-endemic diseases. For onchocerciasis and lymphatic filariasis, there is hope that macrofilaricide drugs will be developed that can kill the adult filarial worm, reducing the need to repeat treatment, which currently has to be continued for years – during the length of time the adult worm lives in the human body and continues to reproduce microfilariae.

The Onchocerciasis Elimination Programme for the Americas (OEPA) has also witnessed successes. In 2013, Colombia became the first country in the world to be verified and declared free of onchocerciasis by the WHO. The WHO's announcement is testament to South America's sustained effort, spearheaded by the US Carter Center in Atlanta, Georgia, to tackle onchocerciasis. The population still requiring mass drug administration of ivermectin is little more than 20,000, and the last new case of blindness attributable to *O. volvulus* occurred in 1995. Elimination efforts are currently focused on the Yanomami people living in the remote regions of the Amazon rainforest on the border between Brazil and Venezuela.

While forty years of control has delivered major benefits to public health and development and much has been learnt from the onchocerciasis control programmes that can be applied to other NTDs, there is no room for complacency. Current estimates suggest that there are still about 100 to 120 million people at risk of onchocerciasis in thirty-one endemic countries; around 37 million people are infected with the parasite, a million of whom are blind or suffer serious visual impairment. The overwhelming majority (99 per cent) of those infected live in sub-Saharan Africa, which carries the burden of so many of the infectious diseases of the twenty-first century, and the vast majority of these are impoverished subsistence farmers and their families living in West, Central and parts of East Africa. The disease is widely distributed in these regions, where it takes two major forms: a savannah form that is primarily associated with blindness and a forest form in which skin disease is a more prominent feature.

Hope for the future

In the past, it was all too common in Africa to see groups of blind villagers holding hands in a chain, led by those who still had their sight. Today, outside the headquarters of the WHO in Geneva stands a statue of a child leading his blind father. This iconic statue, *Sightless Among Miracles*, by sculptor R.T. Wallen commemorates the successful OCP campaign against river blindness conducted in West Africa since 1974. Replicas of the statue have also been placed at a number of other locations including at Merck (New Jersey, USA), to recognize the pharmaceutical company's role in the Mectizan Donation Program, and the Carter Center (Georgia, USA), founded in 1982 by the former US President Jimmy Carter with his wife Rosalynn to advance human rights and alleviate human suffering. The Carter Center has played a major role in the fight against a number of Neglected Tropical Diseases, including onchocerciasis.

Sightless Among Miracles is a poignant reminder of the suffering inflicted by onchocerciasis over the centuries, but at the same time it is a symbol of hope that the disease can be eliminated from those parts of the world where it is still endemic.

Viral Diseases

SMALLPOX

Smallpox was for centuries one of the most dreaded, lethal and common of all infectious diseases. It is caused by a virus which belongs to the genus orthopoxvirus and is transmitted by airborne droplets or the pus from pustules of an infected person. It produces a distinctive pustular rash. The scabs which form fall off after three or four weeks, leaving permanent pitted pockmarks on those who recover. There are two main forms – *Variola major* and *Variola minor*. *V. major* has a case fatality rate of 15–25 per cent, rising to 40–50 per cent in the very young and old. *V. minor* (or alastrim) has a case fatality rate of less than 1–2 per cent. It is probably an ancient disease, but it became increasingly virulent in many parts of the world during the early modern period. The pocked and scarred faces of those who survived this horrific viral infection marked them out for life. No cure has ever been developed, but inoculation against smallpox began to be widely practised in Europe and North America in the eighteenth century, until at the end of the century it was superseded by vaccination. Both procedures aimed to prevent healthy recipients from 'catching' smallpox (i.e. to immunize people), but while inoculation used infections material from smallpox pustules, vaccination, which was safer and more effective, was based on Edward Jenner's discovery in 1796 that cowpox (an infection of cows) could prevent smallpox in humans. By 1979 a worldwide vaccination campaign led by the WHO achieved the ultimate and remarkable goal of completely eradicating smallpox, and in 1980 smallpox was officially removed from the list of world diseases – the only major disease so far eliminated by human intervention.

∽

In the late eighteenth century Edward Jenner (1749–1823), a country doctor in the village of Berkeley in Gloucestershire, became aware of a local story that cowhands and dairymaids who had contracted cowpox from infected cows' udders might be protected from the much more serious smallpox. As Jenner and other country folk observed, 'what renders the Cow-Pox virus so extremely singular . . . is that the person who has been affected is for ever after secure from the infection of the Small-pox'.

Jenner spent some years wondering whether there was a way that this link could be put to beneficial use for humankind. In May 1796 he decided to act on his hunch. He chose the son of his gardener – a healthy eight-year-old boy called James Phipps – and a young dairymaid, Sarah Nelmes, for his experiment. The dairymaid had contracted cowpox from a cow called Blossom. Jenner took a scraping of material from a cowpox pustule on her hand and then scratched it into the skin of young James Phipps. The next stage was to be the tricky one. Six weeks later, he inoculated the boy with smallpox virus taken from a pustule of a smallpox patient. It did not 'take'. The boy did, indeed, appear to be protected against smallpox. He then went on to 'vaccinate' his own son with cowpox and found that he, too, was protected from smallpox. Jenner was convinced that he had found a way of preventing this terrible scourge.

Some twenty years before Jenner's 1796 experiment on James Phipps, a farmer in Dorset, Benjamin Jesty (1736–1816), had come up with the same theory about the protective nature of cowpox. He had rubbed matter from cowpox pustules into scratches on the arms of his wife and two children using a darning needle. However, he did not publish his results, though his gravestone is inscribed with a tribute to his early 'trial'. It may be that Farmer Jesty was the first person to use this novel technique, but it was certainly Jenner – as a doctor – who put vaccination into everyday medical practice and onto the world map.

Jenner's story and the discovery of vaccination has been told and retold many times, as befits a milestone in the history of medicine. In honour of Jenner's discovery, Louis Pasteur later gave wider currency to the term 'vaccination', a word derived from Latin *vacca*, meaning 'cow'.

The speckled monster

The origin of smallpox remains an enigma. It is likely that it is a disease of great antiquity, possibly spreading from person to person around the time of the first agricultural settlements in the river valleys of Egypt, the Middle East, China and India. Smallpox has no animal reservoir, although it may in the dim and distant past have evolved from an animal virus such as cowpox, horse-pox or (the most likely candidate) 'camel-pox'. But once established as a solely human disease, smallpox can be spread only when there is a sufficient number of infectious people in the population in close proximity to a reservoir of people who have no immunity. Lesions found by archaeologists on the mummified face of Pharaoh Ramses V, who died in the early second century BC, suggest he may have suffered from smallpox. To what extent smallpox was widespread in ancient Egypt or responsible for some of the great epidemics and 'plagues' of the Greek world and the Roman empire (such as the Plague of Athens reported by Thucydides in 430 BC and the Antonine Plague of c.166–190 AD) is a topic of lively scholarly debate.

We arrive at a more scientific historical basis of the disease in the tenth century, when the Persian physician al-Razi (c.865–c.925), known in the West as Rhazes, wrote an account in which he differentiated measles from smallpox. At this time it seems that smallpox was a common childhood disease, and not as severe as measles. It is possible that the milder of the two forms of smallpox, *variola minor*, may have been more prevalent than *variola major*. Certainly, over the next few centuries, smallpox did not carry the same fear as bubonic plague – indeed, it was not until some 200 years after the Black Death of the mid-fourteenth century that smallpox emerged as one of the major killers of the early modern world.

The term 'smallpox' came into general usage in the sixteenth century, replacing the word 'variola' (from the Latin *varius*, 'spotted or variegated'). 'Pox' (possibly derived from the plural of an Old English word, *pocke*, meaning 'pustule') was used widely in medieval times to describe a number of 'pestilences', including plague, variola and other diseases with pustular eruptions on the skin. The disease may have been called 'smallpox' to differentiate it from the 'great pox', or syphilis, which struck across Europe with alarming consequences from the late fifteenth century. Perhaps the pockmarks of smallpox, though many, seemed 'small' in comparison with the repulsive pustules that spread over the entire body of the earliest victims of syphilis. It is also possible that at the time smallpox seemed the lesser of the two evils.

In Europe by the sixteenth century, smallpox had become the dreaded 'speckled monster', attacking princes and peasants alike, and accounting for some 10 to 15 per cent of all deaths. It established itself as an endemic disease in cities and as a frightening periodic epidemic in smaller towns and villages. At least 80 per cent of its victims were under the age of ten, and it could kill between 25 and 40 per cent of its victims. Survivors were left scarred and sometimes blind for life. It is estimated that about one-third of cases of blindness in Europe were probably from smallpox.

Famous victims included a number of royalty. Henry VIII's fourth wife, Anne of Cleves (1515–57), survived the disease, but was left badly scarred. In 1562 Queen Elizabeth I (r.1558–1603) became seriously ill with smallpox, though she, too, recovered. She painted her face with white lead and vinegar to cover up her smallpox scars. Mary II, wife of William of Orange, died aged thirty-two in 1694 of 'black' smallpox – one of the very worst forms, with massive haemorrhaging into the skin, lungs and other organs. Prince William, the only offspring of the future Queen Anne to survive infancy, was said to have died of smallpox in 1700, at the age of eleven, ending the Stuart dynasty. In Russia, Tsar Peter II of Russia died of smallpox in 1730, aged fourteen. Tsar Peter III suffered an attack of smallpox in 1744. The 1911 edition of *Encyclopaedia Britannica* commented: 'Nature had made him mean, the smallpox had made him hideous, and his degraded habits made him loathsome.'

Smallpox and the New World

The most devastating impact of smallpox in the early modern period was in the New World. Shortly after the arrival of Columbus in 1492, smallpox crossed the Atlantic from Europe and Africa. It spread rapidly and, according to many sources, quite likely contributed to the collapse of the Aztec empire in Mexico and the Inca empire in Peru. The Native Americans had never before experienced smallpox and, as a 'virgin' population, they were exceptionally vulnerable. Estimates vary and scholars still debate the demographic consequences of the so-called 'American holocaust', but it is possible that a large proportion of the indigenous population may have been wiped out by a complex set of interrelated factors, including 'new' diseases (especially smallpox and measles), starvation and superior European military technologies (guns, steel swords and cavalry).

Accounts tell of masses of corpses piled up along the roadsides, of the stench of death pervading the villages, of dogs and vultures devouring the dead. The Mayans called smallpox *nokakil* – the great fire. One Spanish chronicler, Toribio de Benavente Motolinía (c.1482–1568), wrote of the destruction of the civilization of the Aztecs :

> More than half the population died . . . in heaps, like bedbugs. Many others died of starvation, because, as they were all taken sick at once, they could not care for each other, nor was there anyone to give them bread or anything else. In many places it happened that everyone in a house died, and, as it was impossible to bury the great

Above: Die Pest (*The Plague*) by Swiss painter
Arnold Böcklin, 1898. © *akg-images*

Right: A 'plague doctor' wearing a
seventeenth-century protective costume.
The long, beak-like nosepiece was filled
with aromatic substances to combat
the stench associated with the plague.
Wellcome Library, London

An early nineteenth-century French lithograph shows soldiers lying in the street, exhibiting the listless behaviour which accompanies typhus. *Wellcome Library, London*

Physician John Snow, shown here in 1856, played a major role in the discovery of the waterborne nature of cholera after observing fatalities around the Broad Street pump in London's Soho district in 1854. *Wellcome Library, London*

Ronald Ross, photographed with his wife and some assistants on the steps of his laboratory in Calcutta (Kolkata), India, in 1898. The cages in the foreground are for malaria-infected birds, which he studied to unravel the malaria-mosquito life cycle. *Wellcome Library, London*

A public health campaign against Chagas' disease in Bolivia in 1997 graphically illustrates the mode of transmission of this parasitic infection, via the faeces of the triatomine bug, known also as the 'kissing bug'. © *Balaguer Alejandro/Corbis Sygma*

Hookworm was rife among poor people in the southern states of the USA during the early twentieth-century. Up to 40 per cent of the population may have been suffering from the disease. © *Corbis*

Suffering from onchocerciasis, or river blindness, a group of blind or nearly-blind villagers, clutching sticks to guide themselves, are seen in this 1972 photograph from Chad, Central Africa. Around 99 per cent of infected people live in thirty sub-Saharan African countries.
© Bettmann/Corbis

The global eradication of smallpox by 1980 was made possible through the use of a modern version of the vaccine first developed in the late eighteenth-century by the pioneering physician Edward Jenner, seen here in an oil painting, c. 1884, vaccinating a small boy. Wellcome Library, London

Left: A yellow fever victim in Buenos Aires, Argentina in 1871. The disease is still endemic in a number of countries in Latin America and Africa. *Wellcome Library, London*

Below: A New York City tenement *c*. 1911. The source of the 1916 polio epidemic in the city was blamed initially on slum dwellings such as this one. © *Bettmann/Corbis*

Mary Kosloski, 'March of Dimes' poster girl and polio sufferer, meets Randy Kerr, the first 'Polio Pioneer' to receive the Salk vaccine in 1954. Together, they represented the two aims of the 'March of Dimes': polio treatment and prevention.
© *Bettmann/Corbis*

During the 1918–19 influenza pandemic (the Spanish flu) all sorts of preventive measures were tried. This public-health worker in London wears a mask and is carrying a pump filled with an 'anti-flu' spray for use on buses.
Hulton-Deutsch Collection/Corbis

Wearing protective clothing, officials bury a victim of the Ebola virus in Kikwit, Democratic Republic of Congo (then Zaire), during an outbreak in 1995. Such extreme care is a necessity, as is evident from the 2014 epidemic of Ebola in West Africa – Ebola can be spread during the preparation of infected corpses. © *Gilbert Liz/Corbis Sygma*

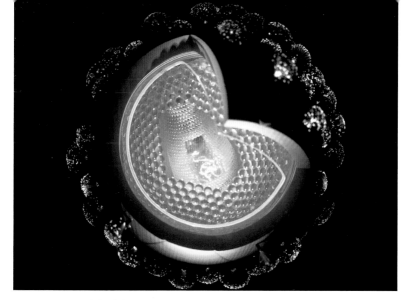

A cutaway model of the human immunodeficiency virus (HIV), the cause of AIDS. HIV is a retrovirus; as a result genetic information for its replication becomes permanently integrated into the host cell's chromosome. *Wellcome Library/John Wildgoose*

Chinese police with wild animals confiscated at a market in Guangzhou, Guangdong Province. Following the suggestion that the 2003 SARS virus entered the human population from palm civets, the Chinese embarked on a culling programme, killing animals suspected of harbouring SARS. © *Wang Bingyu/EyePress/epa/Corbis*

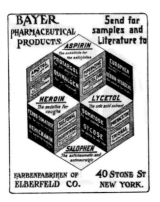

Left: An early twentieth-century advertisement from the Bayer pharmaceutical company offers products including both aspirin and heroin. © *Bettmann/Corbis*

Above: Bloodletting, depicted in the early 1800s, nearly two centuries after William Harvey demonstrated in 1628 that blood continuously circulates through the body. The idea of bloodletting dates back to ancient times and was used to restore the balance of the body's 'humours'. The task was often carried out by barber-surgeons; the red-and-white striped poles still seen outside many barbers' shops are a reminder of the service they once provided. *Wellcome Library, London*

number of dead, they pulled down the houses over them in order to check the stench that rose from the dead bodies, so that their homes became their tombs.

The Spanish conquistador Bernal Díaz del Castillo (c.1492/8– 1584) gave a similar account:

The streets, the squares, the houses . . . were covered with dead bodies; we could not stop without treading on them, and the stench was intolerable . . . all the causeways were full, from one end to the other, of men, women and children, so weak and sickly, squalid and dirty, and pestilential that it was a misery to behold them.

And another observer wrote that 'a man could not set his foot down unless on the corpse of an Indian'.

However, few of the Spanish conquistadors appear to have caught smallpox in the Americas. It may have been introduced, initially, by Europeans, but many of them might have already experienced smallpox and acquired immunity, protecting them from further attacks. The psychological impact on the indigenous populations was said to be as devastating as the physical harm, as the hideous infection sapped their will to resist. As communities broke up and scattered, smallpox was spread far and wide.

Wave after wave of smallpox continued to devastate the indigenous inhabitants of the New World, carried across the Atlantic by traders, soldiers, sailors, slaves and settlers. The disease also hit the newly founded colonial settlements along the eastern seaboard of North America. Boston experienced eight epidemics during the eighteenth century, and in some of these epidemics more than half the population was infected.

Treatments – from bloodletting to cooling remedies

As with so many infectious diseases at the time, physicians tried to treat or relieve the agonizing symptoms with a range of remedies. Some of these were based upon practices that had developed out of the Graeco-Roman tradition: bleeding, purging, vomiting and sweating to balance the humours. Also, following an old idea (known as the 'Doctrine of Signatures') that 'like cures like', the so-called red treatment – involving red curtains, red bed coverings, red shirts and stockings – was sometimes deployed in the smallpox sickroom. Some advised sucking the juice of a red pomegranate or gargling with red mulberry wine. The association with the colour red may have been because of the reddish or crimson appearance of the rash of smallpox sufferers; in severe cases, the pustules are grouped so closely together that they practically eliminate the skin. Another folk remedy involved chewing powdered horse manure.

Thomas Sydenham, often called the English Hippocrates, preferred a cooling regimen for his smallpox patients – by opening windows, letting in light and encouraging patients to drink plenty of fluids. Interestingly, in parts of the Indian subcontinent, smallpox was identified with the Hindu goddess *Shitala Mata* (meaning 'the cooling one' in Sanskrit) who was both feared and worshipped. Traditionally, patients and the goddess were fed 'cooling drafts', such as cold rice and yogurt, while the skin of the patient was rubbed with neem leaves and a cooling mixture of turmeric and flour. Temples dedicated to *Shitala* are still in active use.

Pockmarks, pus and inoculation

The great historian Lord Macaulay (1800–1859), writing about England in the previous century, made this sombre observation:

> The smallpox was always present, filling the churchyards with corpses, tormenting with constant fears all whom it had not yet stricken, leaving on those whose lives it spared the hideous traces of its power, turning the babe into a changeling at which the mother shuddered, and making the eyes and cheeks of the betrothed maiden the objects of horror to the lover.

Smallpox also had graphic figurative names which reflected its dread: the 'Angel of Death', the 'Destroying Angel', and Macaulay's 'most terrible of the Ministers of Death'.

The permanent pockmarks suffered by survivors often caused considerable distress, and fashionable ladies, robbed of their smooth skins, did all they could to mask their scars with paints, potions and beauty spots. At the same time, it was observed that those who carried the telltale signs of once having had smallpox were not likely to catch the dreaded disease again. Adverts for servants often requested that they had already had 'the smallpox in the natural way', and in many parts of the world, parents were anxious that their children should only marry someone who had previously had the disease. John Evelyn (1620–1706) in an entry in his Diary of 1685 described an intriguing idea:

> I went and made a visit to Mrs Graham . . . her eldest son was now sick there of the smallpox, but in a likely way to recovery,

and other of her children ran about and among the infected, which she said she let them do on purpose that they might whilst still young pass that fatal disease she fancied they were to undergo one time or other, and that this would be for the best, the severity of this cruel disease so lately in my poor family confirming much of what she affirmed.

These observations regarding lifelong immunity inspired a method of preventing the disease. This was known as 'variolation' (after *variola*, the scientific name of the disease) or 'inoculation' (from the Latin *inoculare*, 'to ingraft'). Might it be possible to take some of the infectious agent and transmit it to someone who had not yet caught the disease, in the hope that they might get a milder – rather than the full-blown and potentially fatal – form and thus become immune?

This practice, actually, appears to have been used independently in several regions of the world prior to the seventeenth century. In the tenth century the Chinese, for example, removed scabs from the drying pustules of a smallpox patient, pounded them into a powder, and then blew a few grains into the nose of people who had not had the illness – up the right nostril for a boy and the left one for a girl. In other parts of Asia and the Arab world, pus from the 'pocks' of an infected person was inoculated into a scratch in the skin of healthy people.

In the early eighteenth century Lady Mary Wortley Montagu (1689–1762), wife of the British ambassador to the Ottoman court, learned of this practice from the locals during her residence in Constantinople. Her own stunning beauty had been destroyed by an attack of smallpox when she was twenty-six years old, leaving her badly scarred and without eyelashes. In a letter to a friend she described the local 'smallpox parties' in which peasant women would routinely perform inoculation:

> Apropos of distempers, I am going to tell you a thing that will make you wish yourself here. The smallpox, so fatal and so general amongst us, is here rendered entirely harmless by the invention of engrafting, which is the term they give it. There is a set of old women . . . who make parties for this purpose . . . [an] old woman comes with a nutshell full of the matter of the best sort of smallpox, and asks what veins you please to have open'd. She immediately rips open that which you offer her with a large needle (which gives you no more pain than a common scratch) and puts into the vein as much of the venom as can lie on the head of her needle.

Lady Mary decided to have her young son inoculated by the embassy surgeon, Charles Maitland (1668–1748), with a Greek woman familiar with the folk practice in attendance; the child suffered no complications. In 1721, back in England, her three-year-old daughter was inoculated by Maitland. This aroused much publicity. Princess Caroline (1683–1737), wife of the future King George II, was also keen to have her two daughters inoculated and sought the advice of London physician Hans Sloane (1660–1753), best remembered as the founder of the British Museum. Her decision to take this risk followed successful trials supported by Sloane. The first experiment was conducted on six condemned felons in Newgate Prison who were inoculated on the promise of reprieve. Six charity school-children were then inoculated. Once reassured that the attacks following this 'novel' procedure were mild, Caroline went ahead with the two little princesses and helped make variolation widely acceptable amongst the English aristocracy and gentry. Sloane wrote an account of the trials in 1736 which was eventually published in the *Philosophical Transactions* of the Royal Society of London in 1755–6 concluding: 'upon the whole [this operation] is wonderful, which seems so plainly for the public good.' Catherine the Great of Russia (1729–96) also had her family and members of the court inoculated by Thomas Dimsdale (1712–1800), a British surgeon who was awarded £10,000 and a Russian barony for his services. With these royal marks of approval, the technique attracted huge attention in Europe.

Meanwhile, in Boston, Massachusetts, the Reverend Cotton Mather (1663–1728) had learned of the same practice from one of his African slaves, called Onesimus, and had read some of the first reports on inoculation in the *Philosophical Transactions* of the Royal Society. During a severe epidemic of smallpox in Boston in 1721, Mather persuaded the medical practitioner Zabdiel Boylston (c.1676/9–1766) to inoculate those not yet infected. Boylston harvested pus by puncturing with a lancet the pustules of infected patients and then squeezed the fluid into a glass jar. To inoculate the 'healthy', he cut a slit in the arm or leg and liberally dabbed on the infected matter. The idea of interfering in this way with divine providence led to outrage amongst many Bostonians. It is said that a physician in the city tossed a firebomb through a window of Cotton Mather's house. It failed to explode but came with a note that declared: 'Mather, you dog, Damn you, I'll inoculate you with this.' Although some of those inoculated died, the numbers were few by comparison with those who died of smallpox 'in the natural way' – a finding confirmed by careful statistical studies in America and Britain.

One person who refused to have his children inoculated was

Leopold Mozart, father of the famous composer, Wolfgang Amadeus Mozart (1756–91). In a letter in 1764 Leopold wrote:

> They are trying to persuade me to let my boy be inoculated with smallpox. But as I have expressed sufficiently clearly my aversion to this impertinence they are leaving me in peace. Here inoculation is the general fashion. But for my part I leave the matter to the grace of God. It depends on His grace whether he wishes to keep this prodigy of nature in this world in which He placed it or to take it to Himself.

Near tragedy struck in 1767 when the eleven-year old Wolfgang contracted smallpox during an epidemic in Vienna. He became delirious and temporarily blind but was lucky to survive. 'Te Deum Laudamus!' wrote his father. 'Little Wolfgang has got over the smallpox safely!' The music world certainly owes much to his recovery.

Inoculation gradually became more popular on both sides of the Atlantic, especially in the latter half of the eighteenth century when the technique was made safer, cheaper and easier by a number of practitioners, including Robert Sutton (1708–88) and his son Daniel (1735–1819), who was known in England as the 'Pocky Doctor', and James Kirkpatrick (c.1696–1770) of South Carolina. Nevertheless, there were still many who questioned the efficacy and safety of inoculation. One of its main problems, apart from a 1–3 per cent risk of death, was that during the mild attack of smallpox people were actually infectious, and needed to be kept in isolation. In England, one of the earliest smallpox isolation hospitals was the London Small-Pox and Inoculation Hospital, founded in 1746, initially for the care of poor people with smallpox but soon afterwards mainly as a hospital for people undergoing inoculation. Inoculation was, at this time, only a partial solution, and at the end of the eighteenth century smallpox was still exacting a huge toll across the world.

For example, smallpox devastated the Aboriginal population in Australia after the disease first arrived there in 1789, possibly from Indonesia, just one year after the first European settlement in New South Wales. Eyewitnesses described the horrors of finding corpses washed up on the shore. About half of those who had contact with the British settlement of Port Arthur (Sydney) died, and it was probably one of the greatest demographic and psychological shocks in the history of Australia.

Vaccination is adopted across the globe

'Medicine has never before produced any single improvement of such utility . . . You have erased from the calendar of human afflictions one of its greatest . . . Future nations will know by history only that the loathsome smallpox has existed and by you has been extirpated.' US President Thomas Jefferson, in a letter to Edward Jenner, 14 May 1806, some 170 years before smallpox was finally 'extirpated'

When Edward Jenner sent his first report of his cowpox vaccination experiments on young James Phipps to the Royal Society of London in 1797, it met with a cold reception. Although Jenner had already been elected a Fellow of the Royal Society for his work on cuckoos, the Society rejected his paper on the grounds that Jenner 'ought not to risk his reputation by presenting to the learned body anything which appeared so much at variance with established knowledge, and withal so incredible'.

The following year, with more cases and evidence to support

his theory, Jenner privately published a pamphlet entitled *An Inquiry into the Causes and Effects of the Variolae Vaccinae, a Disease, Discovered in some of the Western Counties of England, particularly Gloucestershire, and Known by the Name of The Cow Pox*. Although there were some critics (especially those who feared the consequences of transferring an animal disease to humans), the speed with which vaccination was subsequently adopted around the world was extraordinary. Indeed, by 1801 more than 100,000 people had been vaccinated in England, and by 1811 over 1.7 million in France: the emperor Napoleon managed to have half his army vaccinated. Between 1804 and 1814, 2 million were vaccinated in Russia and the empress named the first vaccinated child Vaccinov. In the USA the practice was taken up with great enthusiasm by Dr Benjamin Waterhouse (1754–1846) of Boston. By the 1820s vaccination against smallpox had spread to much of the world. Its benefits for humankind were quickly recognized, and Jenner was richly honoured and rewarded.

One of the most remarkable aspects of the story is the way in which the vaccines were transported around the world. Dried vaccine on quills and lancets, dried scabs, or cotton threads impregnated with matter from pustules, were just some of the methods used. For long sea voyages the 'serial method' was adopted, in which children (often orphans) were successively vaccinated, one after the other, using ripe pustular matter, until the destination was reached. Between 1803 and 1806 Don Francisco Xavier de Balmis (1753–1819) used this arm-to-arm technique to take the vaccine from Spain across the Atlantic to Spanish America, on to the Philippines and China, and then back to Spain, vaccinating en route possibly as many as 450,000 people. From one small village in Gloucestershire, the vaccine circumnavigated the globe.

Jennerian vaccination even reached Japan, which was still largely 'closed' to the West, via the Dutch who sent information on vaccination to their trading post near Nagasaki. Smallpox was Japan's most devastating disease at the time, and through various professional and social networks Japanese physicians began doing everything they could to propagate cowpox through arm-to-arm vaccination as well as experimenting with alternative methods of using cowpox crusts rather than cowpox lymph. The Japanese vaccinators had a profound influence on the later adoption of Western medicine.

The great advantage of vaccination over inoculation was that the former not only left the recipient non-infectious and immune, but also involved a far milder and less dangerous reaction. (It was realized some time later, however, that vaccination did not give lifelong protection, and people needed to be re-vaccinated after several years.) The vaccine was prepared in large quantities in continental Europe by harvesting the virus on the skins of calves and, with improved production over the course of the nineteenth century, mass vaccination centres were set up.

There were objectors to the practice – on ethical and religious grounds – and a number of anti-vaccinationists and anti-vivisectionists fought hard to suppress it. There was initial concern about the introduction of an animal disease into humans. Cartoons captured this fear of 'bovinization'. Anti-vaccinationists appealed to the public: 'To think of the unparalleled absurdity of deliberately infecting the organism of a healthy person in this day of sanitary science and aseptic surgery with the poisonous matter obtained from a sore on a diseased calf.' Especially unpopular was the policy in some countries, including Britain, of making vaccination compulsory, at least for infants. There was also the possibility of transferring other infections, such as syphilis, via the vaccine, and the risk of complications, such as post-vaccinial encephalitis. A powerful anti-vaccination movement in the nineteenth and early twentieth centuries continued to denounce vaccination, including those who objected to government interference in their lives; those who feared having their babies 'poisoned' (as they thought); and those who believed it was sinful on religious grounds to inject impurities into the blood. The term 'conscientious objector' entered English law in 1898 in an Act which allowed a plea for parents who refused to have their children vaccinated to be heard by a magistrate. This Vaccination Act was eventually repealed in 1909.

But on the whole, vaccination proved highly successful, especially with the refinements and improvements made to the vaccine in the later nineteenth century (though there is still some mystery about whether Jenner's original cowpox vaccine was somehow replaced by a different, but biologically related, virus now known as *vaccinia*). It is difficult to document the success of smallpox vaccination in terms of number of lives saved, but it is highly likely that millions of people in the nineteenth and early twentieth centuries were spared the horrors of the disease – not only death and disfigurement, but also blindness. The development of ancillary containment strategies – isolation and care of the sick (at home, or in isolation hospitals and wards, and even, in London, in 'smallpox hospital ships' moored in the Thames Estuary); disinfection of clothes, bedding and housing; notification of infectious cases and the tracing and vaccination of contacts – were also crucial.

The eradication of smallpox

The widespread practice of vaccination and other measures to prevent and control smallpox were undoubtedly major factors in the decline of mortality rates in the Western world over the past two hundred years. In the early twentieth century, although the incidence of smallpox was significantly less in the industrialized world than it had been a century earlier, smallpox remained endemic in almost every country around the world, with periodic outbreaks of *Variola minor* (the milder form of the disease) in parts of Europe and North America. It was, in fact, not until the late 1940s, with the development of electron microscopy, that the smallpox 'virus', itself, was first seen and identified. And beyond vaccination as a prevention, and isolation and care of the infected, no effective cure – no antiviral drug – was ever found for smallpox.

However, the disease slowly retreated first from Iceland and Scandinavia and then from other parts of the world. By the 1950s smallpox was no longer endemic in Britain and the United States, and by 1967 it had been eliminated from both Europe and North America, as well as from China, Japan and Australia. Smallpox, nevertheless, persisted and remained a serious disease in parts of Africa, Asia and South America in spite of mass periodic vaccination campaigns. In the 1960s, 10 to 15 million in some thirty or so countries contracted the disease each year, with about 2 million deaths.

In a trailblazing decision, the 19th World Health Assembly meeting at Geneva in 1966 agreed (albeit by just two votes) to embark on what they called an 'Intensified Ten-Year Smallpox Eradication Programme'. At the time there were many doubts as to its feasibility, and even the Director-General of the WHO was not optimistic that it would succeed. The programme was nonetheless launched the following year, with the backing of a small multinational team led by the American physician and epidemiologist Donald Henderson (b.1928) of the WHO.

A successful programme of mass vaccination – made easier with the development of a freeze-dried vaccine that remained stable in tropical climates – led to the eradication of smallpox from South America by 1972. In parts of Africa and Asia, however, the task remained formidable. Health workers faced innumerable technical, logistical and cultural barriers. They crossed jungles, deserts and mountain ranges, worked in countries scarred by civil war and transcended political and ideological boundaries (this was one field in which the USA and the Soviet Union fully cooperated during the Cold War).

'Surveillance' and 'containment' – a concept pioneered by William Foege (b.1936), of the US Centers for Disease Control and Prevention (CDC) to replace mass vaccination – soon became the operative words. Wherever the committed and dedicated international and local teams of vaccinators went, their aim was to search for active cases of smallpox and trace and vaccinate contacts, as well as vaccinating the local population, so imposing a 'ring' around each outbreak. Foege describes the development of this idea in his aptly entitled memoirs, *House on Fire: the Fight to Eradicate Smallpox* (2011).

Messages about the campaign were spread via newspapers, radio and posters, and rewards were offered to those who reported active cases of smallpox (reaching a staggering $1,000). Technological developments also played their part: new jet injector guns could vaccinate a thousand people in an hour, while special bifurcated needles, needing only a tiny amount of vaccine, enabled thousands of people to be vaccinated by local health workers.

In October 1975 the last case of *Variola major* smallpox on the Indian subcontinent made headline news. The victim was Rahima Banu, a two-year old girl in Bangladesh, and she survived. The last naturally occurring case in the world was Ali Maow Maalin, a 23-year old hospital cook in Somalia, who contracted *Variola minor* in October 1977. He also recovered. Maalin used his survival to help encourage vaccination in the fight against polio until his death in 2013. The ten-year smallpox campaign had cost in total somewhere in the order of $300 million – large in terms of initial and final outlay, but small by comparison with an estimated saving of over $1 billion per annum.

In 1979 the WHO felt confident enough to announce that smallpox had been completely eradicated from the world. A small official parchment certifying the global eradication of smallpox is one of the most remarkable documents in medical history. It was signed at the WHO in Geneva on 9 December 1979 by the twenty members of the Global Commission for the Certification of Smallpox Eradication, including its chairman, Frank Fenner (1914–2010), an Australian microbiologist. In 1980 smallpox was officially removed from the list of world diseases. Jenner's goal, 'the annihilation of the Small Pox – the most dreadful scourge of the human species', had finally been realized. The pride and pleasure of those who had fought the campaign to 'annihilate' smallpox was nothing less than 'infectious'! The global eradication of this disease was undeniably the greatest success story of medicine.

In some ways, smallpox was easier to deal with than some other infectious diseases. Vaccination had been available and proved effective since the early nineteenth century. Smallpox had no reservoir outside the human population – so there were no complex life cycles to crack, no insect vectors to transmit the disease, no dormant animal reservoirs of the virus to contend with (unlike its 'little cousin', monkeypox, which, though rare, is transmitted by contact with wild rodents). Within the human body, the smallpox virus has an incubation period of about twelve to fourteen days, during which patients are not infectious; it spreads only during the time of the fever and rash making it possible to isolate patients quickly and trace contacts, and thereby break the chain of transmission. In addition, smallpox has no long-term latency – for survivors, once a person is over the attack, he or she is no longer infectious and there are no 'silent' carriers. Finally, the disease makes such distinctive marks on the skin that it was easily recognized, diagnosed and contained. The vaccination procedure also left its distinctive scar, so it was relatively easy to see who had or had not been vaccinated. Despite all these advantages, Donald Henderson of the WHO recalled that the great campaign he coordinated 'only just succeeded'.

The virus lives on

Just prior to the announcement of the global eradication of smallpox, there was, tragically, one further case of smallpox – in Birmingham, England, in 1978. A photographer was working above a smallpox research laboratory, and somehow the virus escaped – possibly through the ventilation system – and infected her. The young woman died. Her mother also came down with the disease, but she survived. The laboratory director committed suicide while in quarantine. There has been no known case of smallpox since that date.

Whether stocks of the smallpox virus and the vaccine should

be kept in laboratories has remained a contentious scientific and political issue. Following eradication, governments began to destroy the stores of smallpox virus, and it was finally agreed that only two heavily guarded laboratories – one in Atlanta, Georgia, USA, and one in Koltsovo, Novosibirsk Region in the Russian Federation – would keep the live variola virus frozen in liquid nitrogen. It has been argued that there is a need to keep such stocks for future research in case there is ever a recurrence of smallpox – for example, if terrorists should ever use the smallpox virus as a biological weapon. The outcome could be disastrous, as many young people today have never been vaccinated, and those who were vaccinated before the 1970s may no longer have the necessary immunity to fight off an attack. Those who oppose the maintenance of the existing stores of the virus point out that, if needed, it should be possible for scientists to reintroduce a vaccine quickly, and efforts today should go into building up stocks of available vaccines.

As the WHO and international scientists continue to debate the issue of the destruction of the virus, in July 2014 employees at the US National Institutes of Health, Bethesda, Maryland, discovered in an unused storeroom some old vials of variola which appear to date back to the 1950s. They were immediately transferred to the CDC's high-containment facility in Atlanta and it is anticipated that these vials will be destroyed.

We can only hope that, following the enormous efforts over the past centuries to eradicate one of the most dreadful diseases of history, there will be no reappearance of this deadly virus in the human population – either naturally or through the deliberate use of the pathogen for bioterrorism.

MEASLES

Measles – or rubeola – is a highly contagious viral disease which affects mostly children. It is transmitted from person to person through the air as a fine mist released from virus-laden droplets in the nose, mouth or throat of infected people, primarily by coughing and sneezing. The first signs of measles are usually a high fever with a cough, coryza (runny nose) and conjunctivitis (red eyes) – the 3 Cs – followed by a reddish rash over the body. Its early history is a matter of conjecture but certainly by the medieval and early modern period it seems to have become a common disease. Although often not serious, measles can prove fatal, especially in populations not previously exposed to it or in malnourished children. A measles vaccine was introduced in the 1960s, and this, like the infection itself, confers lifelong immunity. Many children in Western countries are now protected from the disease. Measles does remain a significant cause of childhood mortality in some parts of the developing world but there is hope that, with mass vaccination, future generations will grow up in a measles-free world.

∽

In 910 the Persian philosopher and physician Rhazes, wrote *A Treatise on the Smallpox and Measles*. His account, which was later translated from Arabic into Latin, is one of the first to draw a distinction between these two highly infectious diseases, both of which cause skin rashes. Rhazes suggested that measles was 'more to be dreaded than smallpox'. Whether a person suffered from smallpox or measles depended, he believed, on their underlying constitution: 'Bodies that are lean, bilious, hot and dry are more disposed to the measles than to the smallpox.'

The earlier history of measles is difficult to document, but it may have evolved from the canine distemper of dogs or, most probably, the bovine rinderpest of cattle (a disease now eradicated). It has been thought that measles emerged several thousand years ago when humans first began to domesticate their animals, though one recent study suggests that a divergence between the 'human' measles virus and the 'cattle' rinderpest virus did not occur until at least the eleventh to twelfth centuries AD. As with smallpox, there is now no known animal reservoir for measles (which makes the prospect of breaking the chain of human transmission and global eradication potentially a possibility).

Diseases such as measles that spread from person to person are often known as 'crowd diseases' or 'diseases of civilization': they need a certain density of population of one-quarter of a million inhabitants or thereabouts before they can establish themselves as endemic. An increasing number of descriptions of measles by the time of the medieval and early modern period suggest that it was becoming a well-established childhood infection in cities by this date. In smaller towns and rural areas, measles was more likely to erupt from time to time in epidemic waves, affecting wide age groups of non-immune or susceptible individuals.

Measles adapts to the Old World

'Count your children after the measles has passed.' Arabic proverb

The Arabic word for measles, as used by Rhazes, was *hasbah*. In the following centuries various names were given to the disease, including *rubeola* (from the Latin *rubeus*, 'reddish') and *morbilli* (a diminutive of the Latin *morbus*, hence meaning the 'little plague'). The origin of the word 'measles' is uncertain, although some scholars trace it to the Old German word *masa*, 'spot', which became in Middle English *maselen*, 'many little spots'. In eleventh-century Japan, the disease was known as the 'red pox' or the 'red rash pox', and in Europe a range of colloquial terms – 'red measles', 'red spots pox', 'red smallpox', 'hard measles', 'nine-day measles' – was used to highlight its characteristic appearance: the reddish rash that spreads rapidly over the body and generally lasts for nine days or so. Thomas Sydenham, wrote a classic description of measles epidemics in London in the 1670s. Although the disease accounted for only a small fraction of all childhood deaths, the London Bills of Mortality record deaths from measles in every year from 1629. It was clearly a disease to be feared.

Some outbreaks seemed to be mild, but others could be deadly. In 1808 a particularly severe epidemic hit the city of Glasgow, as one observer wrote: 'The disease has never before been nearly so mortal there, nor had any infection since the time of the plague, not even smallpox itself, engrossed the burial registers so much as measles did in the months of May and June.' Measles continued to take its toll during the nineteenth century

– its variable impact possibly depending as much on the general health, living standards, nutrition and age group of those affected rather than any differences in the virulence of the disease.

Measles strikes the New World

Measles was totally absent from the Americas prior to the arrival of Europeans. The conquest of the New World has often been described as one of the greatest of all demographic disasters. From a population of anywhere between 50 and 100 million people before Christopher Columbus arrived in 1492, the indigenous population of the Americas was subsequently reduced to perhaps just one-tenth of its original level. Historians have debated the possible reasons for this 'holocaust'. Some have attributed it to the brutality of the conquistadores, others to the ensuing break-up of the social and economic fabric. But many historians concur that it was mainly 'germs' and not 'guns' that wiped out so many people in the post-Columbian era.

Measles, along with smallpox, was one of the major killers of the Native Americans, who had no immunity against such 'new' diseases. All age groups were affected. Young adults were particularly hard hit, and this removed a vital section of the population who might otherwise have provided food and care for their families. The result was helplessness and despair. The Europeans, by contrast, were mostly already immune to measles and smallpox, and thus, as they set about their conquests, found they had the upper hand not just technologically – with horses and firearms and steel swords – but also epidemiologically.

Measles adapts to the Americas

During the later seventeenth and eighteenth centuries, measles became a leading cause of death in the eastern seaboard cities of North America. Mirroring patterns in the Old World, the disease was often mild, but occasionally severe and disruptive. In large metropolitan communities it attained epidemic proportions every second or third year; in smaller communities and areas, outbreaks tended to be more widely spaced and somewhat more severe.

In Fairfield, New Jersey, in 1759 – the 'never to be forgotten year' – a contemporary witness, Ephraim Harris, recounted how:

> The Lord sent the destroying angel to pass through this place, and removed many of our friends into eternity in a short space of time; not a house exempt, not a family spared from the calamity. So dreadful was it, that it made every ear tingle, and every heart bleed; in which time I and my family was exercised with that dreadful disorder, the measles. But Blessed be God, our lives are spared.

Measles in the United States spread westward in the nineteenth century as new areas were opened up by settlers. One of the most serious outbreaks was during the Civil War of 1861–5 when many thousands of Union and Confederate troops are thought to have died of the disease.

Measles touches almost every
other corner of the globe

'Love is like the measles: we all have to go through it.'
Jerome K. Jerome, *Idle Thoughts of an Idle Fellow*, 1886

Over the course of the nineteenth and early twentieth centuries measles was carried by explorers and travellers to many far-flung places of the world. The Faroe Islands, Iceland, Alaska, Australia, New Zealand, Hawaii, Samoa, Fiji and other Pacific islands often witnessed dramatic epidemics and, occasionally, sustained huge losses when they encountered measles for the first time. Two of the best documented cases were the 1846 epidemic in the Faroes and the 1875 epidemic in Fiji.

In 1846 a young Danish doctor, Peter Ludwig Panum (1820–85), was sent to the Faroe Islands – which lie in the Atlantic between the Shetlands and Iceland – to investigate a violent epidemic of measles that was occurring there. Although this was not the first time measles had hit the islands, the 1846 epidemic affected 6,100 inhabitants out of a total population of some 7,800. Those who were over sixty-five years old and had lived through the previous epidemic of 1781, however, did not contract measles. In his report of the epidemic, Panum recognized that measles conferred lifelong immunity.

The number of deaths from measles was relatively low during the epidemic in the Faroes. By contrast, the 1875 epidemic that struck the islands of Fiji killed possibly as many as one-quarter of the Fijian population in little over three months. The disease was introduced by the royal family on their return from a state visit to New South Wales in Australia. The King of Fiji, Ratu Seru Cakobau, had contracted measles in Sydney but was recovering as their ship, the HMS *Dido*, reached the Fijian capital, Levuka, on the east coast of Ovalau Island on 12 January 1875. His two sons, however, were very sick and, undoubtedly, infectious.

The *Dido* did not fly the yellow flag to indicate that there was sickness on board, and no quarantine was imposed. Over the next ten days the royal party entertained a great number of chiefs, their families and entourages, who came from distant islands to welcome home the king and his sons. After the festivities, as they returned home, measles spread like wildfire through the islands. Some 40,000 Fijians – out of an estimated population of 150,000 scattered over 1.8 million sq. km (700,000 sq. miles) on 100 inhabited islands – died in this single epidemic. Some attributed the huge mortality to the practice of 'plunging' young children with a high fever into cold water. Others blamed the disaster on poisoning, treachery or bewitchment. Lack of medical care for those infected was also a serious problem.

Describing the devastating Fiji measles epidemic of 1875, the German physician and medical historian August Hirsch (1817–94) in his *Handbook of Geographical and Historical Pathology* (1883–86) included a quote from a paper given by William Squire to the Epidemiological Society of London in 1877:

> Later in the epidemic, when it is said to be like plague . . . the people, seized with fear, had abandoned their sick . . . the people chose swampy sites for their dwellings, and whether they kept close shut up in huts without ventilation, or rushed into the streams and remained in the water during the height of the illness, the consequences were equally fatal. The excessive mortality resulted from terror at the mysterious seizure, and [from] the want of the commonest aids during illness . . . Thousands were carried off

by want of nourishment and care, as well as by dysentery and congestion of the lungs.

The epidemic has been described as 'one of the great tragic events in Pacific history'.

By the end of the nineteenth century, measles had reached almost every corner of the globe, becoming one of the most ubiquitous of all infectious diseases. As faster steamships replaced the smaller and slower sailing ships, it was much more likely that infected passengers could transmit the disease on arrival to new destinations. Some of the last pockets of population to be visited by measles were the isolated and remote communities of the sub-Arctic region. In 1900, mainland Alaska had an epidemic of measles with rates of mortality that reached 40 per cent among the isolated Native American populations. Iceland was struck several times – in 1846, 1882 and 1904. The 1904 outbreak arrived in late April in the north-west fjords with a crew of whalers from Norway. It spread rapidly after a confirmation ceremony in a little church on a remote fjord. Children and non-immune adults were packed into the church, and by the end of August local doctors were overwhelmed. Further periodic waves occurred in Iceland throughout the twentieth century, becoming even more frequent after the increase in air travel in the 1950s.

'Make measles a memory' – a safe and effective vaccine

The last major 'virgin soil' epidemic of measles was in Greenland in 1951, when only five people out of an unprotected population of 4,262 in the southern part of the island escaped the disease. A decade later, scientists in the United States developed the first effective vaccine for measles. The search for a way of preventing measles had begun in the mid-eighteenth century, when the Scottish physician Francis Home (1719–1813) attempted to inoculate children, either through the skin or into the nose, with cotton swabs soaked in the 'fresh blood of a measly patient' at the height of their fever. Unlike the successful vaccine for smallpox developed in the late 1790s by Edward Jenner, Home's procedure did not catch on, and it was not until 1963 that the first live-attenuated ('weakened') measles vaccine was licensed.

Prior to the vaccine, although there had been a decline in measles as a cause of death in America, Europe, parts of Asia and Oceania (possibly relating to improvements in nursing care, standards of living and nutrition), measles still infected over 90 per cent of children before they reached fifteen years of age. These infections were estimated to cause several million deaths and thousands of cases of blindness annually worldwide.

The first necessary step in developing a vaccine was the identification of the measles virus, which was made possible in 1954. The American microbiologist John Enders (1897–1985) – director of a laboratory at Boston Children's Hospital, and famous also for his work on polio, for which he shared the 1954 Nobel Prize – asked one of his research group, Thomas Peebles (1921–2010), to find a way of isolating the measles virus. Peebles took throat swabs of schoolchildren – his main success involved an eleven-year old boy, David Edmonston, who had an acute measles virus infection and whose name would become attached to the Edmonston-B strain of the measles virus. Enders, Peebles and colleagues then cultivated the virus in human kidney cell tissue and, eventually, succeeded in developing a safe and effective vaccine by the early 1960s. An improved vaccine was soon developed by Maurice Hilleman (1919–2005) at Merck in the US. Hilleman's name is associated with over thirty vaccines, several of which are in use today, including the trivalent MMR (measles, mumps and rubella) vaccine – the first vaccine ever approved incorporating multiple live virus strains.

With the introduction of the measles vaccine (followed by the MMR vaccine) the downward trend of measles was accelerated in developed countries. In the USA a mass immunization programme – which became known as the 'Make Measles a Memory' campaign – was eventually spectacularly successful, and in the year 2000 it was declared that endemic measles transmission had been 'interrupted' and the indigenous virus eliminated from the US. Outbreaks are, however, still occurring following importation of the virus via infected travellers from endemic countries and amongst small clusters of unvaccinated people who oppose the vaccine, often due to philosophical or religious beliefs or on the grounds of its safety.

In 1998 a study published in *The Lancet* linked the MMR vaccine with autism and bowel disease. The findings, reported in a respected journal and the subject of intense media publicity, especially in the UK but also in the USA and elsewhere, triggered a major health scare. Parents became concerned about the safety of the vaccine, and the take-up rates of the vaccine plummeted to levels below those needed for herd immunity. Numerous epidemiological studies published since have provided evidence that no such link exists and the article was subsequently completely discredited and fully retracted by *The Lancet* in 2010. However, the consequences have been profound, and in recent years there have been outbreaks of measles, particularly amongst a generation of adolescents who were not vaccinated as children at the height of the scare. There is currently a 'catch-up' campaign in the UK, with the hope of reaching all those who have not had their two doses of MMR. Although vaccines do carry a small risk, the MMR vaccine is said to be one of the safest and most cost-effective vaccines in the world, and the risk of serious illness and death from measles, mumps or rubella far outweighs the risk of vaccination.

Measles in the developing world

Over the centuries, measles epidemics were, invariably, described as either 'mild' or 'mortal'. In parts of the developing world measles has carried a high death toll, killing between 5 and 10 per cent (sometimes more) of all who are infected. The reasons for this are complex, but it seems clear that for impoverished children living in crowded conditions, suffering from malnutrition or HIV/AIDS, and lacking basic medical care, measles can often lead to severe consequences. Complications of the disease include pneumonia, diarrhoea, otitis media (infection of the eardrum), damage to the nervous system and encephalitis (inflammation of the brain). The risk of a malnourished child dying from diarrhoea associated with measles is especially high. Measles can also precipitate acute kwashiorkor (a form of malnutrition caused by lack of protein) and exacerbate vitamin A deficiency, which may in turn lead to blindness.

The Expanded Programme on Immunization

Recognizing the severity of measles and other vaccine-preventable diseases of children, especially in the poorer countries of the world, in 1974 (shortly before the global eradication of smallpox) the WHO launched the highly successful Expanded Programme on Immunization (EPI), covering six common childhood diseases: measles, polio, tuberculosis, diphtheria, tetanus and pertussis (whooping cough). At the time only about 5 per cent of the world's children were protected from these six diseases, but that percentage has risen markedly since the EPI began. A major public-private philanthropic global health partnership, the Global Alliance for Vaccines and Immunization (GAVI), was established in 2000, backed by the Gates Foundation, and the Global Immunization Vision and Strategy (GIVS) was launched as a collaborative initiative of the WHO and UNICEF in 2006 with the aim of providing a ten-year framework for controlling morbidity and mortality from vaccine-preventable diseases.

As new vaccines have been developed, so additional diseases, including hepatitis B and haemophilus influenzae type B, have been added to the EPI list, and a number of countries are now in the process of including vaccines for two of the leading and often 'forgotten' killers of children – pneumococcal disease and rotavirus (which jointly account for a significant proportion of deaths under five years of age in the developing world). Bill and Melinda Gates, have pledged over US$10 billion of their personal wealth to research, develop and deliver vaccines for the world's poorest countries, calling in 2010 for a new 'Decade of Vaccines'.

Can measles be eradicated?

Other global partnerships, such as the Measles and Rubella Initiative, are galvanizing support to reduce the toll of such diseases while, concurrently, in the highest-burden countries delivering a combination of safe, effective and affordable child-survival interventions (such as combining measles and other vaccinations with vitamin-A supplementation, de-worming medicine, and insecticide-treated bed nets). Indeed, for measles, as for other childhood diseases, there has been a significant reduction worldwide in mortality and morbidity since the EPI was commenced and the 2000 UN Millennium Development Goal 4 set the target of reducing by two-thirds, between 1990 and 2015, the under-five mortality rate. Between 2000 and 2012, over 1 billion children were vaccinated against measles in high-risk countries, resulting in a promising 78 per cent drop in measles deaths since the turn of the millennium. Although the indigenous measles virus has been eliminated from the USA, around 50 to 300 imported cases still occur every year and, with today's high level of global travel, public health experts are urging people to continue to get vaccinated.

Current estimates, nevertheless, indicate that around 20 million people globally are still affected by measles each year, and the disease accounted for 122,000 deaths in 2012. With approximately fourteen people dying from measles every hour, this remains an unacceptably high number for this essentially preventable disease. Over 90 per cent of the deaths occur in countries with a per capita GNP (gross national product) lower than $1,000, more than 75 per cent are in children under five years, and at least 50 per cent of all measles deaths are in Africa.

There is, however, a strong commitment to extend the coverage of measles vaccination for children (there is, as yet, no specific cure or antiviral drug for this disease) with the aim of making measles 'a memory' worldwide. When Rhazes in the tenth century conjectured that measles was 'more to be dreaded' than smallpox, his words would ring true for the twenty-first century. Smallpox has been eradicated – there is still hope that measles will follow it into oblivion.

YELLOW FEVER

Yellow fever – an acute viral disease in which victims become jaundiced and vomit up black blood – was at one time amongst the most dreaded of deadly diseases. It was particularly rife during the era of European global exploration, when sailors, soldiers and slaves may have carried the virus and its mosquito vector from Africa to the New World. For centuries, there were many puzzles about the cause of yellow fever until a remarkable series of experiments in early twentieth-century Cuba finally proved that a species of mosquito, *Aedes aegypti*, transmits the infection. There has been a vaccine for yellow fever since the 1930s, but there is as yet no specific cure. The disease is now largely confined to forty-four endemic countries in two geographical regions of the world – In sub-Saharan Africa and Latin America. A reported 200,000 cases of yellow fever with 30,000 deaths occur each year, with over 90 per cent in sub-Saharan Africa. Like other mosquito-borne diseases, it continues to evade our efforts to eradicate it.

∾

The name yellow fever – reflecting the typical yellow skin and eyes of victims – was first coined by Griffith Hughes in his work *The Natural History of Barbados* published in 1750. The disease can vary in severity. In some cases it is a mild illness of short duration, but in the worst cases yellow fever attacks the liver, leading to jaundice (from the French *jaune*, 'yellow'). The disease can also lead to kidney failure, delirium and coma. Between 20 and 50 per cent of those with the severe or toxic form of the illness will die.

Although yellow fever has probably been around for hundreds of years, it was not until 1900 that it was finally proved that it was transmitted by the bite of infective mosquitoes (notably the female *Aedes aegypti*), and not until the late 1920s that the causative organism was found to be a virus – one belonging to the same family as the virus causing dengue fever.

'Yellow Jack' and black vomit

In the past, yellow fever was so common among sailors that ships carried a special 'Yellow Jack' flag. Infected ships were quarantined outside ports and obliged to fly the flag as a warning. Neither sailors nor passengers were allowed to leave the ship for up to forty days, and, in some cities, anyone trying to escape took the risk of being shot by police or vigilantes. 'Yellow Jack' became such a distinctive emblem that it was often used as a nickname for the disease itself.

While the word 'yellow' in the English name of the disease reflects the outward jaundiced appearance of sufferers, the Spanish name for yellow fever, *vómito negro*, reflects its other notorious symptom: 'black vomit'. This is the result of internal bleeding, especially into the stomach and intestinal tract. Copious bleeding may also occur from the eyes, nose, gums and rectum. In a letter written in 1897 in Memphis, Tennessee, an uncle described his niece's final hours: 'to me the most terrible and terrifying feature was the "black vomit" which I never before witnessed. By Tuesday evening it was as black as ink and would be ejected with terrific force. I had my face and hands spattered but had to stand by and hold her. Well it is too terrible to write any more about it.'

Yellow fever and the transatlantic world

'There was one thing nearly everybody . . . had been agreed upon for nearly two hundred years, and that was this: when folks of a town began to turn yellow and hiccup and vomit black blood, by scores, by hundreds, every day – the only thing to do was to get up and get out of town . . .' Paul de Kruif, *Microbe Hunters*, 1926

Like many diseases, it is hard to know when or how yellow fever began to infect humans. It is possible that for thousands of years yellow fever was a disease of monkeys in the African (and possibly the South American) rainforests. At some time in the past, as people moved into the jungles, the mosquitoes that transmitted yellow fever started to feed on humans.

The first major recorded human epidemics were in the seventeenth century in the Caribbean and the Americas. Some historians have suggested that yellow fever and its vector crossed the Atlantic on slave ships from Africa to the Americas, where it had devastating effects on both the European colonists and the indigenous population, neither of whom had ever before been exposed to the disease. African slaves en route across the Atlantic may have been infected with the yellow fever virus while the mosquito vector of the disease (*Aedes aegypti*) probably thrived and bred in the casks of drinking water carried on board the long voyages.

In 1647 an epidemic of yellow fever struck the Caribbean island of Barbados, where some 5,000 people died of this seemingly new and frightening disease. Called the 'Barbados distemper', the Massachusetts governor, John Winthrop (*c.*1587–1649), established North America's first quarantine regulations to protect his English colony from infection. In the following year the disease hit both Cuba and the Yucatán Peninsula. From that date on, yellow fever regularly visited the ports and cities of the Americas during the summer months – from Quebec in the north to Rio de Janeiro in the south.

With its close trading connections with the Caribbean, the city of Philadelphia became one of the hotbeds of the disease, and in 1793 some 4,000–5,000 people, one-tenth of the city's population, perished in a single epidemic. Around 20,000 fled in panic. Even President George Washington and his cabinet left the plague-ridden city (then the capital of the newly independent USA). A number of neighbouring communities and major port cities such as New York and Baltimore set up quarantines to prevent the influx of refugees and goods from Philadelphia. The physician Benjamin Rush (1746–1813), and one of the founding fathers of the United States, advocated copious bloodletting and powerful purgatives for the victims of yellow fever. A 'violent' disease, he believed, needed a 'violent' remedy.

The question of the effectiveness of quarantine was much debated at the time. Rush was against its imposition, believing the disease to be caused by 'local' meteorological factors and miasmas. Others argued that it was an 'imported' contagious disease that had to be prevented. In 1799 Philadelphia passed an Act making quarantine compulsory – a sentence of up to five years' hard labour awaited anyone found evading these regulations. Similar legislation was enacted in other Atlantic ports. The disruption that epidemics and quarantine created at a time of growing trade and immigration in the US gave yellow fever a heightened national prominence.

Over the following century, ferocious epidemics of the disease continued to erupt at intervals, especially in the southern US cities of New Orleans, Savannah and Charleston, causing panic, terror, mass flight and high death rates. In 1853 in New Orleans there were so many dead that there were not enough gravediggers to bury them all. An epidemic in Rio de Janeiro in Brazil in 1849–50 caused shock waves to reverberate around the region. Even some European ports – including Lisbon in Portugal, St Nazaire in France, and Swansea in Wales – suffered visitations of yellow fever in the mid-nineteenth century. In the US one of the most devastating outbreaks of yellow fever swept across the Mississippi and Ohio valleys in 1878, infecting over 100,000, with some 20,000 deaths.

The baffling 'cause' of yellow fever

To the peoples of the New World, yellow fever proved baffling in every way. Some blamed it on filth and foul smells and burnt bonfires of aromatic herbs in the streets; others believed it was a contagious disease passing from person to person. One doctor attributed it to 'sickly and tasteless' oysters, another to rotting coffee beans.

Mysteriously, during the earliest series of epidemics it seemed that yellow fever was a disease that only, or primarily, afflicted

Europeans – especially newcomers to the New World; it was thus often called the 'strangers' disease'. African slaves seemed to resist it, possibly having experienced it mildly in childhood, giving a rather sinister justification to plantation owners for the use of slave labour. But its origin and epidemiology still remained puzzling, and over the course of time nothing the authorities did seemed to halt its spread. Neither flight nor quarantines were effective in stopping the disease.

In the late eighteenth century, New York physician Valentine Seaman (1770–1817) argued that 'no yellow fever can spread, but by the influence of putrid effluvia' in the malodorous city. To prove his proposition that proximity to noxious airs caused the disease, he produced detailed maps of yellow fever cases along with sites of garbage and human and animal excrement in New York City. A few years later, in the US, medical student Stubbins Ffirth (1784–1820) went to extraordinary lengths to prove that it was impossible to 'catch' this mysterious disease from an infected person. He smeared 'fresh black vomit' from yellow fever patients into cuts on his arms, drank it, and when still uninfected, repeated his experiments using patients' blood, saliva and urine. Ffirth's work had little impact on medical practice, and debates as to the cause of yellow fever rumbled on throughout the nineteenth century.

The role of the mosquito

In the early 1880s Carlos Finlay (1833–1915), a Cuban doctor of Anglo-French descent, conducted a number of experiments and surmised that yellow fever was transmitted by mosquitoes. Finlay was right in his conjecture. Others, however, remained convinced that yellow fever was caused by filth, contaminated clothing and bedding, or poisonous airs arising from stagnant water. It was another two decades before Finlay's hunch was finally shown to be correct.

After the Cuban War of Independence (1895–8) and the Spanish-American War (1898), in which the US army lost more men to disease, including yellow fever, than to enemy action, the American army doctor Walter Reed was sent to the Cuban capital, Havana. Around half a million American troops remained in Cuba after the war, and Reed was appointed head of the US Army Yellow Fever Commission to find the true cause of the disease. Despite a major clean-up of the city, conducted by army medical officer William Crawford Gorgas (1854–1920), and an overall fall in mortality from several diseases, yellow fever deaths had, paradoxically, increased.

By 1900, a number of 'tropical' diseases, including malaria and sleeping sickness, had been shown to be transmitted by blood-sucking insect vectors. British doctors Herbert Durham (1866–1945) and Walter Myers (1872–1901) from the newly created Liverpool School of Tropical Medicine, familiar with these new findings, visited Cuba. They suspected, like Finlay, that mosquitoes might transmit yellow fever. Following up these leads – especially the identification of the mosquito's role in malaria which had been made by Ronald Ross in India in 1897 and confirmed by Italian scientists in 1898, as well as the crucial observations of Finlay about the particular species of mosquito that might be involved in yellow fever transmission in Cuba – Reed and his medical associates soon proved beyond doubt that yellow fever is transmitted by the bite of mosquitoes of the species now known as *Aedes aegypti*.

Mosquitoes, 'filth' and grisly experiments

'The mosquito serves as the intermediate host for the parasite of yellow fever ... and it is highly probable that the disease is only propagated through the bite of this insect.'
Walter Reed *et al.*, 1900

Amongst the first series of critical experiments – or, indeed, self-experiments – to investigate the mosquito hypothesis (using mosquitoes reared from eggs supplied by Finlay) three of Reed's team – James Carroll (1854–1907), Jesse Lazear (1866–1900) and Aristides Agramonte (1868–1931) – undertook a dangerous round of inoculation tests in late August and early September 1900, while Reed was away in the US. Carroll allowed mosquitoes that had fed on patients with yellow fever to bite him. He became very sick, but just about survived. A volunteer army soldier also got yellow fever but recovered. Lazear was not so lucky. While collecting blood from yellow fever patients in a hospital, he was bitten by a mosquito. Lazear deliberately allowed the mosquito, which had settled on the back of his hand, to remain until it had satisfied its hunger. He became desperately ill. Such was the wildness of his delirium that it took five men to hold him down before he tragically died of yellow fever on 25 September 1900.

Lazear's death was a turning point. A telegram to Reed brought him back to Havana to conduct further investigations. He built an experimental establishment outside Havana, which he named 'Camp Lazear' in honour of the dead physician. One group of recruits was put in a mosquito-free but filthy building filled with the vomit- and blood-covered clothing and bedding of yellow fever victims. Another group was left in isolation in a clean and well-ventilated building. This was partitioned into two areas by a fine-mesh wire screen. In one area, volunteers were bitten by mosquitoes that had previously fed on yellow fever patients. Volunteers on the other side of the screen were not exposed to mosquitoes. Only the mosquito-bitten volunteers caught yellow fever, while the group in the 'contaminated' building remained 'as fit as fiddles' – although – we can only imagine – they came out after the experiment gasping for fresh air. Miraculously, no one died.

Not everyone had been persuaded by the Yellow Fever Commission's initial hypothesis. To some it seemed almost impossible that the bite of a tiny insect could cause such a devastating disease. The *Washington Post* on 2 November 1900, for example, had reported: 'Of all the silly and nonsensical rigmarole of yellow fever that has yet found its way into print – and there has been enough of it to build a fleet – the silliest beyond compare is to be found in the arguments and theories generated by the mosquito hypothesis.' However, the Camp Lazear experiment quickly proved to Reed beyond doubt that yellow fever was caused by the bite of infected mosquitoes. Indeed, the team not only proved the mosquito hypothesis with their risky experiments but also confirmed that a lag time of around twelve to sixteen days was required between the insect's acquisition of infected blood and biting of a susceptible individual to induce disease. This timing agreed with that observed by Henry Rose Carter (1852–1925), a US public health physician, who in 1898 had conducted epidemiological studies of yellow fever in two Mississippi villages and had described this as an 'extrinsic incubation period.' We now know that the yellow fever virus must be incubated in the female mosquito over a period of time before she is infective.

At midnight on New Year's Eve, 1900, Reed wrote to his

wife: 'the prayer that has been mine for twenty or more years, that I might be permitted in some way or sometime to do something to alleviate human suffering has been answered! A thousand Happy New Years'. Sadly, Walter Reed died of appendicitis shortly after this great discovery, while a number of other scientists conducting further research in the Americas and Africa died of yellow fever, either through natural or accidental infection.

Armed with the knowledge that yellow fever was a vector-borne disease, strategies were implemented to rid cities of mosquitoes, both in their adult forms as they came into houses to bite or in their larval forms in pockets of water. *Aedes aegypti* lives in close proximity to human settlements, the female laying her eggs in any source of temporary water. Gorgas – who had contracted and survived yellow fever in Fort Brown, Texas, in 1882, and was therefore immune to the disease – carried out a successful campaign of yellow fever eradication in Havana. Water receptacles were oiled or destroyed, houses were screened and dusted with pyrethrum powder, patients isolated and sick rooms mosquito-proofed. By 1901, yellow fever had been eliminated from the city (though it did return again in 1904 and 1905 before being finally extinguished in 1908). With further anti-mosquito programmes in other places, including that which enabled the completion of the Panama Canal in 1914, it was hoped that the disease could be eradicated from the entire globe.

Pouring oil on troubled waters

'The Panama Canal was dug with a microscope.' Attributed
to Ronald Ross

Since the sixteenth century, navigators and merchants had
longed to cut a swathe through the 50-mile (80-km) Panama
Isthmus in Central America to link the Atlantic and Pacific
Oceans. But technical, financial and political constraints, as well
as inhospitable conditions and deadly mosquitoes, were a
serious hindrance to such plans.

In 1851–5 a railroad was built across the Panama region; it is
said that for every sleeper laid, one labourer died. Ferdinand de
Lesseps (1805–94), the French engineer who had masterminded
the building of the Suez Canal which opened in 1869, had to
abandon the first attempt to build a canal across the Isthmus of
Panama in 1889. Tens of thousands of workmen died on the
project, notably from yellow fever and malaria.

When the US took over the Panama Canal Zone in 1904,
Gorgas was appointed chief sanitary officer, and set about the
daunting task of ridding the area of mosquitoes and mosquito-
borne diseases during a renewed attempt to build a canal. His
sanitary brigades tried everything: draining ponds and swamps,
pouring oil over open water to kill mosquito eggs and larvae,
building sewerage systems and hospitals, insisting on screens on
every door and window, and isolating yellow fever patients in
mosquito-proof rooms. Although the death toll for construction
workers was still high, by 1906 Gorgas had successfully eliminated yellow fever from the region. Malaria took longer to control,
but with a combination of anti-mosquito measures and a freely
available supply of the drug quinine as an effective preventive

and therapy, cases and deaths from malaria were reduced significantly. The Panama Canal was finally opened in 1914 – one of the greatest engineering marvels of the modern world. The Canal Zone and the canal were handed over to Panama in 1999.

A monkey puzzle

'There is hardly enough of the poison of yellow fever left in the world to put on the points of six pins; in a few years there may not be a single speck of that virus left on earth – it will be as completely extinct as the dinosaurs.' Paul de Kruif, *Microbe Hunters*, 1926

The last major epidemic of 'urban' yellow fever in the USA was in New Orleans in 1905. Elsewhere, especially in South America and sub-Saharan Africa, yellow fever continued to pose a threat during the early twentieth century. But with vector control to eliminate the 'domestic' mosquito from its breeding places close to human habitations, it was hoped that eradication of the disease would be possible – indeed, yellow fever was one of the first diseases to be proposed for eradication. The Yellow Fever Commission of the Rockefeller Foundation, for example, based on the Gorgas model, set its sights on the ultimate goal of eliminating *Aedes aegypti* from the Western hemisphere and, eventually from the world.

However, just as confidence was high and early activities were proving successful in urban areas, a dispiriting twist in the story was uncovered in the late 1920s and early 1930s. With yellow fever re-emerging in isolated and rural areas in northeastern Brazil, Rockefeller scientist Fred Soper discovered a 'jungle' or sylvatic yellow-fever cycle, transmitted by wild mosquitoes (of the *Haemagogus* genus) with a host in monkeys living in the canopies of trees. As forest areas such as the Amazon rainforest were being opened up, the risk to people working there (e.g. for logging) was especially worrying, as vector control methods were nigh on impossible for this 'zoonotic' form of yellow fever. The existence of an animal reservoir of the disease dealt a blow to the eradication concept.

Identifying the virus and a vaccine

On a more optimistic note, scientists were able to infect rhesus monkeys with yellow fever, thus making possible an animal model. This led in 1927 to the isolation and identification of the causative pathogen of yellow fever, which scientists concluded must be a virus (the first human disease to be identified as a virus). By 1937, South African-born US Rockefeller scientist Max Theiler (1899–1972) and his colleagues had developed a vaccine for yellow fever. Theiler received the Nobel Prize for Physiology or Medicine in 1951 for his 'discoveries concerning yellow fever and how to combat it.'

The vaccine was a powerful new weapon in the fight against yellow fever, and by the 1940s it had been given to millions of people. Yellow fever cases almost vanished from French West Africa following intensive vaccination campaigns. However, there were some serious outbreaks of yellow fever between the 1950s and 1990s in parts of Africa and South and Central America where vaccine coverage was low or absent, and mosquitoes, increasingly resistant to the insecticide, DDT, still persisted in large numbers in both urban and sylvatic settings. The rapidly growing tropical and subtropical cities and slums – with ample opportunities for *Aedes aegypti* to breed in any water receptacle from abandoned rubber car tyres to plastic water bottles – have since intensified the need for vaccination as a way of preventing yellow fever.

Although there were some initial problems with the early batch of yellow fever vaccines, the vaccine used today (known as the 17D vaccine) is now considered safe and highly effective, conferring lifelong immunity. Campaigns led by the WHO and partnerships such as the GAVI Alliance are currently trying to improve the uptake of the vaccine, especially in sub-Saharan Africa.

For reasons which are still puzzling, yellow fever has never been endemic in Asia despite the abundance of the *Aedes aegypti* vector and the prevalence of dengue fever – a closely related mosquito-borne disease. Indeed, with the opening up of the Panama Canal in the early twentieth century there were fears that yellow fever would spread from the West to the East. So far, mercifully, that has not happened. But a valid international certificate of vaccination against yellow fever is still required by many countries for entry of travellers coming from or going to recognized yellow fever zones – an international regulation that dates back to the 1950s when it was introduced to prevent the global spread of yellow fever, as well as, at the time, cholera and smallpox.

Yellow fever is one of a few mosquito-borne diseases (some of which like yellow fever are caused by viruses, others like malaria are parasitic diseases) for which there is a preventive vaccine. But there are others, such as dengue fever, for which there are currently no vaccines. Urbanization, climate changes, deforestation and tourism are bringing more and more people into close contact with infective mosquitoes. Avoiding mosquito breeding sites, as well as liberal use of DEET-based mosquito repellents (especially in areas where mosquitoes such as *Aedes aegypti* bite in the daytime) and insecticide-treated bed nets (where mosquitoes such as the *Anopheles* mosquito which causes malaria bite after dusk) remain vital strategies for travellers to 'exotic' climes.

There are a reported 200,000 cases of yellow fever each year, causing 30,000 deaths worldwide, though the actual figures may be considerably higher. Indeed, there has been a resurgence of the disease over the past two decades in poorer countries, especially in sub-Saharan Africa, which accounts for 90 per cent of all deaths, the remainder mostly occurring in Latin America. For those living in *Aedes aegypti*-infested areas, we can only hope that with continued vector control and a 'push' to increase the vaccination coverage of children, scientists will fulfil the dream of the earlier pioneers who often risked their lives to understand and control the disease and – to quote Walter Reed – that 'in some way or sometime' we will be able 'to do something to alleviate human suffering' from yellow fever.

DENGUE FEVER

Dengue fever, which was often known as 'break-bone fever', is a viral infection transmitted by the bite of a female mosquito. It can cause a high fever and agonizing pain, followed by debilitating after-effects. In the past dengue evoked less fear and horror than many other diseases, but with the recent emergence of more deadly forms of the disease – notably dengue haemorrhagic fever (DHF) or 'severe' dengue – it has become a serious health threat in many parts of the tropical and subtropical world. There are currently no licensed vaccines and no specific medicines to treat the disease, but access to proper medical care lowers fatality rates. Effective vector control measures are vital to prevent the transmission of dengue, which is the most rapidly spreading mosquito-borne viral disease in the world. With a thirty-fold increase during the past five decades and with at least 50–100 million new infections occurring annually in more than 100 endemic countries, dengue is now a major international public health concern.

∾

The origin of the word 'dengue' (pronounced 'deng-gy', the 'g' being hard) is something of a puzzle. One suggestion is that it derives from the Swahili phrase *Ka-dinga pepo*, meaning a sudden, cramp-like seizure caused by an evil spirit. Alternatively, 'dengue' may be a corruption of 'dandy' – slaves in the West Indies called the disease 'dandy fever' because sufferers were crippled with pain and had a 'dandified' manner of walking. Another explanation is that it comes from the Spanish *denguero*, meaning 'affected' or 'finicky', perhaps referring to the stiffness that afflicted victims. It was the American physician Benjamin Rush, one of the signatories of the Declaration of Independence, who first described the disease, aptly calling this crippling condition 'break-bone fever'.

The agonizing symptoms of dengue fever

Benjamin Rush made his historic description of 'break-bone fever' following an outbreak in Philadelphia in 1780: 'The pains which accompanied this fever were exquisitely severe in the head, back and limbs . . . the pains in the head were sometimes in the back part of it, and at other times they occupied only the eyeballs . . . its more general name among all classes of people was the break-bone fever'. To which he added: 'I attended two young ladies, who shed tears while they vented their complaints of their sickness and weakness. One of them very aptly proposed to me to change the name of the disease, and to call it, in its present stage, instead of the break-bone, the break-heart fever'. Rush treated his patients with 'a gentle vomit of tartar emetic' to empty the stomach. He also advised 'a liberal supply of opium, oysters, a generous amount of porter and some gentle exercise in the open air'. To this day there is no cure for dengue or its close relative, yellow fever. But while a safe, effective vaccine for yellow fever has existed since the 1930s, there is still no vaccine for dengue, although candidate vaccines are currently being evaluated.

The classic form of dengue is characterized by the sudden onset of fever, vomiting, a rash, severe frontal headache, intense pain behind the eyes, and searing joint and muscle pains, especially in the lower back. It is not very often fatal, although – as Rush also noted – the disease could leave its victims seriously debilitated and 'uncommonly dejected' for a long time after recovery. One characteristic of classic dengue is known as 'saddleback fever': the temperature soars in the first forty-eight to ninety-six hours, then subsides for twenty-four hours, only to peak again for a couple of days at the end of the fever.

Unravelling the cause of dengue

The origins of dengue fever are uncertain. It may have been endemic in Africa and spread to the West Indies and the Americas via the transatlantic slave trade. Its chief vector, the *Aedes aegypti* mosquito, possibly originated in Africa, but as humans started to travel across the globe the mosquito established itself in far-flung places. Simultaneous epidemics occurred in the 1780s in Asia, Africa, Europe and North America, and throughout the following century there were many outbreaks of dengue fever, mostly in tropical and subtropical regions but occasionally also in temperate areas.

Initially, no one knew how the disease was transmitted. Then, in 1906, following the discovery of the role played by mosquitoes in the transmission of diseases such as malaria and yellow fever, the Australian medical naturalist Thomas Lane Bancroft, using human volunteers for his experiments, suspected that the *Aedes aegypti* mosquito (then known as *Stegomyia fasciata*) responsible for yellow fever also transmitted dengue fever, as it was a day-biter and he was aware of victims who had been bitten only during the day. Other scientists were able to confirm that *Aedes aegypti* was the vector. Some decades later – by the 1940s – the infective agent was found to be a virus. We now know that the virus that causes dengue fever (of which there are four sero-types) belongs to a family of *flaviviruses* (from the Latin, *flavus*, for 'yellow') which also include yellow fever, West Nile virus and Japanese encephalitis. Other *flaviviruses* are transmitted by ticks, such as tick-borne encephalitis (TBE).

Searching for a solution

Following the discovery of the vector, there was considerable optimism. Successful vector control programmes virtually elim-inated mosquito-borne diseases in Cuba and the Panama Canal Zone in the early twentieth century, and there was tremendous hope that mosquito-borne diseases could be eradicated in other regions of the world. The powerful insecticide DDT was widely used in campaigns in the 1950s and early 1960s in an attempt to eliminate the *Anopheles* mosquito which causes malaria, as well as the *Aedes aegypti* mosquito which transmits both yellow fever and dengue fever. But following revelations of the toxic effects of DDT on the environment and problems of mosquito resistance, by the late 1960s DDT was no longer considered a 'magic weapon'.

Dengue fever, historically and globally, did not carry the same fear as yellow fever, though by this time there was an addi-tional preventive strategy of a vaccine for yellow fever. With the problems associated with DDT and the shift to vaccination as a priority for yellow fever control, as well as for many other reasons, the anti-mosquito programmes for *Aedes aegypti*, which had, initially, proved successful in interrupting dengue transmission in much of the Americas, were by the 1970s allowed to lapse. Without sustained vector control and with dengue becoming increasingly 'neglected' by the international health community, the mosquito quickly re-infested a number of regions, followed by outbreaks of dengue in the Caribbean, Central and South America and Asia.

The *Aedes* mosquito breeds close to human habitations. The female mosquito lays her eggs in all sorts of artificial or abandoned water containers, such as old car tyres, plastic bottles, tin cans and even in coconut shells. The adult female is capable of becoming infected for life when she sucks up the virus from an infected host and then, after a period of incubation of seven to fourteen days, transmits the virus back to another human when she feeds on blood. With the growth of uncontrolled high-density urbanization in much of the tropical and subtropical developing world, often without adequate systems of water supply, sewerage and rubbish collection, ideal ecological niches were created for the proliferation of the mosquito to breed, bite and infect people with the dengue virus. By the mid-1990s maps showing the geographical distribution of the insect vector resembled vector maps made thirty years earlier. Poor medical care and deteriorating public health infrastructures were further problems in dengue-endemic regions, while an increase in global air travel aided the worldwide dispersal of the dengue virus and a mixing of its four serotypes.

New and deadly forms of dengue emerge

Partly as a result of these factors, by the late twentieth century there was a massive increase in dengue fever, especially in Southeast Asia, the Pacific region (including northern Queensland,

Australia), the Caribbean, South America and parts of the Middle East and Africa. An average of 900 cases per annum were recorded in the late 1950s, but by the end of the century this had jumped to over a million, with an unprecedented fifty-six countries reporting cases worldwide. Even more worrying has been the emergence of more deadly forms of dengue – dengue haemorrhagic fever (DHF) and dengue shock syndrome (DSS) – now often known as 'severe' dengue.

The first epidemic cases of DHF were reported in Manila in the Philippines in 1953. A small child with dengue fever started bleeding uncontrollably, then other children fell victim to this strange new syndrome. By the following year a serious epidemic of DHF was sweeping though the area, thereafter reaching Thailand and other parts of Asia. The Singapore government in the 1960s instituted measures to reduce its incidence, including fining or imprisoning residents who allowed mosquitoes to breed on their property. By the 1980s cases of DHF were also reported in the Western hemisphere. In 1981 a six-month epidemic of dengue and DHF occurred in Havana, Cuba, killing 158, including 51 children, and further outbreaks occurred in Latin America. In 1998, there was another large epidemic of dengue and DHF in the Western Pacific region.

This apparently new clinical syndrome, then designated as a clinical entity separate from the classical form of dengue fever, seems to have arisen in South-east Asia and the Pacific during and after the Second World War, linked to the movement of troops and populations, and associated with ecological disruption. It has rapidly become a significant public health problem in many towns and cities in the tropics and subtropics. Prior to 1970, only nine countries had experienced cases of DHF; since then the number has increased more than four-fold and continues to rise.

DHF, with its ominous symptoms of pinpoint-sized spots of blood, bleeding under the skin, convulsions and fevers reaching over 104°F (40°C), can lead to multiple haemorrhaging or, in the case of DSS, circulatory shock. It is currently a leading cause of hospitalization and death in Asia and Latin America, especially in young children. There is no specific treatment, but fatality rates can be kept down (to below one per cent) with early detection, good medical care and fluid-replacement therapy. DHF and DSS are puzzling and frightening outcomes of dengue fever – one hypothesis is that they are triggered by a complex hyperactive immune response following a previous (and usually mild) infection with a different serotype of dengue fever. There are four distinct, but closely related, serotypes of the virus that cause dengue. Recovery from infection from one provides lifelong immunity against that particular serotype. However, cross-immunity to the other serotypes after recovery is only partial and temporary and, bizarrely, it is subsequent infections by other serotypes that appear to increase the risk of developing severe and life-threatening dengue.

Dengue – from a Neglected Tropical Disease to a high global priority

There have been further explosive epidemics of 'classic' dengue and 'severe' dengue in many parts of the world in the twenty-first century, with dramatic increases in the number of reported cases and deaths worldwide despite the availability of powerful insecticides and mosquito-abatement efforts directed at the control or eradication of *Aedes aegypti*. Data for 2014 estimate that there are between 50 and 100 million new infections annually, with half a million cases of DHF and around 22,000 deaths, mainly amongst children, though these may well be underestimates. Dengue is now endemic in some one hundred countries through the tropical and subtropical regions, including regions not previously affected by the disease. It is still mostly a disease of urban and peri-urban environments, especially the poor, overcrowded and insanitary slums, shanty towns and favelas of the developing world. But cases are now cropping up even in rural areas, and the likelihood that there is a wild primate reservoir and sylvatic cycle in forested areas, as with yellow fever), adds to the disturbing complexities of this disease. The worsening situation has been described as increasingly worrying, and dengue – the most important and rapidly spreading viral disease transmitted by mosquitoes – poses a major threat to global health.

There is also growing concern about the recent spread of a secondary mosquito vector, *Aedes albopictus* or the Asian tiger mosquito, which can transmit dengue (as well as chikungunya). *A. albopictus* is highly adaptive. It can survive in cooler temperatures and is already beginning to infest temperate areas. In 1985 this aggressive type of mosquito reached the Americas on a shipload of old tyres sent from Japan to Houston, Texas, for re-treading. Since then it has spread rapidly across the eastern states of the USA, raising fears of the possible reintroduction of dengue fever to the USA as well as to Europe, where the last serious outbreaks of endemic dengue fever were in the mid-1940s and the late 1920s, respectively. The international commercial trade in used rubber tyres which easily accumulate rainwater – and provide an ideal breeding ground for mosquito vectors – continues to ring alarm bells. With increased global travel it is also possible that returning tourists and others infected with dengue will act as hosts for local mosquitoes, as dengue expert Duane Gubler has warned: 'The presence of albopictus dramatically increases the probability that exotic viruses will be brought into the urban human environments of the Americas . . . the tiger mosquito will feed on anything, a rat for example, and then turn right around and feed on a human.'

While *A. albopictus* has been implicated in the transmission of dengue fever, it has, so far, not proved a major public health threat in the USA or Europe. But the situation in non-endemic regions now needs careful surveillance and monitoring, as there have already been a number of imported cases of dengue leading to local outbreaks. In September 2014, Japan reported its first cases of dengue fever in almost seventy years, prompting the immediate closure of Tokyo's popular Yoyogi Park, thought to be the epicentre of the outbreak, followed by rapid implementation of anti-mosquito measures including spraying insecticides and draining its ornamental ponds. The vector in this outbreak was the Asian tiger mosquito, *A. albopictus*.

Indeed, dengue is the classic twenty-first century disease driven by an urban, adapted mosquito and easily transported by infected people or the vector through increasing trade, changing land use and expanding urbanization. The recent spread of two other viruses transmitted by mosquitoes, chikungunya (meaning 'to become contorted', transmitted by *A. aegypti* and *A. albopictus*) and West Nile virus (transmitted by mosquitoes of the genus *Culex*, with a host reservoir in birds) highlight that importation and establishment of vector-borne pathogens outside their current habitat represents a serious danger to the world.

Fortunately, awareness of the global impact of dengue and other mosquito-borne viral diseases is, at last, slowly starting to register. Dengue has been grouped amongst the seventeen or so Neglected Tropical Diseases (NTDs) which warrant serious attention in the twenty-first century. In a 2012 WHO report, 'Global Strategy for Dengue Prevention and Control, 2012–2020', the Director-General of the WHO notes that for decades there has been no concerted action to control and contain dengue, and that given the importance of the global dengue epidemic, with its staggering human and economic costs, an international effort to reduce morbidity and mortality is long overdue. A number of pressing issues and multi-pronged strategies are discussed in the report. Improved outbreak prediction, integrated vector management with larvicides and insecticides, early case detection and rapid supportive clinical therapy for severe cases are high on the agenda. So, too, is the push to find anti-viral drugs as well as an effective vaccine that will protect against all four serotypes, and a number of vaccines are now in various stages of clinical trials.

The challenge for national and international health agencies is to reverse the trend of increasing epidemic dengue activity along with the alarming rise in the incidence of DHF, and to meet the goals of the 2012 report which aim to reduce mortality and morbidity from dengue by 2020 by at least 50 per cent and 20 per cent, respectively. As with other NTDs, however, progress will depend not just on specific targets for dengue and its vectors, but also helping to lift the 'bottom billion' people most affected out of poverty. Radical improvements in sanitation, sewerage, rubbish disposal and collection, as well as broader social and economic conditions such as housing, are desperately needed to fulfil these goals.

Football fever in Brazil

'The FIFA World Cup is a major sporting event. The results for dengue epidemiology, and on the football pitch, will be fascinating. We await both outcomes with interest.' *The Lancet*, May 2014

Prior to the (FIFA) World Cup in Brazil in the summer of 2014, the million or so football fans travelling to attend the matches in twelve different cities were warned of potential outbreaks of dengue fever in Brazil during the competition. Rio de Janeiro had major epidemics of dengue in 2002 and 2008. So overwhelming was the crisis in 2008 that the military had to be called in to fumigate houses and to set up tent hospitals to take in the thousands of patients infected with dengue. Brazil reported 7 million cases between 2000 and 2013, with 1.4 million dengue cases in 2013 alone. Brazil now has the highest incidence of dengue fever in the world. Scientists developed an 'early warning system' to alert authorities to the risk of dengue fever outbreaks during the World Cup, and health experts in Brazil stepped up efforts to eliminate mosquito breeding grounds and raise public awareness. Since then, good news has been reported by Brazil – in September 2014 scientists from the research institute Fiocruz released thousands of mosquitoes infected with bacteria of the *Wolbachia* genus, which acts like a vaccine for dengue-carrying mosquitoes by stopping the dengue virus multiplying in the insect's body. The long-term aim and hope is that all future generations of mosquitoes will carry *Wolbachia* and help prevent the transmission of dengue in Brazil and other countries experimenting with this innovative idea.

Cover up – while waiting for a vaccine

In the meanwhile, the best advice to avoid contracting the disease in endemic dengue regions is to cover up with loose-fitting, light-coloured clothing; avoid mosquito bites by having screened or air-conditioned accommodation; remove any potential 'mosquito-breeding' containers; use tropical-strength insect repellents, such as those containing DEET; and remember that unlike the malarial mosquito, which bites after dusk, *Aedes aegypti* likes to bite by day – especially favouring a few hours after sunrise and a few hours before sunset. It is also important for anyone with unusual symptoms to seek medical assistance immediately. A vaccine to prevent dengue, which poses a risk to almost half the world's population, is now also of pressing urgency.

RABIES

Rabies is an acute viral infection of the central nervous system, transmitted via the saliva of an infected animal. Although rabies has not been responsible for devastating epidemics like cholera and plague, it is one of the most frightening of all diseases, with a case-fatality rate approaching 100 per cent. The very word 'rabies' – from the Latin word meaning 'rage or madness' – conjures up images of 'mad' dogs foaming at the mouth and biting people in a frenzied attack, resulting in horrific symptoms and almost certain death for the victim. There are now effective human and animal vaccines for rabies (following on from Louis Pasteur's remarkable trial of the first rabies vaccine in 1885) and there are very few cases in Europe and the Americas. However, there are still parts of the world where rabies – a 'neglected zoonotic disease' – is a very real danger, and more than 60,000 people die of rabies every year, mostly in Asia and Africa.

∾

In the twenty-third century BC, a legal document, called the Eshnunna Code of Babylon, was drawn up in Mesopotamia. It stipulated the amount of compensation that an owner of a 'mad' dog had to pay in the event that the animal caused the death of a person – forty shekels of silver in most cases, or fifteen shekels if the victim was a slave. Today, in the twenty-first century AD, there are all sorts of strict and costly regulations to ensure that domestic animals are vaccinated or put into quarantine before entering a rabies-free country. In the intervening 4,000 or so years, societies have struggled to understand, contain and prevent rabies. It is a story of insights and dead ends, brilliant scientific discoveries, and worldwide fear.

The bite of a mad dog

In ancient Mesopotamia, China, India, Greece and Rome, the consequences of the bite of a rabid dog were all too familiar. In the classic Indian text, the *Sushruta Samhita*, for example, the author writes that 'a person bitten by a rabid animal barks and howls like the animal by which he is bitten' causing him to lose 'the functions and faculties of a human subject.' There was no cure, and the victim had no chance of survival. The word 'rabies' itself has its origins in ancient languages. In Sanskrit, the word *rabhas* means 'to do violence'. The Greeks used the word *lyssa*, meaning 'frenzy', and so-named after the mythological Greek goddess, Lyssa, who was the spirit of rage, fury, madness and frenzy. In Latin the verb *rabere* means 'to rave', and the associated adjective *rabidus*, 'furious, raging', gives us the term 'rabid.' In French, rabies is *la rage* – depicting it as both a horrible disease and a sort of animalistic fury tinged with madness. In Europe in the Middle Ages, the disease was also known as hydrophobia, meaning 'fear of water'. The words aptly describe the symptoms of this terrible and terrifying disease.

The cause of the human form of the disease – the bite of a rabid animal – was one of the most clearly recognized and dreaded diseases of past times and, indeed, one of the only diseases which was understood to originate in animals (and which we would now call a 'zoonotic' disease). But what caused the dogs and other rabid animals to go 'mad' in the first place? For many Roman and Greek physicians, rabies somehow had to fit into their 'humoral doctrine' of disease, based on the idea that the body was made up of four 'humours' or fluids: black bile, yellow bile, phlegm and blood. When these were in balance, a person remained healthy. But if the humours became unbalanced, disease resulted. All sorts of factors could upset the balance. Animals, it was believed, developed rabies following 'a corruption of the humours', caused possibly by cold, heat, poisoning, stress or, as later suggested, by devouring corpses. The next part of the puzzle was how the bite of a rabid animal transmitted the disease to humans.

In the first century AD, Aulus Celsus (*c.*25 BC–*c.*AD 50), the Roman philosopher and writer, used the word 'virus' in connection with dog bites. In Latin *virus* means 'something slimy and poisonous'. Celsus suggested that if anyone was bitten by a rabid dog, 'the virus must be drawn out with a cupping glass'. As it happens, Celsus had the right word for the infection, though it was also thought that the diseased body produced the 'virus' rather than vice versa and it was not until the 1930s that any 'virus' – a tiny micro-organism that can only reproduce inside another living cell – was actually 'seen', using an electron microscope.

For many centuries, the ideas of the ancients about rabies continued to dominate as well as to confuse and perplex. Some narrowed the cause down to 'contagious seeds' or, more specifically and correctly, to the 'poisonous' saliva in the bite of the rabid animal. The Persian physician Avicenna wrote a remarkable account of the manifestations, course and prognosis of the disease and, while adhering to the idea of an imbalance in the four humours within rabid dogs, wrote that: 'Everyone who eats the remaining part of his [a rabid human's] food or drinks his water becomes rabid' – perhaps recognizing the possibility of transmission through saliva. The Italian physician Girolamo Fracastoro (c.1476/8–1553), who also wrote an epic poem on syphilis and published a book in 1546 entitled *De contagione et contagiosis morbis*, suggested for rabies that: 'Contagion takes place in the blood itself through contact with the teeth and foam from the mouth of the rabid animal.'

In 1735 an anonymous contributor to the *London Magazine* wrote that rabies was transmitted by means of 'minute particles or animalculae mixt with saliva' inserted through a wound into the 'nervous juice', and that these particles then affected the brain. The German scientist Georg Gottfried Zinke (d.1813) published a small book on rabies in 1804 and carried out experiments transmitting rabies from animal to animal to try to find the unknown agent of rabies. The contagion theory was strengthened by experimental studies undertaken in the early nineteenth century by François Magendie (1783–1855) and others in Paris when they reported the transmission of rabies to a dog by inoculation of saliva from a human case. Others questioned the physical nature of the disease, suggesting (incorrectly) that its deadly symptoms were a result of imagination and fear.

We now know that rabies is caused by a virus belonging to the genus lyssavirus. The virus is present in a rabid animal's saliva. It is then communicated to humans either by a bite or scratch or by the infected animal licking a break in the victim's skin. (It cannot cross intact skin.) From the site of entry it travels along the nerve pathways to the brain. Some time after the bite or lick (the incubation period is typically one to three months but may vary from less than a week to over a year) the most horrible symptoms manifest themselves. There are two clinical manifestations of rabies – 'furious' and 'paralytic' rabies.

'Furious' rabies is the most common form, and the infected do, indeed, appear to go 'mad' in all sorts of bizarre ways. They foam at the mouth, become vicious and aggressive, suffer seizures, hallucinations and extreme thirst – but when they try to drink they are crippled by severe muscle spasms in the throat; in spite of their desperate need for water, its very sight can lead to terror, followed by delirium and convulsions. In the end, the victim falls into a coma, and death, when it comes, is often due to cardio-respiratory arrest. 'Paralytic' or 'dumb' rabies runs a less dramatic and usually longer course, but also eventually leads to death. There have only been a handful of recorded cases of a person surviving rabies after the onset of symptoms.

To cure or contain

Over the centuries, physicians searched for ways of curing the terrible scourge – drugs and purges, bloodletting and cauterizing the wound with hot irons, surgically excising tissues around the bite, applying poultry dung or goose grease mixed with honey to the wound, ingesting the liver of mad dogs, subjecting victims to electrical shocks or advising them to jump into the sea – but to no avail. In Korea, medicines were made up using cats as the main ingredient – the idea, possibly, being that the cat medicine would neutralize the dog poison. The 'hair of the dog that bit you' ('like for like') was also used as a popular remedy to treat the wound. The French physician Joseph-Ignace Guillotin (1738–1814), who is more commonly associated with the decapitation device that bears his name, wanted to set up some experiments whereby condemned criminals would be bitten by 'mad' dogs and used experimentally to try out various remedies. The idea was not taken up.

All sorts of regulations were also imposed in an attempt to prevent the spread of the disease. In 1793, Samuel Argent Bardsley (1764–1851), physician to the Manchester Infirmary, presented a scheme for 'extirpating canine madness' from Britain by 'establishing an universal quarantine for dogs within the kingdom, and a total prohibition of the importation of these animals during the existence of such quarantine'. He added: 'Our insular situation is peculiarly favourable for the experiment.' His idea of 'universal quarantine' was taken up much later in the twentieth century.

The Victorians became obsessed with the fear of dog rabies and, although there were only around 1,225 recorded cases of human rabies, or hydrophobia, between 1837 and 1902 in Britain (a low figure by comparison with many other deadly diseases) the threat of 'mad dogs' led to a range of drastic measures to deal with the problem. When rabies was present, posters placed in streets warned citizens of 'MAD DOGS' and 'HYDROPHOBIA'. Laws were passed that required all dogs in public places to be muzzled, and allowed policemen to 'shoot on the spot' any unmuzzled dog. In some places, dogs had their teeth filed down to prevent them inflicting deep bites. In Paris fear of rabies led to 'Great Dog Massacres' sometimes called 'canicides'. The poor working-classes were often victimized as irresponsible for letting stray dogs wander the streets, and dog taxes in England and France were created to discourage ownership amongst the poor. Veterinary and medical professionals, governments, local authorities and the public hotly debated the cause of the disease. Some adhered to the idea that it was 'contagious', others that rabies arose from 'spontaneous generation' or 'aerial miasmas'. Anti-vivisectionists and dog lovers, meanwhile, opposed the draconian policies to cull or muzzle dogs.

With no known effective treatment or understanding of the true cause, finding a solution to dog rabies and its risk to humans attracted widespread attention throughout much of the nineteenth century in Britain, France and elsewhere. As Neil Pemberton and Michael Worboys note in their book *Rabies in Britain: Dogs, Disease and Culture, 1830–2000* (2012): 'potentially rabid dogs lurked everywhere: at home, in the yard and on the street, in the press, in novels, in figures of speech, in popular memory, and in the imagination.'

The terror that led to the treatment

'As the death of this child appeared inevitable, I decided, not without deep and severe unease, as one can well imagine, to try out on Joseph Meister the procedure which had consistently worked on dogs.' Louis Pasteur, describing his decision to attempt to vaccinate a rabies victim in July 1885

In July 1885 the story of rabies control was transformed by a remarkable experiment by the French chemist Louis Pasteur, one of the founders of modern bacteriology. As a young child, after hearing reports of the mutilation and deaths of several people when a 'mad' wolf had rampaged through his village in the Jura Mountains of eastern France, biting people on their hands and faces, he witnessed one victim being brought to the blacksmith's shop for treatment. The sight of a red-hot iron cauterizing the young man's still-frothy wounds is said to have given

Pasteur a lifelong fear of rabies, a fear shared by millions. By 1885, Pasteur already had an international scientific reputation. He had discarded the old notion of 'spontaneous generation' (by which it was thought that decaying meat, for example, spontaneously generated maggots), and had replaced it with the 'germ theory' of disease (in which he proved that it was infectious agents or germs that caused the decay and not the other way round). He had also found a way of eliminating microbes from milk ('pasteurization'), and had developed vaccines for chicken cholera (a disease of poultry) and anthrax. But there was still one thing that he was determined to discover: a treatment for rabies.

In the late 1870s and early 1880s, Pierre Victor Galtier (1846–1908), a professor at the Veterinary School in Lyon, conducted some important experimental studies on rabies using rabbits, leading to the concept that post-bite treatment might be possible. Galtier's publications may well have aroused the interest of Pasteur, and after exhaustive trials on specimens from mad dogs supplied by local vets, Pasteur and a team of researchers in Paris, most notably Émile Roux (1853–1933), eventually developed an experimental attenuated vaccine using the dried spinal cord of rabbits. They found this could protect dogs when later challenged with fresh rabies material. But would it work on humans? On 6 July 1885 a badly bitten little boy from Alsace named Joseph Meister was brought to Pasteur by his distraught mother and Théodore Vone, the owner of the rabid dog. The boy was not expected to live. Pasteur took the chance. Under his supervision, two doctors vaccinated the boy (as Pasteur was not licensed as a medical practitioner he could not give the injections himself) and, after another twelve increasingly stronger injections over a period of ten days, he survived. Meister was the first publically acknowledged successful recipient of Pasteur's vaccine and this was the first 'laboratory' vaccination to make an impact on human history (though according to one historian who has studied Pasteur's notebooks, two previous attempts at rabies inoculation in humans had been made).

In October of the same year, Pasteur successfully vaccinated a second child – Jean-Baptiste Jupille, a fifteen-year-old shepherd boy from Pasteur's home district of the Jura, who had been severely bitten as he tried to protect other children from a rabid dog. Reports of these early successes caused a medical and media sensation, and Pasteur was eulogized in the press as 'a man of genius'. When he offered to give the vaccine freely to any rabies victim, hundreds of patients soon flocked to his laboratory (by then transformed to a 'clinic') in Paris from all around the world, including four boys from Newark, New Jersey, who returned 'cured' in January 1886 to much high-profile publicity.

In spite of his initial successes, there was some scepticism and criticism of Pasteur's experimental vaccine in the medical profession. Even Pasteur had to acknowledge that although he suspected the infective agent of rabies to be 'a microbe of infinite smallness', he could not actually see the microbe in question using the microscopes then available. His discovery of the rabies vaccine, like Edward Jenner's vaccine for smallpox nearly a century earlier, was based on intuition and trial and error (albeit originating in a laboratory and not in a cowshed!), and it was many decades before scientists were able to 'see' the lyssavirus responsible and understand how it acted.

Pasteur's rabies vaccine was, however, different from most vaccines with which we are familiar today. It was not given to prevent the disease but to cure it. The long incubation period of rabies, following the initial bite, meant that vaccination (also known as post-exposure prophylaxis) at an early stage could stop the dreaded symptoms from developing. In 1886, even after the long train ride to Paris to seek the vaccine, sixteen out of nineteen Russian peasants mauled by rabid wolves were apparently saved by Pasteur's injections.

In 1888, with money that poured in from donations, a new scientific research centre was inaugurated in Paris, named the Institut Pasteur as a tribute to the great man's achievements. Joseph Meister went on to become the concierge of the institute (though, tragically, Meister shot himself in 1940 shortly after the outbreak of the Second World War). The Parisian Institut Pasteur served as a flagship for a growing syndicate of Pasteur Institutes worldwide which have carried forward Pasteur's commitment to basic laboratory research and its applications to public health needs for the benefit of all humanity. 'Pasteurians' have made many major breakthroughs in understanding, preventing and controlling infectious diseases – from Alexandre Yersin's 1894 discovery of the plague bacillus (originally called *Pasteurella pestis*) to the 1983 discovery by two Nobel laureates, Françoise Barré-Sinoussi and Luc Montagnier, of the virus (HIV) that causes AIDS.

'Mad dogs and Englishmen'

'In Bangkok at twelve o'clock they foam at the mouth and run,
But mad dogs and Englishmen go out in the midday sun.'

Noël Coward, 1931

Pasteur's post-exposure vaccine, with later refinements, has been instrumental in saving the lives of many rabies victims, provided it is received quickly enough to prevent the onset of symptoms. The control of animal rabies has also remained a high priority, and an anti-rabies vaccine was developed for dogs, as well as for cats, sheep, cattle and horses. While human victims from Britain initially went to Paris to receive their post-exposure shots, Pasteur himself felt that the key strategy for Britain, as an island, should be focused on eradicating canine rabies. In 1886, rabies was added to the Contagious Diseases (Animals) Act, giving central government a leading role in con-trolling the disease and quarantining dogs entering the country. By 1922, Britain was eventually declared free of canine rabies. The last human death from a rabid dog bite in France was a couple of years later. Other nations, including the US, with strict measures of inspection, vaccination, quarantine of pets and control of stray animals, also successfully exterminated canine rabies.

However, the fear of '*la rage*' crossing the Channel from con-tinental Europe to Britain continued to be uppermost in many people's minds. There was also the fear of rabid animals being imported from elsewhere as, by the 1930s, rabies was increas-ingly seen as an exotic tropical disease. When Noël Coward composed his popular song, 'Mad Dogs and Englishmen', as a parody of British colonial society, Britons serving overseas or travelling to parts of Asia would (or should) have been all too aware of the dangers of rabid animals where canine rabies con-tinued (and continues) to be a serious problem.

In order to maintain Britain as a 'rabies-free' island, strict compulsory quarantine measures were kept in place during the twentieth century to prevent rabid animals entering the country. Dogs and other pets entering Britain from overseas would be detained in quarantine for six months, and severe penalties, including imprisonment, would be levied against anyone breaking the law or smuggling in pets. At the time of the opening of the Channel Tunnel in 1994, the main terror in the minds of the British people was not about the invasion of armies or even tourists; it was about rabies. This fear has, so far, not materialized, and the quarantine regulations have since been relaxed following the introduction in the early twenty-first century of the Pet Travel Scheme (PETS) for dogs, cats and ferrets, whose owners have to ensure that they have been tagged with a microchip, vaccinated and carry a pet passport. Travel within countries in the European Union, for example, is now permitted after twenty-one days from the date of the rabies vaccination, though globally there is still variation in the rules (and penalties for breaking the laws) for different countries.

Rabid foxes, chicken heads and oral vaccines

Over the last half century, however, it has not just been a fear of 'mad dogs' carrying rabies from endemic to rabies-free countries, it has also been a fear of rabid wildlife which are not subject to inspection at international border controls. Indeed, although 'mad' dogs are usually singled out as the culprit, as far as human rabies is concerned, dogs and other domestic animals can be infected by bites from feral or wild animals, such as wolves, foxes, jackals, coyotes, raccoons, skunks and mongooses. Such animals may also directly infect humans.

For example, at the time when canine and human rabies had become rare in most of western Europe by the outbreak of the Second World War, in the early 1940s a major animal rabies epizootic (primarily in foxes) was observed in eastern Europe. The epizootic moved westwards at an average speed of 20–40 miles (32–64 km) per year, and nearly reached the English Channel.

The horrors of rabies were featured in the media, with headlines such as 'The deadly virus marching across Europe'.

An ingenious solution was pioneered in central Europe in the 1980s to stop rabies spreading across the continent. Chicken heads containing a live oral rabies vaccine were distributed across the countryside, and foxes, eating the bait, became immune. Since then, millions of vaccine baits have been air-dropped over Europe to eliminate rabies, especially in foxes. Other countries, including Canada and the USA, have also used such techniques to eliminate fox rabies – but the cost of such operations is prohibitive for poorer countries.

Wild carnivores and vampire bats

Another alarming reservoir of rabies was detected in bats during the early twentieth century in Central and South America. Cattle were succumbing to a strange paralytic disease. It was soon realized that they were being infected by blood-sucking (haematophagous) vampire bats. The first human deaths attributed to rabies spread by vampire bats occurred in Trinidad in 1929. Since then there have been a small number of cases of humans being infected directly by vampire and other bats. Victims of bat rabies have even been reported in Europe (including Great Britain), as well as in the USA and Canada. In the Americas bat rabies is now more feared than dog rabies.

One case in the USA made headline news when a young girl, too late to be vaccinated, nearly died of rabies in 2004 after being bitten by a bat in her local church in Wisconsin. Her physician, Rodney Willoughby, desperate to save her life, put her in a controlled, chemically induced coma and administered anti-viral drugs in the hope that this would give her immune system enough time to destroy the virus. She mercifully survived, and this so-called Milwaukee protocol has been the subject of much medical interest as well as controversy.

A new rabies lyssavirus, closely related to but not identical to the classical rabies virus, was identified in the mid-1990s in several species of flying foxes (fruit-eating bats) in Australia, and has been associated with three human deaths from rabies-like illnesses. As with many other diseases with a reservoir in wild mammals, breaking the cycle of transmission is far from easy.

World Rabies Day – breaking the 'cycle of neglect'

'One [rabies patient] in particular made a lasting impression. He was a man who was already in the advanced stages of the disease. What especially got to me was the look of terror in his eyes . . . dabbing his lips with water would trigger terrifying convulsions . . . there was nothing that we could do for him . . .' Joseph B. McCormick and Susan Fisher-Hoch, *The Virus Hunters: Dispatches from the Frontline*, 1996

While cases of canine-, wildlife- and bat-mediated rabies are rare in most developed regions including North America, western Europe, Japan and Australia as well as in a few countries in Latin America, the number of humans infected and killed globally, still remains horribly high. Over 15 to 20 million people receive the post-exposure vaccine every year, and worldwide an estimated 60,000 people, particularly children in poor rural areas, die of the disease, though this is thought to be an underestimate of the true toll. The majority of all human cases occur in Africa and parts of Asia (mainly India and China), and almost all human deaths in these continents follow dog bites for which post-exposure vaccination was not or could not be provided. More than 50 million dogs are vaccinated each year. In Latin America, a canine rabies control programme established in the early 1980s has led to a 90 per cent reduction of rabies in dogs and hence a similar decline in human deaths, showing what can be achieved, but in parts of Asia and Africa the vaccine coverage in the dog population (30–50 per cent) is not yet high enough to break the transmission cycle of the disease.

Rabies is now amongst a group of diseases known as 'neglected zoonotic diseases' and there is a pressing need to strengthen collaboration between the veterinary and medical sectors in the global fight against this still very much feared threat to public health. To put the disease on the world health agenda, the Global Alliance for Rabies Control was launched in 2004, and a 'World Rabies Day' occurs every year on 28 September, the date of Pasteur's death in 1895, to raise aware-ness, generate investment and break the 'cycle of neglect'. The modern post-exposure vaccines, although expensive, are safe and highly effective, and additional treatment with rabies immunoglobulin can be given to save the lives of victims. There are preventive (pre-exposure) vaccines not just for ani-mals but also for people visiting high-risk areas or working closely with potentially rabid animals and bats. Pilot projects to tackle the problem of rabies in a number of endemic regions have recently been launched by the WHO and global health partnerships, with funding from the Gates Foundation. Mass vaccination of dogs, and controlling free-roaming (stray) dogs are the cheapest and ultimate aims of these programmes but, until the disease is eliminated in domestic, stray and wild animal populations, it is imperative that vaccines are made more widely available and accessible, especially for the world's poorest and most vulnerable populations.

It is also worth remembering that not all sick dogs or animals infected by rabies display the typically alarming symptoms of foaming at the mouth and hydrophobia. The form of rabies known as 'dumb' or 'paralytic' rabies leaves the animal or human victim listless and progressively immobile. In avoiding rabid animals, it is important to watch out for *any* strange behaviour, as both the 'furious' and 'dumb' forms can mean an almost certain and agonizing death if a person is bitten and left unvaccinated.

The main advice is to steer clear of any dog or animal behaving bizarrely and to avoid bats such as vampire bats and flying foxes. But, if bitten by a suspect creature, clean the wound as quickly as possible and remember Joseph Meister: seek rapid professional treatment.

POLIO

Polio is a cruel disease that has disabled many people – especially children – over the last century or so. It is caused by an enterovirus transmitted from person to person primarily via the faecal-oral route, by ingesting contaminated food or water. In most cases the infection provokes only a mild illness, but in some cases after the virus multiplies in the intestine it can invade the central nervous system, leading to muscle degeneration and paralysis. Its full scientific name is poliomyelitis, so named because of inflammation of the 'grey matter' of the spinal cord (in Greek, *poliós* means 'grey' and *myelós* means 'marrow'). Polio is probably an ancient disease, but it was not until the late nineteenth and early twentieth centuries that outbreaks of polio attracted serious attention. The first vaccines were developed in the mid-twentieth century, and, although there is no cure for polio, with mass immunization the incidence of polio around the world has fallen dramatically. It now persists only in a few countries, and great hopes have been raised that it could be completely eradicated.

∾

In the summer of 1916 in Brooklyn, New York City, a small child lay sick. She was gasping for air, struggling to take each breath. Her desperate parents had no idea what was wrong. Late that

night, the local doctor was summoned. He held the child's hand
and felt her pulse. She was feverish, delirious and clearly in
intense pain. She began to lose all feeling and movement in her
little legs. She lay on her bed soaked in sweat – listless and apparently almost lifeless. The doctor arranged to take her to hospital.
Her parents were distraught that she was being taken away. She
was admitted as an emergency. She had all the signs and symptoms of poliomyelitis or, as it was then known, 'infantile
paralysis', and she was one of the thousands of cases in the
world's first most serious recorded epidemic of polio in
1916–17.

Infantile paralysis

'Infantile paralysis' in 1916 was a diagnosis without hope,
without treatment, and with no known cause. Many children
died; others spent months in hospital. There was little to be done
but to wait and watch. By 1917, nearly 9,000 cases of infantile
paralysis had been recorded in New York City. Some victims
were left permanently paralyzed, and around 2,400 people,
mostly children, had died. Many of the survivors spent the rest
of their (often short) lives in 'callipers' or braces.

The authorities dealt with the epidemic in ways that were
reminiscent of reactions to bubonic plague in earlier centuries.
Road blocks were imposed to prevent people leaving or entering
the city. Some of the wealthier families fled to the countryside,
but many others who tried to escape the pestilential city were
sent back. In the poorer areas of the city, 'polio houses' and
neighbourhoods were quarantined; warning placards and 'Keep
Out' signs were posted; and sick children were forcibly removed
to isolation hospitals. Dogs and especially cats, as possible

carriers, were abandoned or killed; public places, including playgrounds and swimming pools, were shut or avoided; immigrant families were shunned and blamed, including the Italian community where the epidemic had started in the squalid and unfortunately named Pigtown. The city reeked of disinfectant as officials battled to sanitize and contain the spread of this mysterious summer sickness.

A mysterious disease – ancient or modern?

'Of the essential cause of poliomyelitis nothing is known . . . the origin of most epidemics of endemic contagious diseases, such as scarlet fever, measles, diphtheria, cerebrospinal meningitis and others, is equally mysterious.' Report on Poliomyelitis in the USA, 1918

Across the USA, there were 27,000 cases of polio and over 6,000 deaths between 1916 and 1917. Almost all were children under the age of five. Americans were gripped by fear, panic and, above all, hopelessness. It was a terrifying disease, one that struck young children without warning and inflicted appalling suffering. In the first half of the twentieth century, polio became every American parent's worst nightmare – fear of the disease was all the greater because its cause and means of spread were a mystery.

Polio has probably been around for centuries. An Egyptian stele – an upright stone carving dating from 1580–1350 BC – shows a young priest with a walking stick and a shortened, deformed foot characteristic of polio. Other historical carvings and paintings depict people with withered limbs and children walking with canes at a young age. However, there are very few early descriptions of the disease, so we may never know whether these deformities were caused by polio or some other mysterious affliction.

The first known clinical description of polio was by the British surgeon-apothecary, Michael Underwood (c.1736–1820), who, in 1789, called it 'debility of the lower extremities'. The German physician Jacob von Heine (1800–79) in 1840 named the disease 'infantile spinal paralysis' and provided a comprehensive account of the disease as a specific clinical entity. Over the following decades of the nineteenth century, small and sporadic outbreaks of sudden-onset paralysis affecting children were recorded in Scandinavia, France, England and the USA but for reasons that remain tantalizingly obscure, it seems to have become a serious problem only in the last hundred or so years.

Based on experimental studies in the early twentieth century, notably by the Austrian biologist and physician Karl Landsteiner (1868–1943) – later recipient of a Nobel Prize for his discovery of human blood groups – and Simon Flexner (1863–1946) at the New York City's Rockefeller Institute for Medical Research, it was suggested that the disease was 'contagious'. Landsteiner and his colleague in Vienna, Erwin Popper (1879–1955), were the first to 'isolate' the causative agent of polio. In 1908–9, they injected a monkey with an emulsion made from the spinal cord of a polio victim; they then successfully transferred the polio 'virus' from one monkey to another. Flexner, independently, in 1916 described polio 'germs' that he and colleagues had 'seen' under the microscope as 'innumerable bright dancing points, devoid of definite size and form'. The infectious agent of polio seemed to belong to a group of newly identified 'filterable viruses', which could pass through porcelain filters and could be experimentally transferred to live animals but, unlike bacteria, could not, at the time, be grown in laboratory cultures.

Moreover, during the 1916–17 epidemic in the USA – the most serious epidemic that the world had then ever known – no one really knew how the infectious agent or this so-called filterable virus spread. Was it through the air or through water and food? There was no shortage of theories, from both medical and lay people. Some blamed summer fruits, ice creams, candy, maggots in the colon, insects, raw sewage, garbage, dust, poisonous caterpillars, cats, blood-sucking bed bugs, mouldy flour, contaminated milk bottles or even bananas infected by tarantula spiders. Others advised parents to avoid close contact with their children, believing the disease to be transmitted through sneezing, coughing, spitting and kissing.

Dirt, disease and the danger of the housefly

In the USA and Europe in the late nineteenth and early twentieth centuries, polio was predominantly a disease of the summer months. Drawing parallels with cholera, typhoid and other 'filth diseases', doctors linked polio with 'dirty' environments and insanitary conditions, especially in hot, smelly summers. Initially, in the wake of the New York epidemic, as noted above, immigrant ghettos and slum areas were targeted as the likely source of the disease. But in the summer of 1916 it became clear that the epidemic, while striking hardest at the young, affected both rich and poor, long-time residents as well as recent immigrants.

The association between dirt and disease was extended to the idea that maybe the ubiquitous housefly carried the germs of polio – from filth to food, from the allegedly 'dirty' immigrant quarters to the so-called sparkling 'clean' houses of the leafy suburbs. Discoveries in the field of tropical medicine in the late nineteenth and early twentieth centuries had shown that mosquitoes, fleas, flies and lice could transmit diseases like malaria, yellow fever, plague, sleeping sickness and typhus. The housefly was everywhere, buzzing on the piles of horse dung in the streets of New York, swarming in the garbage cans, then alighting on babies or, seemingly, infecting food. A letter from a social worker during the 1916 New York epidemic, reprinted in a New York newspaper, depicted a tragic scenario:

> In one house I went into the only window was not only shut, but the cracks were stuffed with rags, so that the 'disease' could not come in. You can imagine what the dark, dirty room was like; the babies had no clothes on, and were so wet and hot that they looked as if they had been dipped in oil, and the flies were sticking all over them . . . I had to tell the mother I would get the Board of Health after her to make her open the window, and now if any of the children do get infantile paralysis she will feel that I killed them.

Attacking the housefly became a major preoccupation. Garbage bins were sealed, houses were screened, windows shut, flyswatting contests were held, while posters and pamphlets featured images of giant houseflies menacing the children of the city. One newspaper in 1916 showed a picture of a fly grinning evilly at a child accompanied by the lines:

I am the Baby Killer!
I come from garbage-cans uncovered.
From gutter pools and filth of streets,
From stables and backyards neglected,
Slovenly homes – all manner of unclean places.
I love to crawl on babies' bottles and baby lips;
I love to wipe my poison feet on open food
In stores and markets patronized by fools.

We now know that the housefly is capable of carrying over a hundred pathogens and may have played an indirect role in the mechanical transfer of the poliovirus from faeces to food. However, unlike some insects, flies are not hosts in the way that the yellow fever virus or the malaria parasite infects and replicates inside mosquitoes. Indeed, polio has no known vector or animal reservoir. It is spread primarily through contaminated water, food or unwashed hands. The polio enterovirus enters the body through the mouth, is ingested and passes into the gut. It is shed in the faeces, and can then infect those with poor sanitary facilities or inadequate hygiene. This pathway of transmission is known as the faecal-oral route. A high proportion of the population who are infected with the virus develop a mild fever or show no symptoms but can act as carriers (an observation that was first made in Sweden early in the twentieth century). The 1916 campaign in New York, involving quarantine, cleansing and disinfecting, arose out of desperation and uncertainty, but in retrospect some measures were not far off the mark.

A famous victim

In a minority of people, for reasons still not fully understood, the virus moves from the intestinal tract into the bloodstream and then invades the central nervous system (the brain and spinal cord) where it causes serious damage, leading to muscle weakness, paralysis, respiratory failure and sometimes death. In the early decades of the twentieth century, finding a way of helping those who survived 'infantile paralysis' was as problematic as understanding its cause. Some doctors recommended heavy massaging and exercising affected limbs, while others suggested putting them into plaster casts or callipers, recommending long periods of immobility to prevent deformities. Various experimental therapies such as lumbar puncture and injections of anti-polio blood serum were tried out in hospitals. Bloodletting with leeches, cupping, purgatives and blistering agents were methods that harked back to ancient times. Home remedies and preventions included anything from 'earthworm oil' to bathing in 'ox blood'.

Heart-rending images of children crippled by infantile paralysis and confined in solitary isolation became all too familiar, but when in the summer of 1921 a prominent member of a wealthy New York family was struck down with polio, it became clear that the disease could strike anyone, no matter how old or how privileged. The victim was Franklin Delano Roosevelt (1882–1945), a rising star in the Democratic Party, and later four-times president of the USA. Roosevelt, then aged thirty-nine, had been taking his summer vacation on the island of Campobello, off the coast of New Brunswick and Maine, when, on the night of 10 August 1921, he was suddenly struck by the disease.

Roosevelt survived, but was paralyzed from the waist down, and for the rest of his life he battled with his pain and disabilities. In 1924 a therapeutic visit to a rundown spa at Warm Springs, Georgia, inspired him to purchase the facility and to open its doors to polio patients from all over the country. He also began to put the needs of the disabled on the political agenda.

Some historians have recently speculated that Roosevelt suffered from Guillain-Barré syndrome, another neuro-muscular disorder, but others have argued that whether Roosevelt had polio or not is historically irrelevant – his doctors believed he had polio, so did Roosevelt and so did the nation – and it was this diagnosis which propelled subsequent events in polio care and research.

The March of Dimes

'We have a gospel to preach. We need to make America "polio conscious" to the end that the inexcusable case of positive neglect will be entirely eliminated.' Franklin Delano Roosevelt, 1932

As president of the United States from 1933 until his death in 1945, Roosevelt shouldered many burdens, first taking upon himself the task of mitigating the worst effects of the Great Depression, and then leading his country through the Second World War. He also had his own physical disability to cope with, but this was one thing he was determined to hide from the press and the public: as far as we know, there are very few pictures of him seated in his wheelchair. While hiding his affliction, he remained deeply committed to finding a way of helping his fellow sufferers.

Roosevelt recognized that more money was needed to transform his spa facility in Georgia into a hydrotherapy and rehabilitation centre for those suffering the effects of polio. Fund-raising for the Georgia Warm Springs Foundation began on 30 January 1934, his birthday. At the suggestion of his political ally, Henry L. Doherty, this took the form of a 'President's Birthday Ball'. Events were held simultaneously across the nation under the motto of 'We dance so others will walk.' Over a million dollars was raised from the 600 balls held that first night, and the money was channelled into rebuilding Warm Springs. The Birthday Balls became a highly successful annual event. What started out as Roosevelt's personal mission at Warm Springs became in 1938 the National Foundation for Infantile Paralysis (NFIP), whose aim was to 'lead, direct, and unify the fight against every aspect of the killing and crippling infection of poliomyelitis'.

Roosevelt's former law partner, Basil O'Connor, became director of the newly founded NFIP, and further fund-raising initiatives were launched, most notably the 'March of Dimes' – a catch phrase for the polio crusade dreamt up by the entertainer Eddie Cantor, a take-off of the news feature, 'March of Time', shown at film theatres of that era. Cantor took to the air on his radio show to urge everyone to send their dimes (10 cents) to the President at the White House to fight polio. Soon the tiny donations from many Americans started to build up, and between 1938 and 1962 the March of Dimes raised $630 million. This was the first and largest public health organization in the USA to rely on the general public for funds.

Celebrities including Judy Garland, Humphrey Bogart and Mickey Rooney took part in the campaign by starring in powerful short films on the dangers of polio and pushing the NFIP into the nation's consciousness. One propaganda film, *The Daily Battle*, features a nearly invisible figure leaning on a crutch. This figure, known colloquially as 'The Crippler', stalks the land intoning the sinister but true words: 'And I'm *especially* fond of children.' Luckily the young actress, Nancy Davis (later better known as Nancy Reagan) comes to the rescue and beats back 'The Crippler'.

The Foundation did much to provide long-term care for sufferers and to promote awareness of the disease, and was subsequently also instrumental in funding research for the development of a vaccine. In the meantime, others were also working towards finding a solution for those 'crippled' by this devastating paralytic disease.

Iron lungs

'Escaping the city's heat entirely and being sent off to a summer camp in the mountains or the countryside was considered a child's best protection against catching polio ... so the privileged lucky ones disappeared from the city for the summer while the rest of us remained behind to do exactly what we shouldn't ... unmindful of how our imprudence might be dooming any one of us to lifelong incarceration in an iron lung ...' From Philip Roth's 2010 novel, *Nemesis*, set in Newark, New Jersey, in 1944

The thermal baths at Warm Springs were a therapeutic treat for those with limited mobility. The most seriously affected polio survivors, whose respiratory muscles were paralyzed, experienced severe breathing and swallowing difficulties, and for them life hung in the balance. In the late 1920s, Philip Drinker (1894–1972) and Louis Agassiz Shaw (1886–1940) at Harvard School of Public Health, Boston, developed an airtight chamber that pushed air in and out of an immobilized polio patient's lungs. In 1928, a young girl at Boston Children's Hospital became the first to use this so-called 'iron lung'. Commercial production of this large, cumbersome, expensive and noisy device in which the patient was placed horizontally, and which pushed and pulled the chest muscles to make them work in order to aid artificial respiration, began a few years later.

A cheaper model, known as the 'Both Respirator', was designed by an Australian, Edward Both (1908–87). One of Both's machines was given to British industrialist William Morris (1877–1963), best known for his Oxford Morris motor cars. Morris (then Lord Nuffield) was so impressed with this design that in 1938, on hearing a plea for an iron lung on the radio, he turned over half his car factory shop floor to producing these 'iron lungs' and offered to donate them to any hospital in Britain and the British empire that requested one; nearly 2,000 Both-Nuffield respirators were distributed.

Patients who were confined to iron lungs to aid breathing were sometimes known as 'responauts'. One patient vividly remembers a night in the early 1950s when suddenly the harsh hum of the iron lungs ceased. The night nurse had tripped over the cable that supplied power to the machines, and those encased within their iron lungs gasped for breath. The nurse quickly switched the power back on, and the 'swooshing and pulsing sounds' of the iron lungs – the familiar background noise of polio wards – returned.

For some patients, the iron lung provided temporary assistance, giving them much-needed time to recover their own respiratory muscle power. Others found themselves condemned to spend the rest of their lives in this fearsome and isolating experience. Many people put into the machine never survived. Gareth Williams, in his book *Paralysed with Fear: The Story of Polio* (2013), has summed up the experience of the iron lung: 'At its best it was a life-saver and a sanctuary from the panic of suffocation. At its worst, it was a terrible tomb in which to die.'

In Copenhagen in 1952, during one of the worst recorded polio epidemics in Europe, a shortage of iron lungs inspired the invention of an alternative method of artificial respiration. This involved making a surgical cut in the patient's trachea or windpipe (tracheotomy) and ventilating the patient using tubes and rubber bags. Some 1,500 medical students took their turn in assisting with the 'bagging method', devoting over 165,000 hours to saving the lives of many small children during the course of the epidemic.

Today, the iron lung (a negative pressure device) has mostly been replaced by the positive pressure ventilator, but it is still in use in some countries – an iconic symbol of the devastation and fear wrought by polio.

Sister Kenny

Iron lungs, tracheotomies, crutches, braces, splints and casts were all used with the best of intentions, albeit immobilizing patients and restricting the use of their paralyzed limbs. In the 1930s Sister Elizabeth Kenny (1880–1952), a colourful and imposing lady from the Australian outback, pioneered an alternative approach to try to get polio survivors back on their feet. In 1933, she opened her first clinic in Townsville, Queensland, for the care of polio victims, and in 1940 went to the United

States with the aim of revolutionizing the treatment of polio, establishing the Sister Kenny Institute in Minneapolis, Minnesota.

She was staunchly opposed to the orthodox treatment of extended immobility. Her 'Kenny method', which combined physical and psychological techniques, involved hot packs, gentle 'retraining' of muscles, optimism and determination. Even toddlers were expected to be 'active and knowledgeable participants in muscle exercises'. Her therapies were based on distinctive ideas about polio as not solely a neurological disease but also one that affected muscles and skin.

For the lucky patients for whom this method seemed to work it was close to a miracle, enabling them to reuse their weakened limbs with perhaps only the aid of a walking stick, so giving them a new lease of life. Sister Kenny's methods were popular with the public and at times controversial with the medical profession but, until her death, she kept up her message that it was vital to 'remind the brain how to walk'. In 1952, a Gallup poll identified Sister Kenny as the most admired woman in America.

Polio vaccines – Salk's shot and Sabin's sugar lump

In the year of Sister Kenny's death in 1952, the USA was once more hit by a major outbreak of polio. Some 58,000 people were afflicted: 3,000 died and another 21,000 were left paralyzed. As other classic scourges such as cholera and plague had receded in Western nations, the unpredictable outbreaks of polio left people gripped in fear. Epidemics of poliomyelitis featured ever more frequently in newsreels, with images of 'crippled' children supported by crutches or incarcerated in iron lungs. Tried and tested public health measures seemed powerless to prevent the disease. And while antibiotics were revolutionizing the treatment of bacterial infections, attempts to find a remedy for viral diseases, including polio, eluded the scientific community. There was not, and perhaps never will be, a cure for polio. But could scientists come up with a vaccine?

Early twentieth-century experimental studies by Landsteiner, Flexner and others had laid the foundation for the knowledge of the cause of polio, but over the succeeding decades many aspects of the polio 'virus' had remained a mystery. Indeed, mistaken ideas about how the virus spread within the community, as well as within the human body, had impeded the development of a vaccine or, at worst, led to the development of premature and potentially dangerous vaccines. To complicate (or, in the long run, significantly, help) matters, Australian researchers Frank Macfarlane Burnet (1899–1985) and Jean Macnamara (1899–1968) had discovered in the early 1930s that there was more than one type of the poliovirus. Three distinct varieties of poliovirus were subsequently identified, so that a successful vaccine would need to include all three 'serotypes' of poliovirus.

The difficulties of growing the virus in the laboratory had also hampered research endeavours. However, a major breakthrough in polio research came in 1948–9. John Enders, Thomas Weller (1915–2008) and Frederick Robbins (1916–2003) at the Children's Medical Center in Boston, Massachusetts, succeeded in growing the poliovirus in non-neurological human tissue in the laboratory – a discovery that set the stage for the development of a vaccine and led to a shared Nobel Prize for Physiology or Medicine in 1954.

Funds raised by Roosevelt's March of Dimes and the National Foundation for Infantile Paralysis (NFIP) had mostly been diverted to the care of survivors. By the early 1950s, the time was ripe to invest more into the search for a vaccine. Fear and hope fuelled the endless flow of dollars for the Foundation's cause, and it backed the researches of a number of scientists who were by then in a competitive race to come up with a polio vaccine. And, indeed, in 1955 the USA celebrated the success of the first large-scale immunization of over 400,000 children with a safe and effective vaccine. The man who had developed the vaccine, supported by the NFIP, was the American virologist Jonas Salk (1914–95), working at the University of Pittsburgh, Pennsylvania.

Salk had first tested his prototype vaccine in 1952 on 'volunteers', including himself, his laboratory staff and family, as well as on children in residential institutions. Salk's vaccine was based on an inactivated (i.e. 'killed') poliovirus administered by injection. In 1954, the inactivated polio vaccine (IPV) was tested in a double-blind trial involving nearly 1.8 million schoolchildren (known as the 'Polio Pioneers'), with some receiving the vaccine, others a placebo and the rest acting as unvaccinated controls. When the results of the successful trial were announced on 12 April 1955, church bells pealed throughout the US, the media covered the 'story of the year', and Salk became a national hero overnight. The Salk vaccine was quickly licensed for use in the US.

But, as with so many stories in the history of medicine, it was not all was plain sailing. As a number of companies rolled out the vaccine, children who had been administered a vaccine prepared by the Cutter Laboratories in California were struck down with polio, leading to several thousand cases of the disease and ten deaths. It was soon realized that the 'vaccine' contained virulent, non-attenuated poliovirus. A storm of controversy followed the 'Cutter Incident' in the USA, and Salk was devastated by the tragedies. However, with further safety and inspection checks on the production of the vaccine, Salk weathered the storm; his vaccine programme was resumed and cases of polio plummeted in the US.

Meanwhile, other scientists had been working on vaccines based on a 'live' attenuated virus. Rivalry between supporters of the two different approaches to polio vaccines ('killed' versus 'live') flared up into one of the great feuds in medical history, with the players in the saga either at each others' throats or not on speaking terms. Hilary Koprowski (1916–2013), an American virologist, was the first to develop and test a live-attenuated vaccine, though his experimental vaccine lost out to his competitors and his field trials in the then Belgian Congo in the 1950s later (and sadly for Koprowski) became the subject of an erroneous and unsubstantiated claim that connected his vaccine to the origin of HIV/AIDS. It was, however, another American scientist, Albert Sabin (1906–93), who became the leading figure on the scene, displacing his rivals' vaccines with his own oral live poliovirus vaccine.

Sabin, based at the University of Cincinnati, Ohio, and also funded by the NFIP, conducted trials on a range of subjects, including his own family and prisoners in federal penitentiaries, followed by a large-scale immunization of several million children in the Soviet Union and Czechoslovakia in collaboration with Mikhail Chumakov (1909–93), director of Moscow's Polio Research Institute. Eventually, by the early 1960s, it was Sabin's oral polio vaccine (OPV), which was more easily administered than Salk's IPV, that became the accepted standard in most countries (much to Salk's chagrin). On 'Sabin Sundays', about 100 million Americans received the vaccine free of charge, and the decline in polio, already underway during the Salk programme, continued. By 1979 there were no further cases of paralytic polio caused by endemic transmission of 'wild' poliovirus in the US.

Sabin's OPV, delivered by child-friendly cherry-flavoured syrup or on a simple lump of sugar impregnated with the live attenuated poliovirus, was subsequently instrumental in all but eliminating the disease in the rest of the world.

On the verge of global eradication?

'In the same way that during my Microsoft career I talked about the magic of software, I now spend my time talking about the magic of vaccines.' Bill Gates, 2011

While both the Salk IPV vaccine (in the initial years) and the Sabin OPV vaccine (in subsequent years) dramatically reduced the threat of polio in much of the Western world, there were many countries that continued to be blighted by the disease. In the early 1970s, at a time when vaccinations against numerous childhood diseases were becoming routine in the developed world, there was a growing feeling that these benefits to children's health could and should be extended to the world's poorest nations. In 1974, the WHO set up an Expanded Programme on Immunization (EPI) initially targeting six vaccine-preventable diseases – measles, polio, tuberculosis, diphtheria, tetanus and pertussis (whooping cough) – with the goal of immunizing 80 per cent of the world's infants by 1990.

The EPI has, in many respects, been highly successful but in the late 1980s 'wild' polio was still endemic in over 125 countries on five continents, paralyzing more than 1,000 children every day. Its highest incidence was in the Indian subcontinent, and children crippled by polio begging on crutches on the streets of Calcutta (Kolkata), Delhi and other Indian cities was a common and haunting sight. A further major international effort was needed to combat polio using the OPV, which had proved to be safe, effective and simple to administer. In 1988, following the success of smallpox eradication in 1979, the World Health Assembly, inspired by Rotary International, passed a resolution to eradicate polio by the year 2000 so that 'no child will ever again know the crippling effects of polio'.

This marked the launch of the Global Polio Eradication Initiative (GPEI), spearheaded by national governments, the WHO, Rotary International, the US Centers for Disease Control and UNICEF, with further funding from private donors including the Gates Foundation – the largest public-private health initiative the world has ever seen. Underpinning the effort has been a global network of more than 20 million volunteers who have collectively immunized more than 3 billion children since the initiative began, as well as offering other health benefits, such as Vitamin A, which helps children to fend off a range of infections. As part of the GPEI, special 'National Immunization Days' have been held and in remote and war-torn localities; 'Days of Tranquility' have also been negotiated so that the vaccine teams – using all manner of transport from donkeys to motorbikes to helicopters – can reach children living in conflict zones. Amongst the countless and dedicated members of the polio eradication programme was Ali Maow Maalin, the last person in the world to be infected naturally with smallpox in 1977. Following his own lucky survival, Maalin became an advocate for vaccination and devoted his remaining years (he died in 2013) to playing an instrumental role as a district polio officer in his home country of Somalia.

Although the goal of global eradication was not reached by the turn of the millennium, the achievements of the GPEI have been nothing short of amazing. In 1994, the WHO Region of the

Americas was certified polio-free, followed by the Western Pacific Region in 2000, and the European Region in 2002. Even more remarkable was the announcement in March 2014 that the WHO South-East Asia Region had been certified polio-free, meaning that transmission of wild poliovirus has been interrupted in this bloc of eleven countries stretching from Indonesia to India. The eradication of polio from India, especially, is a tremendous success story and has been hailed as a 'historic milestone'. Long recognized as one of the most difficult places in which to eradicate polio, India stands as an example of how to mount a successful disease response effort under the most complex circumstances, and owes much to the tireless efforts of millions of vaccinators.

In 2014, there are only three countries with endemic polio – Afghanistan, Pakistan and Nigeria – recording a total of some 160 cases in 2013, with an additional 256 cases in non-endemic countries (this compares to a global total of 350,000 cases in 1988). However, it is these last remaining hotspots that are proving difficult to tackle – conflicts, suspicion of the vaccine, religious objections and many other political, logistical and cultural factors confound the efforts of dedicated vaccinators.

To further strengthen the programme, the GPEI has launched a new and intensified Polio Eradication and Endgame Strategic Plan 2013–2018, as well as a Global Polio Eradication Emergency Action Plan to try to reach every last child with the polio vaccine and secure a polio-free world. (Ironically, given the mid-twentieth century battles over whose vaccine was best, there has recently been a switch back to using Salk's 'inactivated' vaccine rather than Sabin's 'live' polio vaccine. This is to prevent the rare risk of vaccine-derived cases of polio. Current trials are now underway using both types of vaccine to boost immunity.)

But there are still hurdles to overcome. Especially worrying has been the recent spread of imported polio to formerly polio-free countries, including Syria, embroiled in civil conflict. In May 2014, the WHO declared polio as a public health emergency of international concern, with fears of the renewed spread of polio across country borders.

Polio puzzles and post-polio syndrome

While polio remains on 'the verge of eradication', there are still a number of unresolved puzzles about the disease. A curious feature of polio is why one in 200 infections leads to irreversible paralysis while many of those infected with the virus have no symptoms at all, and the rest only a mild fever. This varying severity may depend on the virulence of the polio strain, genetic factors, immune deficiency, or possibly excessive muscular activity while the disease is incubating or during its early onset. For those seriously disabled by the disease, 'Why me?' is a haunting question with no obvious answers.

Another puzzle is why, over the course of the first half of the twentieth century, polio in the West became associated with increased prosperity and cleanliness. A disease spread by the faecal-oral route that flourished at a time of improved hygiene is something of an epidemiological paradox. It has been suggested that over the past two millennia infants were constantly exposed to the poliovirus in areas of poor sanitation and, while developing a mild fever, they were able to build up lifelong immunity. Maternal antibodies may also have protected babies. Only when general standards of hygiene and public health improved did the mild form of the disease cease to be a constant part of life so that, when it did strike, children and adolescents had little early exposure, and thus little or no immunity. While this might explain the long-term historical evolution of polio, the disease today is most rapidly spread in areas without adequate sanitation.

For those who survived but were seriously affected by polio in the pre-vaccination era, life has often been a struggle. Some polio survivors have been dependent on long-term care, but many have faced the aftermath of this crippling disorder with resilience and strength. For them there was always the reassurance that, unlike diseases such as multiple sclerosis and muscular dystrophy, polio was not a progressive disorder.

In the late 1970s a disturbing and unexpected trend began to appear. A number of people who had suffered from polio in the past began to experience alarming symptoms of severe fatigue, muscle weakness and a range of debilitating, polio-like symptoms. Some, who had been able to function with the aid of canes or crutches, now found their mobility severely limited. This is known as post-polio syndrome (PPS) or late effects of polio (LEP). Various theories have been proposed to explain PPS, though it is not believed to be related to persistence of the virus itself. The condition remains something of a mystery.

The final 'push' . . .

Polio was once a disease feared worldwide, striking suddenly and paralyzing mainly children for life. Today, the story of polio is not yet finished. There are still many children and adults living with the consequences of paralytic polio, and polio represents one of the greatest causes of disability worldwide. While the disease now survives in only a few places amongst the world's poorest, war-torn and most marginalized communities, it continues to stalk vulnerable children, and the threat of it spreading to parts of the 'polio-free' world remains high on the agenda of global health agencies.

If the goal of global eradication can be reached in the coming years, it will be the second major viral infectious disease, following smallpox, to be wiped off the face of the Earth and a triumph for all who have been part of the 'polio story'. If the last cases cannot be eliminated (99.9 per cent victory is not enough, as extinction must be absolute), it will be one of the most expensive and saddest missed historical opportunities of the early twenty-first century. We can only hope that with concerted international efforts in this final 'push' towards eradication, the spectre of 'The Crippler' will no longer haunt the dreams of the world's children.

INFLUENZA

Influenza – commonly referred to simply as 'flu' – is a highly infectious viral disease that affects the respiratory tract. Many winter and spring outbreaks of 'seasonal' influenza have been recorded over the past 500 or so years, but it is the pandemics – those that are global in scale – that have created the greatest mystery and misery. The disease was called influenza in the eighteenth century because it was assumed that some heavenly 'influence' must be at work in striking so many people over such vast areas in a short space of time. The 1918–19 pandemic (the so-called Spanish flu) killed at least 50 million people across the globe – the highest death toll of any single pandemic in the annals of human history. In the late twentieth century, it was feared that a new and highly pathogenic strain, known as 'avian' or 'bird flu', might result in a similar global catastrophe. So far, this has not happened, though the 'swine flu' pandemic of 2009, during which the virus was readily transmitted from person to person through airborne droplets and spread rapidly around the world and resulted, according to recent estimates, in the deaths of approximately 200,000 people. Influenza is one of the world's most intractable viruses and, whether in its seasonal or pandemic forms, remains a major public health challenge.

∽

In 1918–19, as undertakers around the world worked to bury the millions of people who had died from influenza in what has been described as 'the greatest single demographic shock that the human species has ever received', children sang this ditty:

> *I had a little bird*
> *And its name was Enza*
> *I opened a window*
> *And in-flu-enza.*

So often, when we feel ill, we say we have 'a touch of flu', and, until quite recently, a trip to the doctor with a bit of a fever might have been met with a shrug and the response, 'It's just a virus.' A bout of flu, which is usually spread from person to person by coughing and sneezing or touching infected objects, can be miserable – involving aches and pains, a high fever, a head cold, a runny nose, a cough and a sore throat – but may need no more than a week in bed, plenty of fluids and a lot of handkerchiefs. But some types of influenza, as in 1918–19, can be much more serious – indeed deadly. And for centuries there was no cure, no vaccine and no real understanding of how this complex disease could so quickly infect large numbers of people right across the world, with – at times – such catastrophic consequences.

A blast of the stars

In April 1658, after an exceptionally cold winter, a 'distemper' suddenly arose in many parts of the world. The English physician Thomas Willis (1621–75) said it was as if:

it was sent by some blast of the stars, which laid hold on very many together, that in some towns, in the space of a week above a thousand people fell sick together. The particular symptom of this disease, which invaded the sick, as a troublesome cough, with great spitting, also a catarrh falling down on the palate, throat and nostrils: also it was accompanied, with a feverish distemper, joined with heat and thirst, want of appetite, a spontaneous weariness and a grievous pain in the back and limbs ... such as were indued with an infirm body, or men of a more declining age, that were taken with this disease, not a few died of it; but the more strong, and almost all of an healthful constitution recovered.

The disease was widespread, and it was said that 'a third part of mankind almost was "distempered" with the same in the space of a month'.

An epidemic in the winter of 1732–3 was described as 'the most universal disease upon record'. It visited every country in Europe and raged in America and the Caribbean. 'The uniformity of the symptoms of the disease in every place was most remarkable', wrote the Scottish physician, John Arbuthnot (1667–1735). And in 1781–2, within the short space of six weeks, some three-quarters of the British population was infected by another epidemic, which also reached the Americas and many parts of the known world.

This 'universal' distemper was called by a number of names, including 'the hot or epidemic catarrh' or 'epidemic catarrhal fever'. Seasonal or more localized attacks were often described as 'the fashionable cold', 'simple catarrhal fever', 'vernal' or 'spring fever'. The French called the contagion *la grippe* (from the verb *agripper*, meaning 'to grasp or seize'). The Italians, however, had come up with the name by which we now know the disease: influenza. The original Italian phrase was *una influenza*. Its Latin equivalent was *influentia coeli*, which literally meant 'heavenly influence', as it was believed that some ominous celestial configuration of the planets and stars might account for this seemingly mysterious disease. The English adopted the word 'influenza' in the mid-eighteenth century and, like their Italian counterparts, thought that some 'blast of the stars' could be the only explanation for the sudden and widespread global visitations. Curiously, perhaps by coincidence, there is also a similar-sounding Arabic phrase, *anfal-'anza*, which means 'the nose of a she-goat': female goats were once thought to be carriers of disease.

Influenza is probably an ancient disease which was first spread when humans started to settle down into farming and urban communities some 10,000 or so years ago. The virus may have 'jumped' from wild birds to domestic fowl and then to pigs and humans, though early outbreaks are hard to document. Possibly the first influenza 'epidemic' (affecting a large number of people) in Europe was in AD 1173. As Europeans discovered the New World, Native Americans in 1493 on the island of Hispaniola were hit by an epidemic which is now thought by some historians to have been a 'swine' influenza virus carried by pigs aboard Columbus' ships. In 1510, and again in 1580, a disease described as a 'gasping oppression' was observed to spread along the trade routes from Asia to Africa and then 'attacked at once and raged all over Europe not missing a family and scarce a person'. These are said to be the first unequivocal descriptions of influenza pandemics.

In the fifteenth and sixteenth centuries a strange and

mysterious disease called the 'sweating sickness' or 'English sweat', with horribly foul symptoms and causing rapid death, erupted on several occasions and then apparently 'vanished'. Some historians have wondered whether this might have been influenza, but it still remains one of the great puzzles of historical epidemiology

A mysterious but not very dangerous disease?

By the seventeenth and eighteenth centuries, physicians, like Thomas Willis, who documented the outbreaks were struck by the way the disease targeted the weak, aged and infirm. While countless numbers were sick and the disease 'scarce spared any one family', it was noted that the infection was very often only fatal to 'consumptive old men, asthmatics, cachetic, phlegmatic, gross bodied, plethoric people' or those recently afflicted with one of the many other fevers around at the time. The healthy and robust fell sick, but generally survived. Bleeding, rest and nourishing food were variously recommended in terms of treatment.

Over the course of the nineteenth century, recurrent waves of influenza continued to 'explode' at unpredictable intervals or times of year. The disease was rarely life-threatening, unless complicated by bronchitis or pneumonia, though as one nineteenth-century cartoon from the periodical *Punch*, entitled 'The Prevailing Epidemic', reminded sufferers: 'Ah! You may laugh, my boy; but it's no joke being funny with the influenza!' The first recorded epidemics and global pandemics of influenza – from the sixteenth to the nineteenth century – gave rise to many puzzles about its origin and mode of transmission, especially in the days before people were able to travel around the world by rapid means of transportation. Influenza in its brief visitations caused misery, suffering and sometimes death, especially amongst the elderly, but overall it did not seem as dangerous or frightening as some of the other great plagues, poxes and pestilences of the past. All this was to change at the end of the nineteenth and early twentieth century.

The Russian flu of 1889–1893 – panic and hysteria

In the autumn of 1889, an outbreak of influenza was reported in St Petersburg in Russia. This so-called 'Russian flu' proved to be exceptionally virulent and widespread, rapidly progressing in a westward direction. Its transcontinental spread from one European capital to another was linked to the railway system and, by the following spring, influenza had laid low hundreds of millions of people. Via shipping connections, the disease reached North America. It is estimated that around a million people worldwide died in this pandemic as it erupted in waves over the next few years. In Britain alone, it is thought that 110,000 people perished between 1889 and 1893, including the Duke of Clarence, second in line of succession to the British throne, who succumbed to influenza in 1892, aged just twenty-eight years.

Although the overall mortality rate of the Russian flu was probably less than one per cent of all those who were infected, its near instantaneous reporting via the worldwide telegraphic network meant that its impact was tracked in 'real time'. As Mark Honigsbaum in his book, *A History of the Great Influenza Pandemics: Death, Panic and Hysteria, 1830–1920* (2013), has shown, the pandemic had an 'unusual grip on the Victorian imagination'. At the time, scientists had no real idea of the 'cause' of the disease but the tone of many of the newspaper reports, for example in Britain, was both 'alarmist' and 'sensational'. The sense of shared suffering and danger was, moreover, sustained by the promotion of patent medicine manufacturers of quack 'cure-alls'. The 'Carbolic Smoke Ball' (which released a puff of acidic smoke into a tube inserted into the nostril of the user – to expel 'germs') was one of many remedies that was presented as a panacea that would 'positively cure' influenza within twenty-four hours, as well as some sixteen other diseases (and could even prevent snoring!).

While the Russian flu attracted immediate newspaper coverage (indeed, news of the outbreak in St Petersburg reached British journalists within twenty-four hours) and led to fear, panic and even hysteria, the next global influenza pandemic – the so-called Spanish flu of 1918–19 which went on to destroy millions of people in their prime of life – was, initially, according to one newspaper at the time, 'stoically accepted'.

A forgotten pandemic?

In 1976 the medical historian Alfred Crosby wrote a book on the history of influenza called *Epidemic and Peace, 1918* (later reissued as *America's Forgotten Pandemic: The Influenza of 1918*). For historians this was a grim reminder that the 1918–19 influenza pandemic was one of the greatest single mortality crises of all time.

The Black Death of the mid-fourteenth century (possibly both bubonic and pneumonic plague) had killed around 25 million, or one-third of the population of the known world over a period of four or five years. The 1918–19 flu, or Spanish flu as it was known, resulted in the deaths of millions of people in the course of some six months. Crosby and others put the figure at around 20 million – higher than the death toll from the First World War. Moreover, half of all deaths were among those aged between twenty and forty years. Influenza on this occasion did not just kill the weak and elderly. It struck right at the heart of the most active sections of the population. Crosby's book was a wake-up call for historians to look more deeply at the great outbreaks of influenza of the past, in particular the 1918–19 pandemic.

But beyond scholarly and scientific circles, it was, for many, 'a global calamity that the world had forgotten'. This global calamity has now become hot news. With the threat of 'bird flu' and 'swine flu' in the early twenty-first century, and fears of another major human influenza pandemic, there is every reason to go back to this historical case study. Indeed, it is now thought that up to 50 million people may have died in this single pandemic, and some have suggested that the toll was as high as 100 million.

Yet for many decades, it had been an episode 'sketched' rather than 'etched' in people's memory. As historians have pointed out, most people knew more about the horrors of bubonic plague in medieval Europe than they did about this shocking tragedy, which killed so many millions of their grandparents and great-grandparents. There are no memorials, few contemporary novels evoking the heartbreak, no remembrance services or lengthy lists of the deceased. Unlike the devastation and brutality of the two world wars, the unleashing of one of the most deadly pathogens of all times had, until recently, almost been forgotten.

The Spanish flu erupts, circulates and 'disappears'

'Never since the Black Death has such a plague swept over the face of the world; never, perhaps, has a plague been more stoically accepted.' *The Times*, 18 December 1918

The recent interest in the 1918–19 influenza pandemic has brought to light startling new facts and figures, as well as scientific confirmation that the disease really was influenza. But this brief and deadly episode still holds many mysteries for historians and virologists. The disease, at the time, was called the Spanish flu – not because it started in Spain but because Spain was not a belligerent country and its press was not prevented by government censors from freely reporting its alarming impact when it struck there in May 1918.

In fact, no one can say for certain when or where the disease began, or map precisely its route of dissemination. Some think that it was first seen amongst the Allied troops in France in 1916–17 (where it was known as 'Flanders grippe' or 'purulent bronchitis' by the British, and '*Blitz Katarrh*' by the Germans). Others believe that it began in the military cantonments of the Midwest United States in the spring of 1918 when the Americans were preparing to join the Allied forces in Europe. It has also been suggested that, like the recent bird flu outbreak, it may have originated in mainland China or Hong Kong.

But whatever the origin of the first wave (and there may have been several points of origin), in late August 1918 a second and far more virulent wave seems to have erupted simultaneously in three widely separated locations: Boston, Massachusetts, USA; Brest in Brittany, France; and Freetown in Sierra Leone on the west coast of Africa. These three ports were all engaged in dispatching troops and supplies to the trenches of the Western Front. By the time the Armistice was signed on 11 November 1918, ending the Great War, the disease had spread like wildfire around the entire globe, infecting one-quarter to one-third of the world's population. From the bloody battlefields of Europe to the isolated islands of the South Pacific, from the Arctic Circle to Australasia, from the tropics to the tundra, north, east, south and west, the 'grim reaper' of the early twentieth century felled soldiers and civilians, killed healthy young men and women, infants, pregnant mothers and the elderly.

It touched the lives of nearly every human being on Earth, leaving millions sick or bereaved and countless children orphaned or bereft of one or other parent. Its impact was severe enough to lower average life expectancy by twelve years for Americans. In India, one of the worst-hit places, at least 17 to 20 million died, and in Western Samoa in the central Pacific, around 8,000 out of a population of 38,000 died in November and December 1918. During the whole pandemic only St Helena in the South Atlantic, New Guinea and a few Pacific islands escaped infection. Australia, possibly through strict quarantine measures, was not as badly hit as other continents.

While initial reports during the first wave had tried to downplay the severity of the disease (perhaps for fear of alarming the public), by the second wave, the gravity of the Spanish flu was becoming clear. On 28 December 1918 the *Journal of the American Medical Association* reported:

> 1918 has gone: a year momentous as the termination of the most cruel war in the annals of the human race; a year which marked, the end at least for a time, of man's

destruction of man; unfortunately a year in which developed a most fatal infectious disease causing the death of hundreds of thousands of human beings. Medical science for four and one-half years devoted itself to putting men on the firing line and keeping them there. Now it must turn its whole might to combating the greatest enemy of all – infectious disease.

Contemporary descriptions of the disease began to paint a graphic and grim picture of its horrors. People died quickly – often forty-eight hours after onset, some seemingly drowning in their own phlegm as their lungs filled with fluid. Blood oozed from noses, ears and lungs. Some literally dropped down dead in the streets, slumped forward while driving trams and streetcars, or toppled off horses and buggies. In the crowded military bases and troop ships, soldiers collapsed in feverish delirium. Everywhere undertakers worked round the clock to keep up. Nurses and doctors rapidly succumbed to the disease, and there were desperate requests for volunteers to help cope with the terrible burden of sickness and death. Images from the time show overflowing hospitals, horrendous scenes of people being buried in mass graves, and glimpses of some cities simply overwhelmed by the circumstances of the catastrophe.

In the absence of vaccines, anti-flu drugs or a scientific understanding of the origin or cause of influenza (although it was clear that it was highly infectious and probably airborne), efforts to prevent its spread – especially once its severity was evident – relied on public and personal health measures. These included the prohibition of public gatherings, quarantining ships, closing schools, disinfecting streets and homes, sterilizing water fountains, banning shaking hands, spitting (which, in some places, became a punishable offence), encouraging frequent hand-washing and enforcing the wearing of gauze masks. Graphic posters with slogans such as: 'Spit spreads death', 'Wear a mask and save your life!', or 'Don't cough or sneeze into anything but your handkerchief', warned the public of the dangers of the flu but advertised that there were common sense methods of prevention. Military metaphors, seen through the lens of the Great War, echoed across many of these messages, encouraging people to be determined to 'fight' the 'enemy' of influenza.

Groups of practitioners, including homeopaths, osteopaths and chiropractors, came forward to challenge what they regarded as the intellectual 'mainstream' medical profession and offered their 'alternative' treatments. Some people invoked folk remedies, such as cinnamon, garlic, sulphur, cucumbers or potatoes to ward off infection, and any number of patent medicines and lung tonics were sold as 'sure cures' – but they were probably mostly of little avail. Nursing and ancillary care for the sick and dying was, however, of vital importance, and in the USA, for example, the American Red Cross (founded in 1881 by Clara Barton as an American branch of the international Red Cross) recruited thousands of volunteers, mostly women, to participate in the struggle against the Spanish flu.

The Spanish flu had exploded in the autumn of 1918, circulated the globe over the following winter and spring, briefly erupted again in the winter of 1919–20, but by the spring of 1920 it had begun to 'fade away' as mysteriously as it had arrived. It had done most of its brutal killing in little more than six months. Indeed, not only did the death toll far outnumber those killed in combat on the battlefields during the First World War, but, by way of analogy, in twenty-five weeks influenza had destroyed the lives of more people than those killed by HIV/ AIDS in its first twenty-five years.

The reaction throughout the world had varied from initial denial, censorship of newspaper reports, fatalism and inaction, to reassurance and confidence that medical science would provide answers – and then to shock, bewilderment, betrayal, loss and overwhelming personal sorrow and grief. But, for various reasons that are still puzzling, there was far less panic than during many other great plagues of the past – perhaps because it was overshadowed by the trauma and sadness of the First World War, or as one anonymous writer of *The Times* in 1921 put it: 'so vast was the catastrophe and so ubiquitous its prevalence that our minds, surfeited with the horrors of war, refused to realize it.'

Historian Nancy Bristow, in her book *American Pandemic: the Lost Worlds of the 1918 Influenza Epidemic* (2012), evocatively describes the many complex and varied reactions of Americans to the Spanish flu. She highlights the dilemmas at the time of how to confront and deal with the disease, and the paradox of the nation's 'public amnesia' following the pandemic (emphasizing the optimism and opportunities that the coming of peace after the First World War brought in its wake). And she also reminds us, through her 'recovery' of letters, diaries and oral histories, of 'long-silent voices' and the ways in which the tragic event lived on for the bereaved at an intimate personal level 'in vivid memories and in lives indelibly marked' by losses and experiences.

Why was the 1918–19 flu such a killer?

She lay on a narrow ledge over a pit she knew to be bottomless . . .

Then, as she climbed back from that depth:

> pain returned, a terrible compelling pain running through
> her veins like heavy fire, the stench of corruption filled her
> nostrils, the sweetish sickening smell of rotting flesh and
> pus; she opened her eyes and saw pale light through a
> coarse white cloth over her face, knew that the smell of
> death was in her own body, and struggled to lift her hand.

This passage comes from the haunting novella, *Pale Horse, Pale Rider*, by the American writer Katherine Anne Porter (1890–1980), first published in 1939. Porter was one of the few contemporaries to write a fictional account of the horrors of the 1918–19 flu, during which her fiancé had died, and she herself had almost succumbed.

The symptoms of the Spanish flu were, indeed, far more dramatic than any other human flu pandemic before or since. The worst symptom – signalling imminent death – was known as 'heliotrope cyanosis', when the lungs were starved of oxygen and the patient's cheeks, lips and ears would turn purple, black or blue. Physicians struggled to understand the reasons for this terrible 'purple death' – some even feared it was the Black Death. There was general agreement that it was a contagious disease spread from person to person, though a number of scientists at the time, including the German microbe hunter Richard Pfeiffer, mistakenly thought that influenza was caused by an infectious bacillus (rather than a virus). The supposed agent was known as Pfeiffer's bacillus or *Bacillus influenzae*. (Today this bacterium is called *Haemophilus influenzae*.)

Since the publication of Crosby's study in the mid-1970s, various explanations have been put forward (or ruled out) to explain the unusually high global mortality and why, unlike most influenza outbreaks, the 1918–19 pandemic struck down young and healthy adults. Both biological factors and the unique historical context of the pandemic may have interacted and contributed to this deadly scenario. The appalling conditions and logistics of the First World War, together with the mass movement of troops, could have played a key role in the initial dissemination of what was, undoubtedly, a particularly virulent and novel strain of influenza virus, though eventually many badly affected countries were outside the theatres of war.

Associated complications may have been caused by opportunistic infections or secondary bacterial pneumonia (for which, at the time, there were no antibiotics). It has also been suggested that a massive immune response (known as a 'cytokine storm') meant that young adults, paradoxically due to their healthy immune systems, mounted a too-strong and damaging response to the infection as it invaded and replicated in lung tissues. In some regions, such as the Indian subcontinent, where the death rate was at least twelve times higher than that of the USA or Europe, the combination of overcrowding, crop failures, poverty, poor nutrition and lack of good nursing care may have been influential in heightening the mortality risks of influenza.

The absolute numbers who died from influenza around the world (50 to 100 million) far surpassed any other single pandemic in human history, and its symptoms were more alarming than 'typical' influenza. Although the overall case fatality rate or the fraction killed out of all those infected (averaging 2.5 to 5 per cent globally but reaching 10 to 20 per cent in some countries) was not as high as the Black Death in mid-fourteenth century Europe (30 to 50 per cent) or the recent outbreaks of Ebola in Africa (up to 90 per cent), the sheer 'ubiquity' of the pandemic – its vast global geographical scale and the huge numbers of young people infected or killed by the disease – together with the circumstances of its eruption and spread during and following the First World War makes the 'recovered' memory of this human tragedy so poignant and significant.

Discovering the influenza virus

At the time of the Spanish flu, while scientists developing the 'germ theory' had already begun to identify the causative agents of a number of bacterial diseases (and Pfeiffer in 1892 had been misled into thinking that influenza was a bacterial disease), the agents of some diseases, including influenza as well as smallpox and rabies, could not, actually, be seen under the light micro-scopes of the time: they were 'ultra-microscopic'. Furthermore, they were so small that they passed through filters that were capable of blocking the passage of bacteria. Yet, based on labora-tory studies (and dating back to researches conducted on the tobacco mosaic disease in the late nineteenth century), it seemed as if these 'invisible' organisms were, like bacteria, also infec-tious and were often called 'filterable viruses'. New interest was sparked in 1931 when the American scientist, Richard Edwin Shope (1901–66), announced that a combination of a bacillus and a filterable virus produced a disease in pigs – 'hog flu' – analogous to human influenza.

A real breakthrough came in London during an epidemic in 1933, when Wilson Smith (1897–1965), Christopher Howard Andrewes (1896–1988) and Patrick Playfair Laidlaw (1881–1940) at the National Institute for Medical Research in London managed to transfer filtered nasal fluids and throat garglings from a sick researcher into ferrets. Within forty-eight hours the ferrets started sneezing and displaying signs of an influenza-like disease. Their work using ferrets enabled the virus to be studied and experimentally manipulated, and in July 1933 they published an important paper in *The Lancet* identifying a 'virus' as the primary causative agent for influenza.

With the development of the new electron microscopes from the late 1930s, investigators were able to 'see', photograph and study the structure of influenza viruses. They also began to realize the complexities of the disease and the problems associated with the development of vaccines. Indeed, it is often said that influenza is not just one disease but a host of rapidly mutating pathogens. There are three main 'types'. The virus isolated in 1933 by the London team became known as influenza type A and, over the following years, types B and C were isolated and identified. We now know that type A infects humans, a variety of birds and certain animals, most importantly, swine. Types B and C generally infect only humans.

In 1948, the newly established WHO set up a Global Influenza Surveillance Network – one of its first initiatives. This was created as an international network for influenza monitoring and control, and as a global centre to share information between laboratories, identify suspected new strains and to recommend the appropriate vaccine composition to be used.

The Asian (1957–8) and Hong Kong (1968–9) flu pandemics

Attention soon focused on why in most years there were relatively mild epidemics but every ten to forty years there were major pandemics of a serious illness. It became apparent that most cases of flu and all the major pandemics were due to influenza type A. Further important discoveries were made about key molecular components of the virus. Two glycoproteins on the surface of the virus were called haemagglutinin and neuraminidase. Haemagglutinin (HA) facilitates the attachment of the influenza virus to the surface of the cell, thus allowing its entry. Neuraminidase (NA) permits the release of newly formed viruses from an infected cell.

The significance of haemagglutinin and neuraminidase in influenza pandemics was first recognized in the outbreak of Asian flu which began in China in 1957. The virus that caused this pandemic was found to have novel haemagglutinin and neuraminidase subtypes, which were subsequently named Haemagglutinin 2 (H2) and Neuraminidase 2 (N2), while those which were present on the previously circulating strain of influenza (which had caused the Spanish flu) were, retrospectively, labelled H1 and N1.

The Asian flu of 1957–8 (influenza A H2N2) spread across the globe, infecting around one-third of the world's population and, although there were large numbers of fatalities (an estimated 1 to 2 million), the overall mortality rate was below 0.5 per cent. Another pandemic began in Hong Kong in 1968 and was found to have a new haemagglutinin which was named H3. The Hong Kong flu of 1968–9 (influenza A H3N2) was similarly widespread, possibly infecting about a quarter of the world population, but the final death toll of around half to 1 million was, mercifully, not on the same scale as the 1918–19 pandemic. Although anti-viral drugs for influenza have been developed only recently, for those suffering from secondary bacterial pneumonia during the Asian and Hong

Kong flu pandemics, antibiotics were available, and the first live vaccines against flu were produced in the 1960s.

An ever-changing virus – antigenic 'shift' and 'drift'

Of the many alternating subtypes or different strains of influenza that have now been identified, some are called 'mild' while others are labelled 'highly pathogenic' or just plain deadly. The intriguing and, indeed, worrying aspect of influenza is why and how the virus mutates and when another deadly strain is likely to emerge. As more and more research was conducted on this protean RNA virus, scientists found that major, and often abrupt, changes can occur in type A influenza viruses to produce a completely new and unfamiliar subtype. This is known as 'antigenic shift'. Consequently, people are not immune to such strains and the infection can cause severe disease. Why does a major change happen? It seems that occasionally genetic material from a bird and perhaps a pig strain becomes mixed with a human virus (usually in an intermediate host such as swine or domestic fowl) to produce a novel human strain through a process known as genetic reassortment. Antigenic shift can also occur through direct bird-to-human transmission. The new strain may further evolve and adapt to spread easily from person to person, causing a global flu pandemic.

But there is also what is known as 'antigenic drift' between pandemics. Influenza viruses are changing by antigenic drift all the time. This can lead to minor changes in the shape of the surface haemagglutinin and neuraminidase proteins. Antigenic drift produces new virus strains that may not be as virulent as those arising from antigenic shift, but if they cannot be recognized by antibodies to earlier influenza strains, it can explain why people can 'catch' flu more than once. One of the most frustrating challenges facing the pharmaceutical industry in its efforts to produce vaccines since they were first developed in the 1940s, is that, in any given year, we never know which 'old' or 'new' strain of influenza will emerge and circulate.

Bird flu (H5N1) shocks the world

In 1996, in the Guangdong province of China, a new influenza virus – type A subtype H5N1 – was identified in some geese, and came to be known as bird or avian flu. Bird flu received little attention until the disease spread through the live poultry markets in Hong Kong in May 1997 and went on to infect eighteen people, of whom six died. A three-year-old boy in Hong Kong is thought to have been the first human casualty of this new H5N1 avian flu virus. The authorities took drastic steps to stop the outbreak: disinfecting the bird markets, banning the sale of ducks and geese, culling millions of birds and destroying Hong Kong's entire poultry population. By taking such quick action in this early wave, the authorities in Hong Kong were credited with averting a global influenza pandemic.

However, in December 2002, in Kowloon Park in Hong Kong, numerous water birds were found dead. The culprit was, again, H5N1. The following year, two further human cases and one fatal outcome of H5N1 occurred in Hong Kong (though, by then SARS was also a major concern) and, by late 2003, unprecedented outbreaks of H5N1 among poultry were reported in ten Asian countries, leading to massive culling and attempts at vaccination of poultry. In May 2005, a highly pathogenic (HP) H5N1 variant emerged in wild birds in Qinghai Lake, China, that not only killed domestic poultry but also wild aquatic birds.

The H5N1 strain spread to a great many countries in Asia, Africa and Europe, where it was repeatedly recovered from migratory birds and was the cause of multiple outbreaks in poultry. By June 2007, 315 human cases of H5N1 and 191 fatalities had been reported to the WHO from a wide range of countries.

The news of bird flu captured the headlines and, as it spread more widely through wild birds to domestic fowl, it proved devastating for poultry farmers in many parts of the world. There was also a tremendous fear that, given historical precedents, this 'new' H5N1 virus would spark off another major human pandemic. As one expert quoted by John Barry, author of *The Great Influenza: The Epic Story of the Greatest Plague in History* (2004), put it: 'The clock is ticking. We just don't know what time it is.'

During the widely publicized outbreak of bird flu, a great deal more knowledge was amassed about the complexities of influenza. It had long been suspected and, from the 1930s onwards, confirmed that humans are not the only ones who can catch flu: it can also affect wild birds, poultry, pigs, ferrets, horses and other animals. It now seems that the natural reservoir and ultimate origin of all subtypes of influenza A viruses is, indeed, aquatic wildfowl. While in humans the virus replicates in the respiratory tract and can be readily passed by coughing and sneezing (even before symptoms in the infected are apparent), in birds the virus replicates in the intestinal tract. This means it can be shed through bird droppings as well as in saliva and nasal secretions. Migratory wildfowl act as carriers, transmitting the virus via their faeces which can then easily contaminate the water and bird feed of domestic poultry, enabling the disease to spread rapidly through entire flocks.

At the height of the bird flu outbreak, a number of scary

scenarios were posited for the future. First, once the bird flu virus entered the human body it might mutate so that it could then be readily passed from person to person – and with rapid air travel across the globe it could well descend 'like a blast of the stars'. A second, related possibility, was that if a person had even a mild form of influenza (the 'it's just a bout of flu' type) and then contracted H5N1, the two viruses would combine and evolve to become a 'new' lethal human strain. With increasing evidence that 'reassortment' can take place, when genes of bird, animal and human viruses mix together into new combinations – with swine, in particular, acting as an intermediate host reservoir – there were fears that a new and unfamiliar virus could emerge in this way and spread to humans.

Fortunately, it seems that, unlike some influenza variants, H5N1 cannot readily 'jump' the species barrier from birds to swine to humans and is thus not adaptable or easily transmissible as an airborne, human-to-human infection. Indeed, almost all the human cases and fatalities of bird flu have, so far, related to people who have handled sick birds, breathed in dust particles contaminated with bird faeces or eaten uncooked infected poultry products, and further human-to-human transmission has not occurred on a wide scale. However, for those infected with bird flu, the consequences of H5N1 can be horrible. The virus causes massive destruction of lung tissue, and the case fatality rate of this highly pathogenic virus can be as high as 30 to 60 per cent.

The 2009 pandemic of 'swine flu' (H1N1)

'We are all in this together, and we will all get through this, together.' Margaret Chan, Director-General of the WHO, 11 June 2009

In April 2009, with world attention still focused on bird flu, news of an outbreak of a mysterious influenza-like illness in the village of La Gloria in the state of Veracruz, Mexico, was picked up by HealthMap, an online information service that scans the internet for reports of unusual disease outbreaks. Two other isolated cases were also identified by the US Centers for Disease Control and Prevention (CDC) in California. By 24 April, it became clear that patients in Mexico and the US were infected with a similar virus – possibly, it was thought, of 'swine origin' – and the WHO issued a health advisory on the outbreak of 'influenza-like illness in the United States and Mexico', noting that this was of 'high international concern'. The infection then spread rapidly, with the number of confirmed cases rising to over 2,000 by early May, despite aggressive measures taken by the Mexican government to curb the spread of the disease. The disease became known as 'swine flu', and the story was widely covered and sensationalized by the media, with renewed fears of a possible global catastrophe.

Because the disease was called 'swine flu', there were also concerns about contact with pigs or consumption of pork products. Scientists were, nevertheless, quick to identify and unravel the cause of this outbreak. It was a novel influenza virus (type A, subtype H1N1) virus that probably did have its origins in pigs, but by the time it was detected the new virus was circulating among humans and not among pig herds. The virus isolated from patients in the US was found to be made up of genetic elements from several different flu viruses: North American swine influenza, North American avian influenza, human influenza and swine influenza typically found in Asia and Europe. Quite a 'mix'!

It is likely that pigs infected with these different viruses had acted as 'mixing vessels', facilitating the reassortment of influenza genes and creating a new influenza virus. This new strain had, then, 'jumped' into the human population (though when, where and how remain puzzling questions) and had adapted to become a human virus capable of being transmitted as an airborne respiratory infection from human to human. The appearance of such a 'reassortment virus' in the Northern hemisphere during spring was thought to be highly unusual – as was the fact that the virus had, apparently, emerged from an animal host in North America rather than in South-east Asia, which was where most flu experts had been expecting the next pandemic to come from.

As the infection spread around the globe with around 30,000 confirmed cases in seventy-four countries by early June, the WHO on 11 June 2009 announced: 'the world is now at the start of the 2009 influenza pandemic' – categorizing it as a Phase 6 'full-blown' pandemic and designating it the first global influenza pandemic since the 1967–8 Hong Kong flu. On 25 October 2009, US President Barack Obama declared H1N1 a national emergency.

Public health responses ranged from advising against air travel for those who were ill to checking temperatures and feverish symptoms of passengers arriving at international airports (using thermal imaging systems) and, in some places, imposing quarantine measures on those suspected of either harbouring the virus or having been in contact with others who might have been infected. The WHO's Global Outbreak Alert and Response Network and Global Influenza Surveillance Network remained on high alert, and a number of other international, national and independent forecasting organizations also tracked the pandemic across the globe. Scientists exchanged reports, while the media and internet kept the public up to date with the latest facts and figures (reminiscent of the Russian flu in the 1890s when news of the pandemic travelled rapidly via the telegraphic system and was graphically reported by the newspapers).

As hotlines were set up for patients or family members to ring medical centres, physicians and nurses struggled to advise or treat countless numbers of patients and their close contacts. Traditional personal hygiene measures, such as hand-washing, were recommended, along with bed rest and 'self isolation' of infected patients to prevent further spread in the community. Face masks to protect against infection became popular in some countries, and posters reminding people that 'coughs and sneezes spread diseases' were widely advertised. Two anti-flu drugs were also available – Tamiflu (oseltamivir) and Relenza (zanamivir) – and, indeed, some countries began to stockpile these drugs as the situation seemed to worsen (although this policy and the effectiveness of the drugs are still the subject of clinical inquiry). A massive effort to produce a vaccine resulted in the approval by the US Food and Drug Administration (FDA) of four vaccines by September 2009, though trying to distribute them globally proved challenging.

Many very sick and vulnerable patients were hospitalized, putting a huge burden on the health sector, and by the end of

May 2010, the WHO update stated that '214 countries and over-seas territories or communities have reported laboratory confirmed cases of pandemic influenza H1N1 2009, including over 18,138 deaths.' Thankfully, however, the pandemic was successfully contained, and on 10 August 2010 the WHO declared that the H1N1 influenza pandemic was over, saying that world-wide flu activity had returned to typical seasonal patterns.

The official death count between April 2009 and August 2010 was 18,500. Studies published, since, including in *The Lancet*, have, however, suggested that the actual toll was far higher – anywhere between 105,700 and 395,600 deaths – or possibly ten to fifteen times more than the total of confirmed deaths, with the burden falling heavily on people younger than sixty-five years. It is also likely that the number of people who succumbed to or died from the disease in the developing world, including sub-Saharan Africa and South-east Asia, was significantly greater than actually reported in the official statistics. Indeed, one of the tragedies and dilemmas that has emerged in the aftermath of the 2009 pandemic (and which was not widely broadcast at the time) was the great disparities around the world in the severity of the pandemic based on the availability (or lack of availability) of drugs, vaccines and medical care. The so-called 'swine flu' was not the disaster that had been anticipated and feared but, in hindsight, it has highlighted global inequities across the world that remain to be addressed.

Revisiting the Spanish flu of 1918–19

The history of influenza reminds us how this protean disease can manifest itself; at times, as a benign infection and, at other times, as a plague-like, destructive pandemic. Once assumed to have descended on the globe from some ethereal 'heavenly influence' or possibly caused by miasmas and meteorological and atmospheric disturbances, over the course of time a deeper scientific understanding of the complexities of this viral disease has evolved. By the late twentieth and early twenty-first centuries, naming novel flu outbreaks and pandemics had shifted from associating them with a particular country (the Russian flu, the Spanish flu, the Asian flu and the Hong Kong flu) to identifying the specific types (influenza A, B and C) and sub-types of the virus (e.g. H5N1, H1N1 and several recently identified subtypes called H7N9, H10N8, H3N2 and H5N8). 'Popular' names for the disease, according to their avian or mammalian source of origin, such as 'bird flu' and 'swine flu', are also now familiar.

As scientists have been addressing such concepts such as 'reassortment', 'antigenic shift' and 'antigenic drift' to explain the way human influenza viruses can evolve and spread, so, too, are answers being sought to explain the likely cause and severity of the now 'not forgotten' Spanish flu of 1918–19. To what extent migratory birds, domestic fowl or non-human mammalian species, such as swine, might have contributed to the 1918–19 influenza pandemic became a topic of increasing interest during the bird flu outbreak. Prompted also by fears of another major pandemic, scientists (including Jeffery Taubenberger in the US and John Oxford in the UK) began to search though past records of the Spanish flu. They found and examined stored autopsy lung tissues both from American soldiers who had died during the pandemic and which had been preserved at the Armed Forces Institute of Pathology in Washington, DC, and from British victims whose pathological specimens were discovered in the Royal London Hospital. Researchers also exhumed influenza victims buried in permafrost in Norway and Alaska to try and unravel more clues.

In 2005, Taubenberger and colleagues announced, in the journal *Nature*, the completion of the entire genome sequence of the 1918–19 influenza virus. From this evidence it was revealed that the 1918–19 pandemic may have been a new variant and highly pathogenic avian H1N1 influenza A virus that acquired mutations to infect humans. Moreover, by reconstructing the virus genome, the study suggested that the entire 1918 virus was novel to humans, in, or shortly before 1918, and that it was not likely to have been a 'reassortment virus' such as those that caused the 1957 and 1968 pandemics. It was more likely, they proposed, 'an entirely avian-like virus that adapted to humans *in toto*'. It has even been suggested that humans then transmitted the virus to pigs, and they in turn (and after reassortment) gave it back to us in the form of the variant 2009 H1N1 pandemic.

There are still ongoing studies and discussions about these theories and the origins of the pandemic (why, how and where it first started). But if the Spanish flu did make a direct leap from birds to humans and was disseminated, perhaps initially by birds, the little ditty about the bird called Enza has a strikingly ironic twist to it, and justifies the concern that direct transmission from birds to humans of a novel, highly pathogenic virus, followed by adaptation in the human population and human-to-human transmission via coughs and sneezes, is a real possibility.

With luck, such a scary scenario (given the speed of air travel today) will not be repeated in the twenty-first century. In the meantime, global surveillance networks (including the WHO Global Influenza Surveillance and Response System, or GISRS), will continue to monitor the circulating flu viruses, enabling pharmaceutical companies to produce appropriately targeted vaccines and, one hopes, new and better drugs to protect against flu during both pandemics and seasonal outbreaks. The latter are by no means to be sneezed at, as seasonal influenza causes misery and can result in a quarter to half a million deaths each year, mostly amongst the very young and elderly. A close watch is also being kept on any potentially lethal new viruses that may suddenly emerge (through antigenic shift) in any region of the world, so that the necessary public health and containment measures to prevent these becoming serious human pandemics can be rapidly implemented. The ultimate goal is that scientists will, one day soon, be able to come up with a universal vaccine that will protect against all flu strains and save many lives.

EBOLA

Ebola – also known as Ebola haemorrhagic fever (EHF) or Ebola virus disease (EVD) – is a highly infectious viral disease and one of the deadliest to have emerged in recent decades. The first identified human case occurred in Africa in 1976, near the Ebola River in the Democratic Republic of Congo (formerly Zaire), and sporadic, localized outbreaks of the disease have since occasionally flared up in a number of countries in sub-Saharan Africa. In the spring of 2014 news of a tragic outbreak of Ebola in West Africa began to hit the headlines, and in August 2014 the WHO declared it an international emergency. Ebola is characterized by massive internal and external bleeding, and death from surgical shock and respiratory arrest occurs in some 50 to 90 per cent of all cases. The risk for anyone in contact with the Ebola virus is so great that the disease is classified as a 'Biosafety Level-4' pathogen, which requires the strictest safety precautions for laboratory investigation, as well as stringent infection control measures for patients and health care workers. There are as yet no licensed specific treatments or vaccines for Ebola, and many aspects about its origin remain puzzling.

∾

In late August 1976 a schoolteacher called Mabalo Lokela living in Yambuku, a remote town in northern Zaire, developed a fever. At the local mission hospital they thought he might be suffering from malaria, but an injection of chloroquine failed to control his feverish symptoms. A week later he returned to the hospital, critically ill. He had begun to experience uncontrollable vomiting, acute diarrhoea and a blinding headache. He was also severely dehydrated, and had trouble breathing. Frighteningly, he then started bleeding from his nose, gums and eyes, and there was blood in his stools. There was no doctor in the hospital, but the Sisters who ran the Catholic mission did all they could to care for him. They had no idea what was wrong. Mabalo Lokela died on 8 September 1976.

Funerals, families, friends and health workers

Lokela's body was cleansed and prepared in the traditional way for his funeral. Not long afterwards, many of his family and friends who had attended the ceremony succumbed to the same symptoms, and several of the staff at the mission hospital became desperately ill. Panic broke out: it seemed as if people were literally bleeding to death. The mission hospital at Yambuku was eventually closed on 30 September, and the whole area sealed off by the Zairian army. Epidemiologists were sent from the National University of Zaire to investigate the epidemic at Yambuku. The disease ultimately spread to more than fifty villages in the vicinity of Yambuku, as well as to Kinshasa, the capital of Zaire, resulting in a total of 318 cases and 280 deaths – a mortality rate of nearly 90 per cent.

Some two months earlier, an ominously similar disease had broken out in Nzara and Maridi in the south of Sudan, a country bordering Zaire in the northeast. This outbreak had led to the deaths of 151 people out of 284 cases (a 53 per cent mortality rate). The local hospital soon turned into a morgue, and many of the patients, as well as relatives and hospital staff, succumbed to the disease.

As later in Zaire, people were petrified – it is said that some of the fearful victims in the last stages of the dreadful disease threw off their clothes and staggered out naked into the streets, while the surviving medical staff panicked and simply ran off to escape.

Identifying the cause and finding a name

The Sudan outbreak did not initially receive international attention. But when news of the terrible mortalities in Zaire reached the WHO headquarters in Geneva, and at the same time reports of the Sudan outbreak arrived, alarm bells rang.

One of the first to identify the virus was young Belgian scientist, Peter Piot (now director of the London School of Hygiene and Tropical Medicine and author of *No Time to Lose: A Life in Pursuit of Deadly Viruses*, 2012). In late September 1976 he received a cheap blue plastic thermos flask containing blood samples (flown on a passenger airline) from a Belgian nun who had died in Zaire from what was thought to be yellow fever. Without realizing the risk he was taking in examining this sample at the time, Piot, in the laboratory in the Institute of Tropical Medicine in Antwerp, isolated an unusual 'worm-like' structure. Meanwhile, the WHO were quick to recognize the potential danger of exposure to this disease and insisted that all further investigations should be carried out in high-security laboratories such as at Porton Down in England and the CDC in Atlanta.

Piot and other scientists examining this virus were both shocked and puzzled. The disease initially appeared to be similar to another scary 'new' haemorrhagic fever – Marburg disease or green monkey virus. This had first been identified a decade earlier and named after the German town of Marburg, where a shipment of African green monkeys had infected laboratory staff at a pharmaceutical research company. In 1967 clinicians at a hospital for infectious diseases in Marburg had been alarmed and mystified to see several severely ill patients whose fever was accompanied by agonizing pain and bleeding from multiple sites on the skin and the mucous membranes. It turned out that all the affected patients had worked for the same pharmaceutical company, and had acquired the virus from infected African green monkeys. The monkeys, half of whom had been dead on arrival from Uganda, were used in the preparation of cell cultures for vaccines. Seven of the infected lab workers died. Further cases occurred in Belgrade, Serbia (then part of Yugoslavia) and Frankfurt, Germany.

Common features of the disease that had broken out in Zaire and Sudan with Marburg disease included the high mortality and the severe haemorrhagic fever (the word 'haemorrhage' comes from the Greek words *haima*, 'blood', and *rhēgnunai*, 'to break forth'). Both diseases seemed to be caused by viruses that looked like threads or spindly filaments. There were, however, serological differences between the two. In October 1976, scientists at the CDC confirmed that this latest was, indeed, a 'new' virus (but, as yet, without a name).

A number of teams of international scientists, including Karl Johnson from the CDC, were sent to identify the causes of the outbreaks of this 'new' virus in Africa and to see whether further epidemics could be prevented. Piot joined those investigating the disease 'on the ground', and went to Zaire (formerly a Belgian colony) to help unravel how the virus was spreading. While in Yambuku, he and his colleagues realized that this 'new' disease needed a name, and in early November 1976 it was decided to call this novel, highly pathogenic virus 'Ebola', after a small river in the vicinity of Yambuku (rather than associate it with the village of Yambuku itself). Ebola has since been placed, along with Marburg, in a new family of viruses, the Filoviridae or filoviruses (after the Latin word *filum*, 'thread').

Ebola starts with symptoms not unlike many feverish infections, but progresses to severe and often fatal symptoms including high fever, vomiting and diarrhoea, painful sore throat (so sore that patients can hardly bear to swallow their own saliva), haemorrhaging and central nervous system damage. Although it seems as if people literally bleed to death, patients are more likely to die from shock from fluid loss rather than loss of blood. Therapy consists of maintaining fluid and electrolyte balance, with the administration of blood and plasma to control bleeding.

Ebola shocks the world

'As a rule disease can scarcely keep pace with the itch to scribble about it.' English chemist and physiologist John Mayow (1640–79)

For Western medicine, the 1950s and 1960s had been decades of tremendous optimism. Books on the history of disease were published with titles that incorporated such promising phrases as 'the rise and fall of infectious diseases', 'the conquest of disease' and 'the eradication of infectious diseases'. Epidemic infectious diseases seemed to be becoming a thing of the past. The eradication of smallpox in 1979 was an especially key moment in medical history.

But from the 1950s through to the end of the twentieth century, previously unknown and deadly diseases, including a number of haemorrhagic fevers, had begun to surface in various parts of the world. The real significance of these diseases was not fully recognized in the West until their impact began to be felt in Europe and the USA. Marburg fever (first identified in Germany in 1967), Lassa fever (recognized in Lassa, Nigeria, in 1969, when it struck down an American nurse), Lyme disease (first observed in the town of Old Lyme, Connecticut, in 1975), Legionnaires' disease (which caused the deaths of twenty-nine members of the American Legion attending a conference in Philadelphia in 1976), Ebola in 1976 and, especially, HIV/AIDS in the early 1980s – all these shattered the general mood of complacency.

By the 1990s books had begun to appear with such titles as *The New Killer Germs* and *Quest for the Killers*, reminding readers that poxes, pestilences and plagues were by no means vanquished. Laurie Garrett's *The Coming Plague: Newly Emerging Diseases in a World out of Balance* (1994) attracted worldwide attention. In her description of the 1976 outbreak in the Sudan she wrote: 'Weak, emaciated men and women lay about the mud-and-stick chamber, staring out of ghost eyes at the white men. The virus was so toxic that it caused their hair, fingernails and skin to fall off. Those who healed grew new skin.' Richard Preston's chilling account of Ebola and other haemorrhagic fevers in the bestselling 1994 book *The Hot Zone*, was subtitled *A Terrifying True Story*.

Ebola was perhaps the grisliest of the new plagues, provoking, as one scientist has put it, 'convulsive shudders' in the public imagination. Ebola made it not only into the news, but also into gruesome novels and movies, and images of scientists in protective spacesuits arriving in African villages and carrying lethal viruses back to high-security labs, not to mention graphic depictions of ghastly symptoms and agonizing deaths, scared many people. While reports of internal organs dissolving into mush and victims squirting blood from every orifice were exaggerated, there is no doubt that when Ebola first hit the headlines, it was seen as the most frightening and lethal of the newly emerging diseases (though its wider impact was later eclipsed by the HIV/AIDS pandemic, which, it now turns out from retrospective analysis of stored blood samples during the 1976 Ebola outbreak, was already present in Zaire, including in the village of Yambuku).

The virus hunters

While scientists in high-security laboratories were wrestling to identify and understand the Ebola virus, others in remote parts of Sudan and Zaire were tracking down the epidemiology of the disease and doing all they could to arrest its spread. These 'disease cowboys', as the medical detectives in Africa were called, faced almost insuperable difficulties as they tried to contain the nightmare of Ebola.

Joe McCormick and Susan Fisher-Hoch, in their 1996 book *The Virus Hunters: Dispatches from the Frontline*, narrate just how tragic it was to witness the impact of this deadly virus in parts of Africa where there were limited health facilities and few safety precautions, and where the population was consumed by grief and terror. Jonathan Mann (1947–98), in his preface to

Laurie Garrett's book *The Coming Plague*, described the disease cowboys – comprising both international and local teams of scientists and health workers – as: 'Heroes of a special kind: bonding science, curiosity and humanitarian concern combined with a practical attitude . . . who [went] into the field armed only with . . . will, intelligence, and confidence that a way forward would be found.' Their stories could have been written a hundred years ago by their predecessors in tropical medicine – men and women who had grappled to understand and control diseases such as malaria, yellow fever and sleeping sickness.

Many significant discoveries about Ebola were made during these first outbreaks. It appeared that the Sudan and Zaire epidemics of Ebola were coincidental and probably unrelated. Both, however, spread rapidly through personal contact, especially within hospitals and clinics, via infected bodily fluids, blood, tissues and organs. Funeral customs – handling and cleansing the corpses – were also instrumental in spreading the infection. A particularly rapid transmission of the virus occurred through the practice of using and reusing unsterilized syringes in medical centres. In Yambuku, following Mabalo Lokela's illness and death, it is thought that about 300 to 600 people a day were injected at the mission hospital with the same five hypodermic needles. Some patients came for a minor complaint or antenatal care, only to leave with the deadly virus then in their bloodstream.

Over the course of the next decade, Ebola experts continued to monitor and identify localized outbreaks of the disease in Central Africa and put in place every precaution needed to contain the disease. The Ebola-Zaire strain appeared to be the most lethal, with death rates as high as 90 per cent, while the Ebola-Sudan strain was killing about half of all known cases. The reasons for this varying mortality rate, and why some people survive the disease, are still not fully understood (though follow-up studies of survivors may provide clues, as, for example, to an immune response to the disease).

Monkey alarms

In 1989 alarm bells rang again – this time in the USA. A shipment of one hundred cynomolgus monkeys, also known as crab-eating macaques (*Macaca fascicularis*), was sent from Manila in the Philippines to a quarantine laboratory in Reston, Virginia, for research. The monkeys started dying. Officials of the US Army Medical Research Institute were called in and found that the monkeys were dying from a form of Ebola virus – which was labelled 'Ebola-Reston'. While it was highly lethal to monkeys, no humans were infected, though four of the animal handlers developed specific antibodies to this form of Ebola. The remaining monkeys were destroyed and the laboratory decontaminated. But this was not the only scare. Several more times in the course of the next few years, both in the USA and in Italy, monkeys shipped from the same export facility in the Philippines were found to be infected and dying of Ebola-Reston.

Five distinct species of the Ebola virus have now been identified and named: Zaire ebolavirus, Sudan ebolavirus, Bundibugyo ebolavirus, Taï Forest ebolavirus, and Reston ebolavirus. The first four have been found to cause haemorrhagic fever in both humans and animals though the Taï Forest virus has not been associated with major outbreaks of Ebola. Reston ebolavirus is the only form that has not so far caused clinical illness in humans. However, while no locally acquired human cases of Ebola have been found outside Africa, the presence of the virus in monkeys in Asia has remained an extremely worrying aspect of this deadly and mysterious disease. Reston viruses have also recently been detected during several outbreaks of a deadly disease in pigs in the Philippines as well as in the People's Republic of China.

Ebola 2014 – an international health emergency

Between the first reported cases in 1976 and the WHO's cumulative count in 2013, there were around 2,387 cases and nearly 1,600 deaths from Ebola, with fatality rates in each of the outbreaks varying from around 25 to 90 per cent. Most outbreaks occurred primarily in African villages (in the Democratic Republic of Congo, Sudan, Côte d'Ivoire, the Republic of the Congo, Gabon and Uganda). Although there were two laboratory-acquired infections in 2004 – one in the USA and the other in the Russian Federation – in recent years Ebola has been 'out of the news' in the West. Other scary global health threats, such as HIV/AIDS, 'mad cow' disease, SARS, bird and swine flu have taken attention away from the more localized outbreaks of Ebola in remote parts of Africa.

By early to mid-2014, all this was to change, and Ebola – with its alarming symptoms and shockingly high mortality – was back in the headlines as it erupted in West Africa. Indeed, since then there has not been a day that has gone by without an update and report on Ebola, with horrific and tragic images of sufferers and bereaved families; new graves being dug and poignant funerals; frightened people hiding the sick and dead or fleeing from 'infected' homes and isolation units; the imposition of road blocks; and, as featured in earlier graphic movies such as *Outbreak* and *Contagion*, scientists and health workers dramatically garbed in full protective regalia. Rioting has even broken out as petrified people have objected to enforced quarantine. The economic impact – especially for farming communities and the agricultural sector – has been also of huge concern, with added fears of food shortages in these afflicted countries. Restrictions on travel and trade are having further repercussions. Moreover, although Sierra Leone and Liberia, two of the major countries concerned, have managed to rebuild their economies after emerging from civil wars, there are serious worries that all the good work that has been achieved could be reversed and Ebola might damage Africa's economic revival of recent years.

So where, what and why is this happening? The first cases of the latest crisis probably originated in late 2013 in south-east Guinea, bordering Liberia and Sierra Leone. This region had not, prior to this, reported any cases of Ebola. By March 2014, Ebola was present in all three countries and by July it had reached Nigeria. Alarm bells rang as a Liberian patient was treated in its capital city, Lagos, which is one of the fastest-growing cities in the world and an international transit hub. Unlike diseases that have a respiratory route of transmission, however, human-to-human transmission of Ebola is limited as it can be caught only by direct contact (through broken skin or mucous membranes) with the blood, secretions, organs or other bodily fluids of infected people, or, more rarely, indirect contact with articles such as bedding contaminated with such fluids. Burial ceremonies in which mourners have close contact with the body of the deceased person can also play a significant role in the transmission of Ebola. Nevertheless, although not predicted to be transmitted rapidly across the globe like SARS and influenza, its high mortality rate and the speed and extent of its spread across West Africa have engendered widespread panic and massive disruption to some of the poorest countries in the world.

On 8 August 2014 the WHO declared the outbreak to be 'a public health emergency of international concern'. It is proving to be one of the biggest, most complex outbreaks of Ebola the world has ever seen. Indeed, by August 2014 there had been at least 3,000 cases, with numbers rapidly escalating and around half of all patients dying. At the time of writing, in October 2014, the latest figures from WHO reveal that approximately 8,400 people have been infected with Ebola, leading to over 4,000 deaths mostly in the worst-affected West African nations of Sierra Leone, Liberia and Guinea, though the true extent of the horror remains unknown and the number of cases being reported increases daily. By October 2014 over 400 health-care workers were known to have developed Ebola and over 230 had died. There are stories in the press about the spread of Ebola outside of Africa, notably Spain and the USA, although these have been contained. Only time will tell when this terrible disease will be brought under control and it is predicted that the number of cases and deaths will continue to rise.

Behind each number lies a tragic human story, and for people contracting the disease and for families, local care workers, medical and humanitarian agencies (such as Médicins Sans Frontières) who have tried to help patients during both the earlier eruptions and now in this ongoing outbreak in Africa, it has been terrifying and deeply traumatic.

Where did Ebola come from?

There are many outstanding puzzles about the Ebola virus, especially regarding its origins prior to its spread via human-to-human transmission. Where did it come from, and why did it suddenly infect humans in the mid-1970s in Central Africa and, again, erupt in West Africa in 2014 with such ferocity during this current, ongoing, deadly epidemic? During the first outbreaks, it was speculated that Ebola, like a number of newly 'emerging' diseases, was a 'zoonotic' disease of animal origin. Numerous species of animal and insect vectors were collected and tested by the 'virus hunters' in an attempt to track down a non-human reservoir. Bedbugs, mosquitoes, pigs, cows, squirrels and other rodents showed no signs of the Ebola virus in either Zaire or Sudan. It was subsequently shown, however, that a number of non-human primates – including monkeys, chimpanzees and gorillas – seemed to be susceptible to the virus, along with forest antelopes and porcupines. These animals also appeared to be able to transmit the disease to people.

Mabalo Lokela, the first identified Ebola victim in 1976, had eaten antelope meat shortly before he showed his initial symptoms, and he and another patient had also handled fresh monkey meat. In 1994 a scientist contracted the disease in the Taï Forest of Côte d'Ivoire while performing an autopsy on the carcass of an infected wild chimpanzee. In 1996, in the Mayibout area of Gabon in West Africa, a chimpanzee was found dead in the forest and eaten by people hunting for food: nineteen people involved in the butchery of the animal became ill, with other cases following in family members. In total, twenty-one people died.

In some remote equatorial African regions the consumption of 'bushmeat' (the meat of wild animals) is a traditional supplement to the diet. It has been suggested that political instability, a rising population and worsening economic conditions have forced many more people to become dependent on bushmeat, either by selling it or by consuming it. Hunters usually either use wire snares to trap the animals, or simply shoot them. While conservationists are concerned about over-hunting and the threat to wildlife, epidemiologists are worried about the risk of infected wild animals spreading diseases like Ebola to the human population, as well as the risk of Ebola for populations of great apes. Researchers in the region straddling the border between Gabon and the Republic of the Congo believe that some 5,000 gorillas have been wiped out by Ebola, with suggestions that the disease is passing from gorilla to gorilla through direct contact.

However, while the consumption of bushmeat might provide one link in the chain enabling the virus to 'spill over' into the human host and then spread from human to human through bodily fluids, non-human primates in the wild may not be the original source. The high mortality among monkeys infected with the Reston ebolavirus in the USA suggested, for example, that these non-human primates might, like humans, be 'new' to the virus and also 'accidental' hosts. The search has continued for a primary host in the wild.

One of first cases in the 1976 Sudan outbreak had been employed in a local cotton factory. The factory was also home to a number of bats and, although none were found to be harbouring the Ebola virus at the time, bats remained a possible, but not proven, suspect in some of the early outbreaks. Laboratory observation then showed that fruit- and insect-eating bats experimentally infected with Ebola do not become ill or die, and this raised added speculation that these mammals may play a role in maintaining the virus in the tropical rainforest. In 2005, Ebola viral RNA was found in three species of bats in Central Africa. As the 2014 outbreak hit the headlines, the WHO stated that 'fruit bats of the *Pteropodidae* family are considered to be the natural host of the Ebola virus.' In West Africa, fruit bats are eaten as a delicacy by some local populations and, indeed, it is now thought that the family of the first two-year-old victim (dubbed 'Child Zero'), in southeastern Guinea, hunted bats.

Understanding and breaking the transmission cycle of Ebola is fraught with difficulties. Indeed, even if the true reservoir is bats, there is still the intractable question of how to deal with Ebola once it spreads via human-to-human transmission.

Preventing current and future outbreaks

Since the 1980s international health agencies have recognized the serious threat presented by 'new' diseases, as well as by re-emerging 'old' diseases such as malaria and tuberculosis. Quests to find either a vaccine or cure for diseases such as Ebola are of immediate priority, and, in an almost unprecedented step, in August 2014 the WHO gave its approval to the use of a number of experimental treatments, including ZMapp (a mixture of three humanized monoclonal antibodies against the Ebola virus produced in tobacco plants), concluding that in the circumstances of the Ebola outbreak, use of unproven treatments is ethical. ZMapp (pronounced 'Zee-Map') was first used to treat two American health workers in Liberia who were then evacuated to an isolation suite at Emory University Hospital in Atlanta in the US. Both survived. ZMapp was also used to treat a volunteer British nurse, who was evacuated from Sierra Leone to a special isolation unit at the Royal Free Hospital in London in early September 2014. He, too, survived and returned to Sierra Leone in October 2014 to help combat the 'horror and misery' of the disease. However, the supply of even experimental drugs is not sufficient to tackle the present crisis. A vaccine for Ebola, co-developed by the pharmaceutical company GlaxoSmithKline and the US National Institute of Allergy and Infectious Diseases (NIAID), began early trials in late September 2014, and scientists are trying to fast-track the vaccine through clinical trials in the hope of using it to prevent the spread of Ebola in West Africa. Again, only time will tell if this or other vaccines, currently being developed in a number of countries, will be able to prevent a 'crisis' becoming a 'catastrophe'.

In the meantime, it remains imperative to raise awareness of the risk factors. Warning people about the dangers of contracting Ebola from bats as well as from various forest animals such as monkeys, chimpanzees, gorillas, antelopes or any other suspect animal source (especially if found ill or dead in the rainforest) is a key factor in breaking the chain of infection. Also vital to prevent the spread of Ebola once it appears in the human population is the rapid and safe disposal of liquid and solid wastes as well as of corpses whose bodily fluids still harbour high quantities of virus. This latter precaution has been one of the most complex aspects of the current outbreak. Traditional funeral practices in the region involve close contact with the deceased, and changing burial rit-uals, which are deeply embedded in the cultural fabric of societies, is not easy. Tension between local populations observing their tra-ditions and international agencies coming in wearing their 'spacesuits' and taking charge, initially led to a number of rumours and conspiracy theories. Increasingly, though, there is progress in reducing mistrust about the disease amongst local communities, with a better understanding and acceptance of the public health efforts needed to combat this deadly virus.

It is also recognized that intensified efforts to introduce var-ious infection control measures need to be urgently and more widely put into place to contain the disease. Immediate diagnosis is paramount, followed by strict isolation and the use of barrier nursing techniques – not only involving hand-washing in disinfectant, wearing protective clothing and disposable gowns, masks, goggles, and gloves, but also the sterilization of all contaminated medical equipment and soiled bedding and clothing. Severely ill patients require intensive supportive care. Ebola victims have the best chance of survival if their fluid and electrolyte balance is maintained, and, in the case of the critically ill, if blood and plasma are given to those who are haemorrhaging. Contact tracing and monitoring or isolation for twenty-one days of anyone who comes into contact with a sick Ebola patient, followed up by testing for the disease, is also part of the fight to contain the spread of the disease.

Avoiding risks, barrier nursing for those infected, and contact tracing remain, at present, the main defences. But in many of the poorest parts of Africa struck by Ebola, such strategies are not always easy to implement or impose. Moreover, the levels of care needed to diagnose, support the sick and prevent the spread of the infection are often beyond reach. Liberia and Sierra Leone each have only about a hundred practising doctors; Guinea is only marginally better off, with fewer than 1,000 doctors for a population of 11 million. Nevertheless, the world has witnessed some unbelievably moving accounts of people who are trying to cope with the outbreak, often with very basic and totally inadequate health facilities. Many doctors, nurses, health care workers and volunteers have put themselves at a tremendous personal risk to nurse and care for the sick and dying.

A number of international agencies, humanitarian emergency relief teams and charities have responded to the crisis and, while trying to 'contain' the spread of Ebola, there is increasing recognition of the urgent need to build better health facilities to treat victims of the disease. This crisis has highlighted that there is, moreover, in the longer term, a desperate need to improve the fragile health infrastructure in African countries.

Will Ebola become the next global pandemic?

The WHO says that there is a very low risk of the disease spreading as a global pandemic, though all international health agencies remain on high alert and some countries have begun to introduce screening at airports. For the affected nations of Africa, Ebola is one more merciless microbe that has been tragically unleashed on a continent that already suffers the heaviest burden of old and new diseases on Earth. The incidence and demographic impact of Ebola in Africa not yet on anything like the same scale as that of malaria, HIV/AIDS and tuberculosis, or even diarrhoeal diseases and pneumonia (and, indeed, another huge concern is that the scale of the crisis is diverting resources from the treatment of these other major infections). But Ebola – one of the most virulent diseases known to humankind – still has the ability to destroy lives and shatter families and communities, and the power to spread terror across the rest of the world.

HIV/AIDS

AIDS – acquired immune deficiency syndrome – is one of the leading causes of death in the twenty-first century. It is also one of the greatest tragedies of the modern era. First recognized and named 'AIDS' in the early 1980s, its causative agent, identified in 1983, became known as the human immunodeficiency virus (HIV). It is a retrovirus that is transmitted from one person to another through sexual intercourse, contaminated syringes and needles or infected blood products, and can also be passed from mother to baby. HIV leads to a progressive breakdown of the immune system, which if left untreated eventually develops into AIDS. There has been much speculation about the origin of HIV and how it entered the human system. It is now known that the pandemic strain of the virus 'jumped' from chimpanzees in the African equatorial forests of southeastern Cameroon to humans sometime in the early twentieth century and later smouldered in Léopoldville (now Kinshasa) a city situated on the Congo River. But the apparent sudden emergence of HIV/AIDS in the human population in the early 1980s was a huge shock and, since then, the disease has claimed more than 39 million lives. As a global pandemic, HIV/AIDS has touched the entire world, though its greatest impact has been in the poorest regions, especially sub-Saharan Africa, and it continues to be a major global health priority. For those who can afford them, there are effective antiretroviral drugs which, if taken daily, help people infected with HIV to manage their condition and lead a normal life. Public educational campaigns have also significantly helped to reduce the number of new infections in recent years. It remains to be seen if preventative vaccines will be developed and whether, as optimists suggest, we are in sight of an AIDS-free generation.

∽

On 5 June 1981 the Centers for Disease Control and Prevention (CDC) in the USA published a short article in their *Morbidity and Mortality Weekly Report*. The article described five cases in Los Angeles, California, of *Pneumocystis carinii* pneumonia, a rare infection of the lungs almost exclusively limited to patients with a profoundly depressed immune system. The five young men were all active homosexuals, but had previously been healthy individuals. Yet, as the editorial note to the report stated:

> The occurrence of *Pneumocystis* in these 5 previously healthy individuals without a clinically apparent under-lying immunodeficiency is unusual.

It went on to add:

> The fact that these patients were all homosexuals suggests an association between some aspect of a homosexual life-style or disease acquired through sexual contact and *Pneumocystis* pneumonia in this population.

This was the first published medical alert about a syndrome that did not yet have a name. It prompted additional case reports from New York, San Francisco and other cities in the USA of patients with very low levels of white blood cells, which play a key role in how the body fights disease. Something was destroying the immune systems of these people, leaving them prey to opportunistic infections, including pneumonia caused by *Pneumocystis carinii* (usually a harmless fungus), cytomegalovirus infection and oral candidiasis. Cases of a rare skin cancer called Kaposi's sarcoma amongst young homosexual men were also noted. The 'syndrome' was initially called GRID ('gay-related immune deficiency') while some referred to it as the 'gay plague'. As further reports of this strange new syndrome cropped up, vague connections began to be made, and in July 1982 the disease was officially named by the CDC as AIDS (acquired immune deficiency syndrome).

The story of AIDS had begun, but it was a story that had been silently unfolding over many decades. At some time and somehow, a lethal virus had entered the human population, and had been slowly smouldering until it was ready to unleash its devastating effects on the whole world.

Stigma and science

When the American clinicians reported to CDC their first cases of a 'mysterious' disease in 1981, little did they know that they were publishing the first observations of what would become the greatest and most tragic pandemic in recent history. This was a time of great optimism and faith that infectious diseases could be conquered, if not entirely eradicated. Indeed, in 1979 the WHO had just announced the eradication of smallpox. Life expectancies, even in some of the poorer countries of the world, were rising. When the first AIDS cases were identified, the syndrome was thought to be rare, affecting only certain high-risk groups, primarily homosexuals and intravenous drug users (IDUs). Politicians were slow to grasp the enormity of the impending crisis. Activist groups in the USA and Europe took centre stage, lobbying for more public funding, overcoming prejudices and demanding a greater awareness of the gravity of the disease. In 1982 AIDS organizations were launched, including the San Francisco AIDS Foundation; the AIDS Project Los Angeles; the Gay Men's Health Crisis group in New York; and the London-based Terrence Higgins Trust.

When a number of haemophiliacs were diagnosed with AIDS in 1982–3, having received Factor VIII (a clotting factor) prepared from contaminated blood, some began to distinguish between such 'innocent victims' and the so-called 'guilty perpetrators'. Collectively, all of the sufferers became known as the '4-H Club': homosexuals, Haitians (originally targeted and blamed for having introduced the disease to the USA), heroin users and haemophiliacs. Blaming, shaming and discriminating against these marginalized groups were the most regrettable responses in the early days.

Scientists were quick to start searching for an explanation of the disease. Its bizarre manifestations, the dramatic effect on the immune system and the likely transmission through sexual intercourse or blood products provided some early clues. Between 1983 and 1984 the cause of AIDS was identified by a number of scientists as a 'new' virus – a retrovirus – that had not hitherto been seen in the human population. The virus was termed HIV in 1986 and was shown to belong to the genus *Lentivirus* of the family *Retroviridae*. Such viruses – which take their name from the Latin *lente* for 'slow' – are characterized by a long incubation period. At the time there was a groundswell of hope that with the causative agent known, followed by the availability of a diagnostic test and a method of screening blood products, scientists would soon come up with a means of curing or preventing the disease.

From HIV to AIDS

In spite of some bitter exchanges as to who could claim priority for the discovery of the AIDS virus and who could own the patent on an HIV-antibody blood test, in 1987 French scientist Luc Montagnier (b.1932) of the Institut Pasteur, Paris, and American scientist Robert Gallo (b.1937) at the National Cancer Institute, Bethesda, Maryland, were recognized as the co-discoverers of HIV. Eventually, however, in 2008, it was Luc Montagnier and his colleague Françoise Barré-Sinoussi (b.1947) who were awarded a Nobel Prize in Physiology or Medicine 'for their discovery of human immunodeficiency virus' – their groundbreaking publication, in the journal, *Science*, in May 1983, was recognized as the first to describe the virus that became known as HIV.

HIV is a retrovirus which means that genetic information for its replication becomes permanently integrated into the cell's DNA of its host. It is an extraordinarily complex microbe. Soon after the discovery of this 'new' retrovirus further insights were revealed about this extraordinarily complex microbe in the laboratories of Montagnier and Gallo, as well as in a number of other international research centres. In the UK, scientist Robin Weiss (b.1940) and his colleagues published a seminal paper in *Nature* (1984) showing that 'the CD4 antigen is an essential component of the receptor for the AIDS retrovirus'. CD4 is a glycoprotein found on the surface of immune cells such as T-helper cells – so-called because one of their main roles is to send signals to other types of immune cells, including CD8 killer cells, which can then destroy an infectious particle. However, the HIV virus attaches itself to and infects the CD4 cells, damaging and destroying them in the process. If CD4 cells become depleted, as for example in untreated HIV infection, the body is left vulnerable to a wide range of infections that it would otherwise have been able to fight. The CD4 count is a critical prognostic test of the progression from HIV infection to the development of AIDS, alongside measuring the amount of free virus in the bloodstream.

At the time of initial infection with HIV, people might have some slight feverish symptoms. During this early period of infection, large amounts of virus are produced and there is a high risk of transmission (through unprotected sexual contact, contaminated syringes and needles, blood transfusions and from infected mothers in pregnancy to their unborn babies). The infection then moves to a clinical latency stage – often without symptoms – though it remains transmissible. Only after a prolonged period of incubation (from five to fifteen years) in which the virus progressively destroys the immune system, leaving the body open to all sorts of life-threatening opportunistic infections and some tumours, does the disease progress to full-blown AIDS, with rapid weight loss, sickness and death. In the absence of treatment, 90 per cent of people infected with HIV will eventually develop AIDS. The ability of HIV to subvert, alter and destroy the function of the immune system is one of the most striking and devastating characteristics of this slowly incubating disease.

AIDS alert in Africa

Recorded cases of HIV/AIDS in the USA had jumped from zero in 1980 to 7,699 by 1984, and of these 3,665 had died. In Europe there were some 762 cases by the end of 1984, with 108 cases and 46 deaths in the UK. Over this period, AIDS appeared to be predominantly a disease of homosexuals and IDUs, with poor urban minority groups taking the brunt of the impact. The first AIDS conference to address the disease took place in Atlanta, Georgia, in 1985.

As the toll of people with AIDS (known as PWAs) continued to rise in the USA, the Caribbean and Europe, so too did its incidence elsewhere, especially in sub-Saharan Africa, become slowly but alarmingly apparent. In Uganda, people were dying of a mysterious disease, dubbed 'Slim', which caused severe weight loss. Doctors in Uganda and Zambia then began to notice an increase in cases of aggressive Kaposi's sarcoma which pointed to a connection with AIDS. Meanwhile, in Belgium, travellers returning from Central Africa were also showing signs of AIDS. Belgian scientist Peter Piot (co-discoverer of the Ebola virus in 1976) went to Zaire (formerly the Belgian Congo and now the Democratic Republic of Congo) in 1983 to investigate the situation. In 1984 he sent samples from people with clearly manifested clinical signs of AIDS to Montagnier – 97 per cent of which tested positive for HIV. Piot, together with Jonathan Mann (1947–98) from the CDC, set up a project in Zaire, jointly coordinated by the Institute of Tropical Medicine in Antwerp, Belgium, and the CDC. This was called Projet SIDA (Syndrome d'Immuno-Déficience Acquise – the French acronym for AIDS) – the first and largest AIDS research project in Africa.

Especially worrying were signs that the disease was slowly evolving amongst the heterosexual population of sub-Saharan Africa, suggesting a very different pattern of transmission from that in the USA and Europe and one, Piot feared, that posed an enormous potential for harm across the population as a whole. There was also evidence of mother-to-child transmission. These first studies of HIV/AIDS in Central Africa would, ultimately, prove vital for tracking the origin of the AIDS pandemic. There was immediate resistance to the idea that HIV could be transmitted from women to men, and Piot's first 1984 report sent to *The Lancet* was, initially, rejected as being 'of local interest only'.

Scientists held a meeting in the Central African Republic in 1985 to discuss the issue, though in its early stages, as in the West, there was denial, blame-mongering and a hybrid of moralistic and scientific explanations. Governments were slow to grasp the scale of the emerging crisis, and the long incubation period and lack of distinctive symptoms made it difficult to detect cases and see what was really happening. But within a few years, in sub-Saharan Africa, the disease had spread east, west, north and south along the truck routes (the 'AIDS Highways'), out of the commercial overnight sex stops and into the heterosexual population, from cities to villages, from men to women, women to men, old to young, and from mothers to babies.

As quoted by John Iliffe in his book, *The African AIDS Epidemic: A History* (2006), one epidemiologist in Kampala, Uganda, poignantly wrote: 'It all started as a rumour. Then we found we were dealing with a disease. Then we realized that it was an epidemic. And, now, we have accepted it as a tragedy.' Indeed, by the time HIV causing AIDS had been identified in 1983, for many in Africa it was already too late. The HIV virus had already seeded itself in people from all walks of life. HIV/AIDS was no longer a disease to be marginalized or ignored. It was already a global problem.

Stop AIDS: the world reacts

As the unfolding tragedy began to make headline news in the mid-1980s, especially following deaths from AIDS of well-known personalities such as the Hollywood star Rock Hudson in 1985, activists in the West continued their campaigns. Randy Shilts, a gay reporter for the *San Francisco Chronicle* (who died from AIDS in 1994), played a prominent role in making HIV/AIDS a news item with the publication of his 1987 book: *And the Band Played On: Politics, People, and the AIDS Epidemic*. In the US a giant commemorative tapestry of quilts went on display in the Mall in Washington, DC, in 1987, designed to remember some of those who had died of AIDS. Each square of the quilt, stitched and embroidered by families and friends, represented an individual or group of people who had died. In the same year, the WHO launched its Global Programme on AIDS, estimating that as many as 5 to 10 million people could be infected with HIV worldwide. In a number of countries various self-help and charity organizations were set up to deal with the epidemic and to combat the prevailing stigmatization of HIV/AIDS. The AIDS Coalition to Unleash Power (ACT UP) was formed in 1987 by New York activists to demand access to experimental drugs and to lobby for a co-ordinated national policy to fight the disease.

As the world reacted to the realization of the enormity of this newly emerging global disease, many questions were posed and dire predictions made. Where had the disease come from? What could be done to control and prevent its spread? What would be its long-term impact on the world? Complacency, denial and recrimination were accompanied by shock, fear, hysteria and further confusion about how to deal with this unforeseen epidemiological crisis.

The questions surrounding HIV/AIDS raised important medical, racial, political and ethical issues. Trying to unravel its country of origin led to further recriminations. As with syphilis four centuries earlier, no country wanted to take the blame. Comparing AIDS to past plagues and pandemics led to endless debates as to how to stop its spread. Mandatory testing of young adults and quarantining of HIV-infected people was experimented with in Cuba, but most activist groups and governments, as well as the WHO, lobbied against coercive measures, which, given the long incubation period of HIV, would mean isolating the infected for long periods. In fact AIDS quickly proved to be so different from any other disease known in history (except possibly syphilis in its first wave from the late fifteenth to the sixteenth centuries) that what had been tried before was unlikely to work, or be acceptable, in the late twentieth century. The importance of acknowledging individual human rights, the realization that a 'police-style' approach to the control of disease was not appropriate or likely to be successful, and the need to enlist the support of those most at risk led to a liberal consensus (in some but not all countries) as to how to approach the new epidemic.

But amidst the doom and gloom of the AIDS crisis in the second half of the 1980s there was a clamour for action, and campaigns for prevention and behavioural changes became the key targets of national and global health organizations. In the US and a number of other countries, soon after the discovery of the virus, blood supplies began to be screened for the presence of HIV to prevent potentially deadly transfusion-related infections, as had tragically occurred amongst haemophiliacs. Around the world people were advised about the risks of contracting HIV/AIDS and the ways of avoiding or spreading it. Posters, media voices and images dropped through letterboxes spelt out the messages of 'safe sex' or abstinence, and the importance of the use of condoms and clean needles. In the UK the government used the slogan 'Don't die of ignorance', and delivered a leaflet about AIDS to every household in the country. The world's first needle exchange for drug users was set up in Amsterdam in 1984, and in the UK the first was in Dundee in 1986. The 'Stop AIDS' campaign became one of the biggest health education drives the world had ever seen.

AZT – the first drug for HIV/AIDS

As the Stop AIDS campaign got underway, activist coalition groups lobbied the pharmaceutical industry to find a cure. One drug, azidothymidine (AZT), which had been tested (unsuccessfully) in the 1960s as a treatment for cancer (and had been shelved) was investigated again because it was already known to inhibit a retrovirus in mice. Following re-testing of AZT *in vitro* and in rodents, the first double-blind, placebo-controlled randomized trial of AZT, conducted by Burroughs-Wellcome, showed that it could significantly reduce the replication of HIV in patients, leading to clinical and immunological improvements. The trial began in 1985 and was terminated in 1986, enabling AZT to be approved by the US FDA using its then new, accelerated approval system in March 1987. The time between the first demonstration that AZT was active against HIV in the laboratory and its approval was twenty-five months, the shortest period of drug development in recent history.

This therapeutic breakthrough was not a magic bullet, but it was a start. However, it soon became apparent that AZT was extremely expensive and thus beyond the reach of most of the world's population. It also caused severe side effects and patients became resistant to AZT within three to four months of starting treatment.

A cocktail of drugs

'We stand on the brink of a global crisis in infectious diseases. No country is safe from them. No country can any longer afford to ignore their threat.' Gro Harlem Brundtland, Director-General of the WHO, 1996.

From the first 'curious' cases identified in the USA to the connections made with AIDS in Africa, by the late twentieth and early twenty-first centuries it soon became apparent that the disease was out of control. In 1996 UNAIDS (Joint United Nations Programme on HIV/AIDS) was set up with Piot as founding Executive Director – the first UN organization entirely dedicated to confronting the global AIDS crisis. In the same year the 11th International AIDS Conference in Vancouver adopted the theme 'One World, One Hope.' By this time, with some 33 million adults and children infected with HIV, the AIDS red ribbon had become the international symbol of AIDS awareness, solidarity and hope.

Indeed, there was hope. In 1996, almost a decade after the development of AZT, a 'cocktail' of three or more antiretroviral drugs which included AZT (known as HAART – highly active antiretroviral therapy) was given the go-ahead. In North America and Europe, the efficacy of this combination therapy became known as the 'Lazarus effect' ('bringing life back to the dying'). People infected with HIV, who would once have died from AIDS, were now returning to normal life. In the USA and Canada, death rates from HIV/AIDS dropped significantly between 1996 and 1997. Similar success stories were evident in parts of western Europe. Brazil took the unprecedented step of offering HAART free to all who needed it, but the drugs were mostly only available and affordable in the developed countries.

The drugs (now known as antiretroviral therapy or ART) do not cure the disease, but by slowing down the progress of the virus, suppressing its replication and preventing it from rapidly destroying the immune system, the combination therapy is a breakthrough for HIV sufferers. Other drugs, including antibiotics and painkillers, combined with vaccines and long-term medical care, also helped to prevent opportunistic infections from taking their deadly toll. In the wealthier nations, by the close of the twentieth century, HIV was no longer an inevitable death sentence.

However, even following the introduction of the combined antiretroviral drugs, the cost of ART proved exceptionally high, and the drugs have to be taken daily for life. People with HIV, whether in cities or remote villages, need to be tested, diagnosed, counselled, treated and monitored. ART can make an amazing difference to people's lives, enabling those who are HIV-positive to manage the disease, and ART can also prevent the infection passing to unborn children from pregnant mothers who are HIV-positive. But a major dilemma, especially for the developing world, has been how to reach all those most in need of ART. Limited supplies of even painkillers or drugs to treat opportunistic infections, as well as the practical difficulties of screening blood products before transfusion, have also contributed to the AIDS crisis in many poorer regions of the world.

Reaching those most in need

'What was first reported as a few cases of a mystery illness is now a pandemic that poses among the greatest threats to global progress in the twenty-first century . . . We need a far greater commitment of political will, courage and resources; we need united action on a new scale.' Kofi Annan, Secretary General of the UN, 2006

By the end of the twentieth century HIV/AIDS in sub-Saharan Africa was on a scale unimaginable in the early 1980s. Shocking statistics pointed to the huge reductions in life expectancy at birth following the onset of the HIV/AIDS pandemic, with levels falling to below forty years in the worst affected African countries. At the turn of the millennium, some 6 million African children had been made orphans because of HIV/AIDS; more than 9,000 new infections were occurring every day, or over six every minute; and AIDS had become – from zero reported cases in 1980 – to a leading cause of death in sub-Saharan Africa two decades later. The infection was also spreading even further, to North Africa, Asia, the Middle East, eastern Europe and the Pacific, causing nearly 3 million deaths a year worldwide.

The 13th International AIDS Conference in the year 2000 – under the slogan 'Breaking the Silence' – took place in Durban, South Africa, the first to be held in a developing nation, heightening awareness of the global nature of the pandemic. When the

United Nations member states adopted the Millennium Development Goals (2000–15) they identified as one of the goals the target of reversing the spread of HIV/AIDS. In 2002 the Global Fund to Fight AIDS, Tuberculosis and Malaria (GFATM), an international financing initiative, was launched to increase resources to fight three of the world's most devastating diseases and to direct those resources to areas of greatest need. In the US, President Bush founded the President's Emergency Plan for AIDS Relief (PEPFAR) in 2003 with an endowment of $15 billion and an initial aim to raise the broader profile of the disease in resource-limited settings, including in Africa, and to support ART for several million people.

Further initiatives were set up to raise awareness and funds for HIV/AIDS, including the Live 8 concerts, organized by Bob Geldolf and first held in Hyde Park, London, in 2005. At a historic and unprecedented joint press conference in 2005 the WHO, UNAIDS, the US government and GFATM announced the results of collaborative efforts to increase the availability of antiretroviral drugs in developing countries. Private charities and philanthropic donors have added further impetus to fight the disease. The Gates Foundation, for example, has made a huge financial contribution and commitment towards HIV/AIDS research, drug development and distribution.

In 2001 Yusuf Hamied, chairman of the Indian generic pharmaceutical company Cipla (founded in 1935 by his father, Khwaja Abdul Hamied), electrified the global health industry by saying that his company could produce a cocktail of three antiretroviral drugs in a single tablet at a cost of a dollar a day. The price has since fallen to 20 cents per patient per day. Cipla is now one of the largest suppliers of ART in the world. This humanitarian response to the crisis has encouraged other companies making HIV drugs to drop their prices. The world's commitment to universal access to ART has been the most positive and striking collaborative response to global public health in the modern era. In 2014, it has been estimated that close to 13 million people globally are receiving life-saving antiretroviral drugs with the aim to increase access to all those in need over the coming years. Mother-to-child-transmission can be nearly fully prevented if both the mother and the child are provided with ART through the brief stages when infection can occur, just before and after birth. Early detection, rapid diagnosis and treatment (including a strategy known as 'treatment as prevention' when uninfected people at high risk are given pre-exposure prophylaxis) are also imperative both to improve the health and life expectancy of individuals and to reduce the spread of the virus within populations. Behavioural changes, public educational campaigns, and safe practices to limit the risk of HIV transmission and infection, such as the use of condoms, voluntary medical male circumcision and sterile needles and syringes, continue to be encouraged.

In theory the best solution for HIV/AIDS would be a vaccine – either one that could prevent people from becoming infected with the virus or one that could stimulate the immune system of infected people to attack it effectively. However, HIV – which is a rapidly mutating virus capable of evading both detection and destruction – has proved an unusually complex micro-organism to vaccinate against and, although scientists have been pursuing the 'holy grail' of eventually finding a safe and effective vaccine for the past few decades, it has been a difficult challenge. Following the results of a large-scale vaccine trial in 2009 in Thailand (known as RV144) which showed an admittedly modest 31 per cent reduction in infection in people given the vaccine, hopes for a vaccine are gaining momentum, though it may be at least another decade before a vaccine that can be distributed globally comes to fruition.

The human costs of HIV/AIDS

The number of AIDS-related deaths has fallen by over 30 per cent since the peak of the epidemic in 2005 and, with the success of administering antiretroviral drugs in many parts of the world, HIV infection is, increasingly, seen as a chronic disease rather than a death sentence. Great progress has also been made over the past decade in reducing new infections in children. The downward trends in life expectancies in countries most badly affected by HIV/AIDS are now being reversed. However, HIV remains embedded in both human cells and societies. Across the globe at least 39 million have already died of HIV/AIDS; around 35 million people are still living with HIV; and some 2 million people are newly infected with HIV each year. Sub-Saharan Africa accounts for 70 per cent of the global total of new HIV infections. A parallel rise in tuberculosis fatalities has also occurred – HIV and TB are a lethal synergistic combination, and people with latent TB are several times more likely to develop clinical TB once infected with HIV.

Behind the figures there have, over the past few decades, been countless tragic and heartbreaking stories, especially in some of the poorest regions of the world such as sub-Saharan Africa: a generation of productive people of childbearing age decimated; scarce resources used up to pay for long-term care, expensive drugs and funeral costs; farms, houses and schools abandoned; AIDS orphans with few prospects, many of whom must fend for themselves; households headed by teenagers; impoverished grandparents desperately trying to cope with the children left behind; relatives queuing up at the mortuaries to collect and bury loved ones; the exhausting burden of care for families and health workers; and – in both the developing and developed world – millions of needy, victimized, vulnerable, lonely people living with a death threat. As one young doctor from Zimbabwe once poignantly said:

> What kind of shrivelled wasteland will my nation become? Young orphans and the old eking out a crabbed, hand-to-mouth existence in dusty forgotten rural homes, while in the towns, industry falls silent, businesses and stores lie closed and derelict while the wind blows rubbish and old leaves down deserted, dead streets.

There is clearly a strong link between HIV/AIDS and poverty. HIV is now largely a disease of the poor, and more than 95 per cent of infections occur in developing countries. Within middle- and high-income countries, its incidence is highest, too, amongst the poorest and most marginalized populations. Indeed, trying to disentangle the combined effects of the social and behavioural determinants of HIV/AIDS with the role of opportunistic or coexisting diseases (including TB, sexually transmitted diseases such as syphilis and gonorrhoea and 'tropical' diseases like malaria) is complex. As with so many infectious diseases, the situation can be further complicated in regions affected by natural disasters (such as earthquakes and famines) or human catastrophes (such as wars and civil strife). Nelson Mandela (1918–2013), the South African anti-apartheid activist, whose son died of AIDS, devoted his later years to campaigning against

HIV/AIDS, and set up a charity – 46664 – the name taken from his Robben Island prisoner number. He saw the disease as not merely a medical threat but also a challenge to 'the entire socio-economic fabric of our society', and he came to embody that challenge.

Going back to the origins of HIV/AIDS

'Every once in a while a new disease will emerge and knock the socks off the human population. It happened with HIV/AIDS, and it can happen again.' Anthony Fauci, head of the US National Institute of Allergy and Infectious Diseases (NIAID)

HIV/AIDS has manifested itself as a series of parallel epidemics with patterns, rates of transmission and risk groups varying from country to country and from time to time. Its greatest and most complex impact has been in sub-Saharan Africa, where the variety of circumstances and contexts in which the disease has evolved has been striking. Moreover, even though awareness of the existence of AIDS in Africa came after it was first reported in the US, it is now thought that an epidemic had been incubating on that continent for far longer, and well before scientists realized the gravity of the unfolding human AIDS crisis.

Attempting to trace the origins of the HIV virus has occupied the minds of many people since AIDS first hit the headlines. One of the first and, at the time, most controversial theories in the late 1980s was the 'out of Africa' hypothesis, which led many to object that Africa was being 'blamed' for unleashing a deadly microbe on the world. In the early days, others also suggested it came from the Caribbean island of

Haiti. Some investigators even claimed to trace the disease to 'Patient Zero' – a Canadian flight attendant called Gaëtan Dugas who had crisscrossed the world supposedly infecting numerous sexual contacts with the HIV virus.

In his 1999 book, *The River: A Journey Back to the Source of HIV and AIDS*, Edward Hooper shifted the 'blame' onto Western scientists, including American virologist Hilary Koprowski, who developed the first live oral polio vaccine (OPV) and conducted trials in the late 1950s in the then Belgian colonies of the Congo and Ruanda-Urundi. Hooper claimed that infected cells from chimpanzees had been used to produce the experimental polio vaccine. Subsequent investigations proved that there was not a shred of evidence to support this case and the so-called OPV theory of the origin of HIV has been completely discredited by the scientific community while also exonerating Koprowski and his colleagues.

Moreover, scientists now have evidence that HIV was already circulating in the human population in Africa well before the polio vaccine trials. The current consensus as to the origin of HIV/AIDS – based on the examination of accounts of unusual clinical symptoms in the mid-twentieth century, testing of blood stored from the 1950s (including preserved tissues from patients during the first Ebola outbreak in Zaire in 1976), and computer-generated 'evolutionary trees' of the HIV virus – is that the human disease did probably originate in the western equatorial region of Africa, but possibly as long ago as the early twentieth century. It is, therefore, much older than originally suspected when the shock of AIDS hit the world in the early 1980s.

HIV-1 (the first of the human viruses to be identified) is closely related to the SIV virus (Simian Immunodeficiency Virus) of chimpanzees (SIVcpz) of the *Pan troglodytes*

445

troglodytes sub-species and HIV-1 group M (M for 'major') is the pandemic form. HIV-2 (a less aggressive and less easily transmitted form of the human disease and still confined to West Africa) is more closely related to the SIV virus (SIVsmm) found in the sooty mangabey (*Cercocebus atys atys*), a monkey native to Africa. How, when and why either of these two primate viruses crossed the species barrier – a 'jump' known as 'spillover' – and then mutated from SIV to the human form of HIV, is still a mystery, but many scientists now concur that hunters slaughtering chimps or monkeys may have become infected with the SIV virus, either through cuts or by eating 'bushmeat' (which has traditionally been used to supplement the diet of those living in the tropical rainforests of Africa). There may, in fact, have been a number of 'spillovers' from SIV in non-human primates to HIV in humans but, during the early twentieth century, this dormant infection may have gone unnoticed in remote areas. Moreover, symptoms such as 'wasting', which occur with other tropical infections and malnutrition, and death from opportunistic infections, may not have seemed unusual.

The answer to the next part of the puzzle – how, once localized in the human population in equatorial Africa, HIV then spread around the world – is currently attracting widespread attention from scientists and historians. Amongst debated theories it has been proposed that well-intended, large-scale disease control programmes in colonial Africa, especially from the 1920s to the 1950s, used and re-used unsterilized hypodermic needles and syringes for intravenous injections of a range of drugs, to treat, for example, for sleeping sickness, yaws, syphilis and leprosy. It would, so this theory goes, take just a few people with the mutated HIV infection to enable this to be spread more widely via serial passage as a blood-borne infection. Blood transfusions might also have played a role. It has also been acknowledged that this was a time of profound political, social and economic change in Africa Facilitated by a network of rivers, roads and railways, the movement of migrant labourers (especially of males) to the growing cities and mining, rubber and ivory regions could have led to gender imbalances, accompanied by a rise in prostitution. The result, most likely, was an increased prevalence in sexually transmitted diseases, which, together with a host of other factors, might have enabled HIV to spread along trade and transport routes through human sexual intercourse. According to one recent genetic study, the capital city and commercial hub of what was then the Belgian Congo, Léopoldville (now Kinshasa), seems to have been the epicentre in the 1920s – with HIV-1 group M then spreading to other population centres in sub-Saharan Africa – and igniting the 'silent' beginnings of what would become the global HIV/AIDS pandemic.

Post-colonial disruptions added further fuel to this evolving crisis. For example, following the independence of the Belgian Congo in the 1960s, several thousand French-speaking professionals were recruited from Haiti to work in Zaire, and many were based in Kinshasa. On returning to Haiti, it has been suggested, any one of them might, unwittingly, have taken the virus back to the Caribbean – a region closely connected to the USA. This could explain how the virus 'jumped' across the transatlantic world, unnoticed until AIDS (with its long incubation period) eventually first attracted attention in the US in the early 1980s. Far from 'unleashing a deadly microbe' on the world, Africans were at the mercy of a series of environmental, cultural, medical, social, economic and political circumstances that adds

447

to the poignancy of the origins of the HIV/AIDS tragedy (as we are now currently witnessing with the Ebola virus outbreak in West Africa.

While experts continue to unravel this desperately tragic sequence of events (and we will never know all the answers, or find 'Patient Zero'), the complexities and genetic diversity of HIV are also being revealed. Indeed, there are four different groups of HIV as well as a number of subtypes, with different patterns in different parts of the world. A mystery that remains to be resolved is why the SIV virus from chimpanzees that gave rise to HIV-1 group M became the global pathogen causing the vast majority of AIDS deaths in humans while HIV-2 is much less severe and has stayed primarily in West Africa.

History, sadly, cannot be rewritten, but it is hoped that understanding the origins and ancestral pathways of the 'family tree' of HIV may help with future medical research, as for example, the development of effective vaccines. Moreover, the story of HIV/AIDS (like SARS, influenza, and now Ebola) is a reminder that more attention needs to be focused on early warning signs of zoonotic infections with the potential to jump the species barrier and evolve as human epidemics.

One world, one hope

At the turn of the millennium, several thousand scientists from 189 nations signed a Declaration of Commitment, in which they expressed the expectation that, through international efforts:

'Science will one day triumph over AIDS, just as it did over smallpox'.

The 19th International AIDS Conference was held in Washington, DC in 2012 with the theme: 'Turning the Tide Together: A Declaration to End the AIDS Epidemic'. The Declaration recognized that:

'We stand at a unique time in the history of the AIDS epidemic ... through scientific advances and societal, political and human rights gains, it is possible to turn the tide against AIDS ... and begin to end the epidemic in our lifetimes.'

The most recent, to date, Melbourne Declaration of 2014 added the commitment:

'No one left behind.'

Optimists are beginning to think that an 'AIDS-free generation' is an achievable goal which, they believe, can be brought about by ending HIV transmission through both biomedical and behavioural prevention strategies, even before a vaccine to prevent HIV/AIDS or a wonder drug to 'cure' the infection become a reality. Ambitious new targets have been set up by UNAIDS, the WHO and other global and national health organizations for the post-Millennium Development Goals (2000–15) era.

Indeed, the response to the global pandemic of HIV/AIDS has been exceptional. Over the past thirty or so years, AIDS has united the world in ways that few other crises have. It has mobilized people to come together to break the conspiracy of silence and created a social movement, primarily led and driven by people living with HIV, speaking out for the rights of some of the world's most vulnerable populations. The tragedies, both at the individual and global scale, have been huge; there is continued HIV-related stigma and discrimination; and the current HIV/AIDS statistics remind us that the world cannot be complacent. But the tide does seem to be turning, and global efforts have significantly helped to save many lives. There have been some outstanding achievements across the world in reducing the incidence of HIV/AIDS, and ART has been a remarkable success story – transforming the disease for many from a life-threatening illness to a chronic and manageable condition. Helplessness in the early days has now given way to hope; despair to opportunities. The challenges ahead are great, but the costs of failure will be greater.

SARS and MERS-CoV

In the spring of 2003 the WHO issued an emergency global alert. Reports had come in from Asia of a potentially lethal new disease which became known as severe acute respiratory syndrome – SARS for short. There was a worldwide panic. Airports began screening passengers, and international trade and travel were disrupted. People everywhere held their breath (or put on masks) as this mysterious pneumonia-like disease travelled rapidly via major air routes to every continent of the world, infecting over 8,000 people in around thirty countries, with some 770 deaths. By July 2003 the SARS pandemic – caused by a coronavirus, spread primarily via airborne droplets – was apparently over. Whether it will re-emerge at some time in the future remains to be seen. Recent attention has been focused on another novel coronavirus, known as MERS-CoV (Middle East respiratory syndrome coronavirus) which was first identified in 2012 in a patient from the Arabian Peninsula.

◦◦

On 14 February 2003 a small notice in the WHO's *Weekly Epidemiological Record* mentioned a mysterious acute respiratory infection that was cropping up in Guangdong province, southern China. A total of 305 cases and five deaths had been reported by Chinese health officials between 16 November 2002 and 9 February 2003. This report did not, however, attract media or global attention.

A week later (28 February 2003), Carlo Urbani (1956–2003), an Italian-born WHO specialist in infectious diseases based in Hanoi, Vietnam, rang the WHO regional office for the Western Pacific. An alarming and unidentifiable disease was breaking out in the French Hospital in Hanoi, causing severe, pneumonia-like symptoms and deaths, especially amongst the hospital staff. One key patient in this story was Johnny Chen, who had been admitted to the hospital. After three weeks of dealing with the crisis round the clock, on 11 March Urbani travelled to a medical conference in Bangkok, Thailand. On arrival he felt unwell and told a waiting friend not to touch him but to call an ambulance. He was put into an isolated intensive care unit and died on 29 March.

Between the time of the first notice from China of an unusual 'atypical pneumonia' and Urbani's tragic death, the WHO had become suspicious. Reports of a strange new disease had begun to surface from a number of Asian countries, as well as a city as far afield as Toronto, Canada. On 15 March 2003 the Director-General of the WHO, Gro Harlem Brundtland, took the unprecedented step of alerting the world of the threat of a possible 'new' disease of unknown origin, and at the same time issued an emergency travel warning.

Super-spreaders

The first case of what became known as SARS was probably a young man from the town of Foshan, China. He was admitted on 16 November 2002 to Foshan No. 1 People's Hospital with an unusual respiratory illness. How and why he contracted the disease remains a mystery. The young man recovered and was discharged from hospital, but, like many cases that were to follow, he set up a trail of infection that was to spread rapidly through China, including Hong Kong, and then around the rest of the world.

The complex sequence of subsequent events was pieced together by the WHO in the spring of 2003. What emerged is that while in many individual cases the spread of the infection to others was limited, a number of so-called 'super-spreaders' were, for some peculiar reason, capable of transmitting SARS at an alarming rate and to a disproportionately large number of people, who then carried the virus around the world.

In China the first super-spreader was Zhou Zuofeng, a seafood trader who contracted the disease in late January 2003 in the city of Guangzhou, in Guangdong province. He not only infected staff and patients in three local hospitals, but also transmitted the disease to Liu Jianlun, a professor of nephrology. The professor and his wife travelled to Hong Kong on 21 February for a family gathering and stayed the night at the Metropole Hotel, on the ninth floor. Several days later the professor was dead. By the end of February a number of visitors to the ninth floor of the hotel had become infected. Some were admitted to hospitals in Hong Kong, while others, incubating the virus, had flown to Vietnam, Singapore and Canada.

Johnny Chen was one of the unlucky 'super-spreader' victims. A Chinese American businessman from Shanghai, Chen was en route to Hanoi when he stopped over at the Metropole Hotel – on the ninth floor. When he reached Hanoi he was taken ill with pneumonia-like symptoms and was admitted to the French Hospital. Staff and patients at the hospital were subsequently infected. Among them was Carlo Urbani, who first alerted the WHO as to the potential seriousness of this new disease. Johnny Chen was taken to Hong Kong by his relatives, where he died on 13 March in an isolation facility.

The race to identify the new disease

When the WHO issued its emergency global travel alert on 15 March, no one had any idea what this deadly disease was. It did not even have a name – other than 'atypical pneumonia'. The first reaction was that it might be an influenza virus. The initial symptoms (a high temperature, muscle aches, chills and a cough) were remarkably similar to flu, but tests soon disproved this theory. In severe and fatal cases there was overwhelming damage to the lungs, and while some suggested it might be pneumonic plague, the disease did not respond to antibiotics – ruling out a bacterial infection. It took, however, only a few weeks to identify the cause of this mysterious infection and to discover that it was the first serious 'new' viral disease to emerge in the twenty-first century.

The disease soon became known as 'severe acute respiratory syndrome' (SARS for short), and on 17 March the WHO set up a worldwide collaborative initiative, bringing together some of the leading international microbiologists, virologists, clinicians and epidemiologists. The scientists corresponded daily using teleconferences and a secure website on the internet. They shared their findings and swapped ideas. By early April a scientific paper was published online in *The Lancet* by Malik Peiris and colleagues in Hong Kong entitled, 'Coronavirus as a possible cause of severe acute respiratory syndrome'. Based on clinical studies and laboratory work, they had isolated the virus and found that the lethal pathogen was an entirely new 'coronavirus'. (The name 'coronavirus' is derived from the Latin *corona*, meaning crown or halo, and refers to the crown-like spikes on the surface of the virus.) It appears that the SARS coronavirus (SARS CoV) had never been seen before in humans or animals. Ironically, SARS is of the same family as one of the world's most widespread and harmless diseases – the common cold. How and why one human coronavirus has been around as a mild irritant for centuries and a new and deadly one suddenly emerges is a troubling question.

Controlling the spread of SARS

At the peak of the epidemic in early May 2003, when over 200 new cases were being reported every day around the world, with some 10 per cent of all cases proving fatal, there was still no specific antiviral drug and no vaccine. Controlling the spread of SARS relied on classic epidemiological methods of patient isolation, contact tracing, quarantine, travel restrictions, screening at international borders and infection-prevention measures in hospitals.

Tracking down those who might be incubating the virus, often in distant parts of the world, involved trying to establish who had been in contact with SARS patients in the previous ten to twenty days, and precisely where and when. In Singapore, for example (where the first case was a super-spreader who had visited the Hong Kong Metropole Hotel), a web-based system was set up as the outbreak spread which allowed all hospitals and doctors 24-hour access to daily updated lists of suspect and probable SARS cases and their contacts. A 'prevent-detect-isolate-and-contain' strategy was adopted in the midst of the crisis. Those suspected or known to have been in contact with a

SARS patient were issued with home-quarantine orders, while many others were put on daily telephone surveillance for ten days.

Other affected areas also adopted quarantine measures. In Hong Kong, when over 300 people fell sick from SARS in one of the high-rise apartment building complexes on the Amoy Gardens estate (where the disease was suspected to have been transmitted through the plumbing), the residents were at first quarantined in the building, and then evacuated to isolation camps for ten days. After a woman who had stayed at the Metropole Hotel in February flew to and died in Toronto, of what later turned out to be SARS (while infecting her son, who also died), a chain of cases followed (eventually leading to 251 cases and 43 deaths. Hospitals all across the province of Ontario were quarantined for months, and a number were closed altogether in an effort to contain the disease. The WHO advised against all but essential travel to Toronto.

Strict preventive measures in hospitals included the use of masks, gloves, eye protection and disposable gowns, and of footwear that could easily be decontaminated. Hospital staff were advised to wash their hands before and after contact with an infected patient, and to use disinfectants and disposable equipment. The dedication of staff who dealt with the crisis in hospitals was an incredible part of the story of SARS. The economic impact was also huge, as travel and business patterns were disrupted. In many airports sophisticated thermal scanners were set up alongside the metal detectors to check for passengers with a fever. The fear of SARS in 2003 was as great as the fear of terrorism.

In China, once the government had acknowledged the enormity of the problem – especially following a major outbreak in Beijing that in the end accounted for over a quarter of all SARS cases worldwide – they too responded with amazing speed to try to bring the disease under control. Schools, internet cafés, discos, cinemas and theatres were closed, and weddings suspended. Spitting in public places was prohibited. Nevertheless, the impact on the hospital system was immense – hundreds of doctors, nurses, ambulance drivers and other health workers contracted the disease. On 27 April work started on a new 1,000-bed hospital for SARS patients on the outskirts of Beijing – it took 7,000 construction workers just eight days to build it, at a cost of $170 million. The new Xiaotangshan Hospital treated 680 patients, of whom only eight died, and by the end of June it was no longer needed for the treatment of SARS victims. China was given the all-clear by the WHO on 24 June 2003, and on 5 July 2003 the WHO announced that all twenty-nine countries that had been touched by SARS (with an estimated global total of 8,096 cases and 774 deaths) were free from the disease. The deadly virus had miraculously 'vanished'.

The 'end' of SARS and its continuing mysteries

The speed with which SARS was named, identified as a coronavirus, and contained (without a cure or a vaccine) – after an unprecedented level of international cooperation and collaboration – was both dramatic and impressive. Early detection and rapid response, followed by isolation and quarantine measures, were critical and, fortunately, with SARS (unlike influenza) symptoms tend to appear before, rather than after, a person becomes highly infectious. Thus many patients were hospitalized and placed in isolation before they hit their peak of infectivity and started shedding the virus. The downside was that hospital staff took the brunt of the infection, and health workers in the end accounted for 20 per cent of all SARS cases. SARS – the 'first' new disease of the twenty-first century – was also a frightening reminder of how quickly a novel infectious disease can emerge and be transported across the world. With the massive rise in global air travel, we are now – in our closely interconnected and highly mobile world – facing a situation when any infectious disease is only a flight away.

A few small localized outbreaks of SARS were identified in Asia in 2004 but for the time being it would seem that the SARS pandemic is over. But many mysteries still surround the SARS pandemic, including its origin. Did it come from an animal source like many zoonoses that have jumped the species barrier to become transmissible airborne human infections? At the time of the 2003 outbreak, suspicion fell on the masked palm civet cat (*Paguma larvata*). Following the possibility that the SARS virus entered the human population from civets or from other animals butchered in live animal markets and eaten in restaurants in southern China, the Chinese embarked on a culling programme, killing over 10,000 civets, as well as badgers and raccoons suspected of harbouring SARS. It was subsequently discovered that there might be another source linking the inter-species transmission of SARS from mammals to humans in live animal markets. A report in 2005 suggested that the Chinese horseshoe bat (of the genus *Rhinolophus* species), which is a delicacy in southern Chinese cuisine and whose faeces are used in traditional Chinese medicine, is possibly the natural reservoir for the SARS virus. Indeed, bats appear to harbour many more deadly viruses than was previously thought. SARS has highlighted the critical need to identify zoonotic infections before they 'jump' into the human population and to encourage collaborations between the animal, human and environmental health sectors to detect, monitor and control potential pandemic infections at the earliest possible time.

As scientists continue to solve the mysterious origins of SARS and why and how it jumped into the human population and then mutated in a way that allowed it to spread between people, a second mysterious coronavirus, MERS-CoV, associated with severe respiratory symptoms, has recently shown, once again, the importance of early preparedness and effective surveillance systems.

MERS-CoV – a new puzzling infection

In June 2012, a patient in Jeddah, Saudi Arabia, died of acute pneumonia and organ failure. His doctor, Ali Mohamed Zaki, was unable to identify the infectious agent with routine laboratory tests and sent off samples of sputum to the Netherlands for further analysis. The causative agent was identified by Ron Fouchier and colleagues as another novel coronavirus, but part of the same family that caused SARS. A study published in the *New England Journal of Medicine* in September 2012 alerted the world to this new virus, which became known as Middle East respiratory syndrome coronavirus or MERS-CoV. Other cases were soon identified in the Middle East, as well as in infected travellers returning from the Middle East to their home countries, including the UK, the USA, Europe, Africa and Asia.

With no known cure or vaccine, the disease has a worryingly high mortality rate (greater than SARS) and is, currently, leading to the death of some 30 to 40 per cent of all people contracting this lethal coronavirus. It does not, however, appear to be highly transmissible between people, though those in close contact with patients, including family members and health workers, are at increased risk – most probably through inhaled droplets when an infected person sneezes or coughs – making it vital that infection prevention and control measures in homes, hospitals and elsewhere are introduced to prevent its spread.

By August 2014, there had been a total of 855 laboratory-confirmed cases, including at least 333 related deaths (the majority in Saudi Arabia) but, so far, while the WHO says that MERS-CoV is of 'major global concern', it has not yet been declared an international public health emergency. Nevertheless, vigilance is needed, and many of the lessons learned from SARS are being implemented and revised to prevent the wider transmission of MERS-CoV. Of particular concern has been the possibility that it would spread during the haj in Mecca, Saudi Arabia – the largest yearly recurring religious mass gathering in the world, which attracts over 2 to 3 million Muslim pilgrims from around 180 countries. Fortunately, no cases of MERS-CoV were detected among the pilgrims during the hajj of 2014.

Like SARS and many other newly emerging viruses, scientists are trying to track down the origins of this disease. Bats may be the original hosts though not, necessarily, the direct source in transmitting the disease to humans. A surprising finding came when a close link with the virus was identified in dromedary camels in the Arabian Peninsula. Several of those who have contracted or died from MERS-CoV have been in contact with camels. Until more is known about whether bats or camels are the natural host, the WHO is advising people to take precautions when working with sick animals and to avoid drinking raw camel milk, camel urine or eating meat that has not been properly cooked. In the meanwhile, disease surveillance officials at the forefront of monitoring and forecasting global viruses are watching and waiting – and hoping – that this will not become another pandemic of the twenty-first century.

Lifestyle Diseases

SCURVY

When European seafarers began to embark on long voyages of exploration and trade in the late fifteenth century, they met with many new hazards. One of the most insidious of these was scurvy, which we now know to be caused by a lack of vitamin C. Away at sea for weeks or even months on end, sailors had to put up with filthy, cramped living conditions, and a monotonous and barely nutritious diet of foul water, rations of rum, rancid salt meat, dried fish, seabirds, 'mouldy maggoty biscuits' and the occasional rat. Afflicted with bleeding gums, livid spots on the skin and foetid breath, the 'scurvy sailor' was not a pretty sight – and if the disease went unchecked, the result was an agonizing death. In the mid-eighteenth century James Lind (1716–94) came up with compelling evidence that a daily dose of orange and lemon juice (which contains the critical vitamin C) prevents the disease. Next to famine, scurvy has caused more suffering than any other nutritional disease in history. Fortunately, scurvy is now a rare disease, but other conditions associated with poor nutrition continue to 'plague' the modern world. Striking a successful balance between alleviating hunger and curbing rising obesity is a major global challenge for the twenty-first century.

∾

Of all the hazards of life at sea – storms, shipwrecks, battles and infections – none claimed as many lives as scurvy. Between the fifteenth and nineteenth centuries, it is estimated that as many as 2 million European sailors succumbed to this hideous and painful disease. Scurvy, or scorbutus, became the scourge of the sea.

The disease started slowly and insidiously. The first signs were aching joints and lethargy – sailors showing such symptoms were often flogged for 'laziness'. Then, some weeks later, the visible omens of death would spread over the body: black, bloody patches under the skin, wobbly teeth, spongy and swollen purple gums, seething sores. By the time the disease had taken hold, the afflicted emitted an intolerable stench of putrefaction – just one more stink to add to the cocktail beneath decks of rotting food, urine, faeces and vomit. When death eventually came the victim was sewn into his hammock. The Dutch and the English buried their dead at sea by slipping the corpse overboard, but the French and Spanish took their deceased home for burial.

Long sea voyages

Scurvy occasionally occurred on land, but it was particularly rife on long sea voyages. When the Portuguese navigator Vasco da Gama (c.1469–1524) sailed round the Cape of Good Hope to Asia in 1497–8, it is said that scurvy cost the lives of 100 men from a crew of 160. During the first circumnavigation of the world in 1519–22, the sailors commanded by the Portuguese-born explorer Ferdinand Magellan (1480–1521) under the Spanish flag attempted to stave off starvation and scurvy by eating rats, sawdust and wild celery. Magellan himself was killed in a battle in the Philippines, and when the last ship of his original fleet of five docked in Spain in September 1522, completing the voyage, only 18 out of the original 270 or so crew had survived. One chronicler wrote: 'above all other calamities this [scurvy] was the worst: in some men the gums grew over the teeth . . . so that they could not eat in any way and thus they died of this sickness.' Christopher Columbus and his crew, however, were probably spared – since the expeditions to the New World across the Atlantic were of shorter duration, lasting less than a couple of months.

As other crews endured deadly encounters with scurvy on longer sea voyages, Admiral [Sir] Richard Hawkins (1562–1622), the English seaman and explorer, recorded: 'In twentie years that I have used the sea I dare take upon me to give an accompt of ten thousand men consumed with this disease . . . for it is the plague of the sea and spoyle of mariners.' Many graphic accounts of scurvy entered the literature. English naval surgeon William Clowes (c.1540–1604) thus described the symptoms of his crew:

> Their gums were rotten even to the very roots of their teeth, and their cheeks hard and swollen, the teeth were loose neere ready to fall out . . . their breath a filthy savour. Their legs were feeble and so weak, that they were not scarce able to carrie their bodies. Moreover they were full of aches and paines, with many blewish and reddish staines or spots, some broad and some small like flea-biting.

One English sailor and sufferer wrote: 'It rotted all my gums, which gave out a black and putrid blood. My thighs and lower legs were black and gangrenous, and I was forced to use my knife each day to cut into the flesh in order to release this black and foul blood . . . I rinsed my mouth and teeth with my urine'. Tobias Smollett, in his novel, *The Adventures of Roderick Random* (1748), included the experiences of a surgeon's mate at sea: 'Here I saw fifty miserable distempered wretches suspended in rows . . . each patient breathing nothing but a noisome atmosphere of the morbid steams exhaling from their own excrements and diseased bodies, devoured with vermin hatched in the filth that surrounded them'.

Mariners desperately attempted to search for an answer to prevent the 'plague of the sea' and many remedies were tried.

Oranges and lemons and a peck of scurvy grass

Admiral Hawkins, from his experience of scurvy during his 1590s expedition to the South Seas, astutely recommended 'Sowre Oranges and Lemmons' as 'the most fruitfull remedy for this sickness'. He was not the first or only person to point to fresh fruit as a possible remedy. Indeed, by the beginning of the seventeenth century there was an increasing number of reports commending orange, lemon or lime juice as 'an infallible prophylactic and cure' for scurvy. For example, of four English East India Company vessels sailing for the Spice Islands (Indonesia) in 1601, one escaped devastation by scurvy. This exception was the *Red Dragon*, commanded by James Lancaster (*c.*1554–1618), who every morning had given his sailors a few spoonfuls of bottled lemon juice which he had taken to sea.

In practice, however, it was all but impossible to carry perishable provisions such as fresh fruit on long voyages. Occasionally, if a ship landed at a port, the officers might enjoy the savours of fresh produce for a short while, but for the bulk of the crew, the taste of citrus fruit would have been a rare, and probably unknown, treat.

Another popular remedy, grown in medieval physic gardens, was a plant known as scurvy grass (*Cochlearia officinalis*). William Clowes described 'the cure of two seafaring men that fell sicke at sea of the Scorby': the cure was a mug of new ale spiced with pepper, cinnamon, ginger, saffron, watercress and 'a peck of scurvy grass purely picked and cleane washed'. A story from the seventeenth century tells of a ship ravaged by scurvy just off Greenland. One sailor was so close to death that his ship-mates put him ashore to die, where he 'grazed like a beast' on scurvy grass. He survived.

Scurvy grass, we now know, pales in comparison with fresh fruit as a remedy for scurvy. But it was a lot better than some of the other alternatives tried out to cure scurvy. Bleeding, purgatives, sulphuric acid, vinegar and mercury paste – this last 'cure' smeared onto oozing sores – often proved as dangerous and deadly as the disease itself.

Meanwhile, physicians puzzled over the real cause of this horrifying disease. Was it the salted and smoked meats, the mouldy and maggoty ship's biscuits, or the absence of fresh food? Or perhaps it was the cold damp air of the sea, the lack of exercise, the 'slothfulness' of the sailors, the foul vapours of the air below decks, an excess of 'black bile', or some mysterious miasma or contagion?

James Lind and the first clinical trial

In 1734 Johann Friedrich Bachstrom (1686–1742), a Polish pastor living in Holland, wrote his *Observationes circa scorbutum*, in which he noted: 'Its causes have been generally, though wrongfully, supposed to be, cold in northern climates, sea air, the use of salt meats, etc., whereas this evil is solely owing to a total abstinence from fresh vegetable food, and greens; which is alone the true primary cause of the disease.' With so many pointing their fingers at the importance of a 'missing factor' in the diet, and suggesting that fresh fruit and vegetables might act as a remedy, historians have wondered why it took so long for the medical profession to act on this hypothesis. But how to turn speculation into proof? James Lind, recently qualified as a doctor from Edinburgh, and appointed as a surgeon on HMS *Salisbury* in 1747, was able to do just that (at least in part).

In the early 1740s, shortly before Lind's appointment, the curse of scurvy was dramatically highlighted when 997 out of 1,955 sailors died of scurvy during a voyage to the Pacific of a British fleet under Commodore George Anson (1697–1762). When Lind joined HMS *Salisbury*, then patrolling the English Channel, many of the mariners aboard were already seriously sick with scurvy. Lind decided it was time to test some opposing theories and to base his work on 'attested facts and observations'.

On 20 May 1747, he identified twelve men with similar symptoms: 'they all in general had putrid gums, the spots and lassitude, with weakness of knees.' He sent them down to the ship's sick bay and conducted his now famous 'clinical trial'. For fourteen days each pair of men was to be given an addition to their usual diet:

Pair 1: 'a quart of cyder a-day'
Pair 2: 'twenty-five gutts of *elixir vitriol* three times a-day'
Pair 3: 'two spoonfuls of vinegar three times a-day'

Pair 4: 'a course of seawater'
Pair 5: 'two oranges and one lemon given them every day'
Pair 6: 'nutmeg three times a-day' and 'a decoction', which included garlic, mustard-seed, 'balsam of Peru' and 'gum myrrh' washed down with barley water.

The results were astonishing. The pair receiving two oranges and one lemon daily 'which they ate with greediness' recovered rapidly – even before the meagre supply of fruit had run out after six days. Lind had, or so he hoped, found the obvious 'remedy' for scurvy. In 1753 he published his findings in *A Treatise of the Scurvy*, followed in 1762 with *An Essay on the Most Effectual Means of Preserving the Health of Seamen in the Royal Navy*, noting: 'The results of all my experiments was, that oranges and lemons were the most effectual remedies for this distemper at sea.'

A recipe for 'rob'

But while Lind had produced convincing evidence that a daily dose of citrus fruit was a remedy for scurvy, even he remained confused about the actual cause of the disease. He favoured the idea that the disease was a result of damp, unwholesome air and 'putrefaction' on board ships. Lind was, moreover, realistic about the practicalities of taking fresh fruit on long voyages, and so came up with a recipe for 'rob' of oranges and lemons, a syrupy concoction which would not spoil over time.

When Captain James Cook (1728–79) and the young naturalist Joseph Banks (1743–1820) were sent on a voyage by the British Royal Society and Royal Navy to the South Pacific in 1768, they took with them a number of possible 'anti-scorbutics' – barrels of malt, sauerkraut, carrots, mustard and a small quantity of Lind's 'rob' of oranges and lemons. They stopped wherever possible to supplement their supplies with fresh fruit, plants and water. As Joseph Banks recalled: 'My gums swelled and some small pimples rose on the inside of my mouth which threatened to become ulcers. I then flew to the lemon juice . . . the effect was surprising . . . In less than a week my gums became as firm as ever'. When they eventually returned to Britain in 1771 they were able to report that almost none of the crew had died of scurvy. It was not clear, however, to Cook or those reading his earlier reports, which of the various 'anti-scorbutics' were actually effective – but there was no doubt that the supplements provided to the sailors' diet (as well as Cook's insistence on cleanliness and ventilation) were radical improvements.

British 'limeys'

Some have suggested that had the British heeded the advice of James Lind and the practice of Captain Cook, the War of American Independence (1775–83) might have turned out differently. The British lost many men at sea in the skirmishes, but more to scurvy. By contrast, it has been mooted that during the Napoleonic Wars (1803–15) the British had the upper hand over the French at sea partly because they had begun to tackle scurvy. In 1795 the British Admiralty, following the recommendation of the naval physician, Gilbert Blane (1749–1834), imposed a regulation that after two weeks at sea every sailor should be provided with a daily allowance of an ounce of lemon juice with one and a half ounces of sugar. As a result, Nelson's fleet in the Mediterranean consumed over 50,000 gallons of lemon juice! In 1808, the US Navy also began issuing lemon juice on long sea voyages. Many, like Blane, were convinced that Lind had found a solution: 'But of all the articles, either of medicine or diet, for the cure of scurvy, lemons and oranges are of much the greatest efficacy . . . they are the real specifics in that disease . . . this was first ascertained and set in a clear light by Dr Lind.'

But it was not all plain sailing! Lemons from the Mediterranean were expensive, and difficult to obtain in the required quantities, so the Royal Navy turned instead to limes from the British West Indies – hence British sailors subsequently became known as 'limeys'. Unfortunately, the juice of the lime was far less effective than that of the lemon, and the whole debate was, for a time, thrown open again. Even Lind's long-lasting 'rob' of oranges and lemons (which, because of the preparation process, actually lost some of its potency) was less than ideal. Some physicians began to doubt the efficacy of the citrus fruit remedy. However, by the middle of the nineteenth century, and several million gallons of citrus juice later, scurvy had virtually disappeared from the British fleet.

The preservation of fruit juice at this time was usually done through the addition of rum (popular with the sailors!). In the 1860s Lauchlan Rose (1829–85), a descendent of a prominent family of Scottish shipbuilders, devised a method for allowing citrus juice to remain active as an anti-scurvy agent without the addition of alcohol as a preservative. Sweetening the juice with sugar to prevent fermentation, and sealing it in glass bottles, he patented his method in 1867 and launched Rose's lime juice. Rose set up a factory in Leith, importing limes from the Caribbean island of Dominica, and his company also began to produce soft drinks for public consumption. Indeed, many non-alcoholic beverages today are a by-product of the long search for the prevention of scurvy.

Scurvy on land

Scurvy continued to occur in other environments, causing many deaths in prisons, workhouses and orphanages in Europe and America. During the Irish famine of the 1840s following the failure of the potato crop, scurvy was rife (potatoes are a good source of vitamin C), and in the same decade it severely affected the 'Forty-niners' of the Californian Gold Rush. Elsewhere it debilitated armies. In 1846 American sailors blockading Mexico during its war with the USA suffered badly from scurvy, as did British and French soldiers during the Crimean War and American soldiers during the American Civil War, especially in prisoner of war camps. Many suffered from scurvy during the Siege of Paris in 1870–71. It was also a constant problem for polar explorers. In the late nineteenth and early twentieth centuries, 'infantile scurvy' hit the upper classes of Europe and the USA: mothers who eschewed breast-feeding, preferring to feed their babies with preserved milk products, unwittingly deprived their offspring of vitamin C, which is present in breast milk.

The discovery of vitamin C

For some decades following the discovery of the 'germ theory' in the second half of the nineteenth century, scientists looked for a bacterial cause of scurvy. One naval surgeon proposed that the benefit of citrus juice was simply that it acted as an anti-bacterial mouthwash. It was not until the biochemical studies of the 1910s onwards that scientists such as Frederick Gowland Hopkins (1861–1947) and Christiaan Eijkman (1858–1930), who shared the 1929 Nobel Prize in Physiology or Medicine, became convinced that the key to poor nutritional health lay in the absence of crucial elements or 'accessory food factors' in the diet.

It gradually became clear that nutritional deficiencies of one kind or another were responsible for a number of diseases, including scurvy (a deficiency of vitamin C), as well as pellagra (a deficiency of niacin, a B-complex vitamin), beriberi (a deficiency of vitamin B1), rickets (a deficiency of vitamin D in the diet or caused by lack of sunshine) and iron-deficient anaemia. The word 'vitamin' itself (originally 'vitamine', combining Latin *vita*, 'life', and 'amine', a chemical substance) was coined in 1912 by Casimir Funk (1884–1967), a Polish-born biochemist working at the Lister Institute, London. (The final 'e' was dropped in 1920 when it became clear that not all vitamins were amines.)

Vitamin C was isolated by Albert von Szent-Györgyi (1893–1986), a Hungarian scientist working at the time at Cambridge University. In 1928 he found an unknown compound in adrenal-gland tissue, as well as in cabbages and oranges. Szent-Györgyi thought it was a sugar, but he wasn't sure what kind of sugar it was. The chemical names of sugars (like glucose, fructose, sucrose, etc.) end in the suffix '-ose', so, professing his own ignorance, he called the mystery compound 'ignose'.

When the editor of the *Biochemical Journal* received a copy of his paper describing his discovery (which was to earn him a Nobel Prize in 1937), he sent it back, suggesting Szent-Györgyi rename it. He returned his manuscript, calling the compound 'godnose'. Eventually, the frustrated editor named it 'hexuronic acid' (because it contained six atoms of carbon). It was subsequently called 'ascorbic acid', and is now widely known as vitamin C.

It has since been shown that a deficiency of vitamin C inter-feres with the syntheses of collagen (a substance found in the body's connective tissues and bones), giving rise to bleeding, bruising, poor healing and the eventual onset of scurvy. Since the 1930s the sales of manufactured vitamins and vitamins added to food has been big business.

From malnutrition to a global epidemic of obesity

The story of scurvy is not quite over. The disease can still occur in areas of the world where fresh fruit and vegetables are in short supply, or in people who, for various reasons, have little vitamin C in their diets. Rickets, a deficiency of vitamin D which leads to bone deformities and stunted growth and was once associated with the 'dark' polluted Victorian slums, is now making a come-back. Moreover, a whole range of broader problems associated with malnutrition continue to affect societies, especially in the poorest parts of the world (as well as in times of conflict, natural disasters and famines).

Globally, about 800 million people are estimated to be under-nourished – or around one in every ten of the world's growing population. Forms of severe acute malnutrition – in which there is inadequate protein or calorie intake, mainly affecting young children at the time of weaning – are often known as marasmus (meaning 'wasting away'), kwashiorkor (a Ghanaian word meaning a disease suffered by a child displaced from the breast) and the combined form – marasmic kwashiorkor. Another affliction is iron-deficiency anaemia – poor diet is one major factor but chronic diseases such as schistosomiasis and hook-worm also lead to anaemia (from the Greek word meaning 'without blood'), and a staggering two billion of the world's population are thought to be anaemic. Persistent diarrhoea, pneumonia, measles, tuberculosis, HIV/AIDS and malaria can, additionally, undermine nutritional status, especially of children and pregnant women. Infectious diseases acting in combination with hunger and starvation account for the premature deaths of millions of infants, children and young adults in the developing world. The UN's Millennium Development Goals (2000–15) and the recent 'Zero Hunger Challenge' aim to 'eliminate' both poverty and hunger in the coming decades – though these will be hard goals to achieve.

At the other end of the nutrition scale, by contrast, is now what the media and the WHO call 'a global epidemic of obesity'. This is seen as one of the major 'new' public health problems of the twenty-first century. Associated with obesity and rapidly changing lifestyles has been the dramatic rise in type 2 diabetes, which is estimated to affect around 350 million people worldwide and is predicted to be the seventh leading cause of death by 2030. And this is not just a problem for the wealthier nations. Paradoxically, while low- and middle-income countries battle to overcome conditions resulting from under-nutrition, some 80 per cent of diabetes deaths occur in these countries as they adopt the lifestyles of the industrialized world.

Nutritionists and health experts continue to remind us that children and adults alike need a daily dose of fresh fruit and green vegetables, and warn of the over-consumption of sugar; fatty foods and high salt-intake; the dire consequences of being overweight; the dangers of high cholesterol levels; the problems associated with lack of physical exercise; and the heightened risk of developing diabetes as well as an array of other serious health disorders. Fast foods, chips and burgers may taste better than maggoty biscuits and salt beef, but 'prevention is better than cure', and a balanced and nutritious diet, along with physical activity, remains vital for the future health of us all.

KURU, CJD AND DEMENTIA

Kuru is the name associated with a mysterious and fatal disease that was first observed by scientists in Papua New Guinea in the mid-twentieth century. Their investigations suggested a link between the disease and the ritualistic practice of eating the brains of deceased kinsfolk. Creutzfeldt-Jakob disease (CJD) is a very rare degenerative brain disorder that occurs sporadically throughout the world and was originally described in the 1920s. Scientists have recently proposed that both kuru and a new form of CJD (variant CJD) are caused by infectious agents known as 'prions', which are also linked to a number of animal diseases, including bovine spongiform encephalopathy (known as BSE or 'mad cow disease') in cattle, scrapie in sheep and chronic wasting disease in deer and elk. CJD has also been associated with growth hormone originally extracted from cadavers. In both humans and animals, prion diseases can cause devastating and deadly symptoms, with the tissues of the brain becoming 'spongiform' – riddled with holes, like a Swiss cheese. In humans CJD is associated with 'dementia', but the latter is a very general term for a large number of diseases affecting the brain, the vast majority of which are 'sporadic' and not infectious. The best known form of dementia is Alzheimer's disease, a neurodegen-erative disorder leading to memory loss and cognitive impairment that is very strongly age-related and is currently the most debilitating and distressing of these conditions across the globe. Scientists are now urgently trying to unravel its causes and to link this information to find much-needed effective treatments.

∾

In the early 1950s, J. R. McArthur, an Australian government patrol officer working in the South Fore region of the highlands of Papua New Guinea, came across a strange medical condition amongst the local inhabitants. In a diary entry for 1953 he noted: 'Nearing one of the dwellings I observed a small girl sitting down beside a fire. She was shivering violently and her head was jerking spasmodically from side to side. I was told that she was a victim of sorcery, and would continue thus, shivering and unable to eat, until death claimed her within a few weeks.' The Fore people used the word *kuru*, which translated means 'trembling' or 'fear', to describe what McArthur had witnessed. The group of tribespeople had been virtually isolated from the rest of the world until the late 1940s. They claimed that the untreatable condition, which they attributed to the malevolent activities of sorcerers in their midst, was a relatively new affliction and had spread slowly within living memory. McArthur realized that this was an important new mystery – and one that needed a solution.

Kuru – the trembling death

Over the next few years, Vincent Zigas (1920–83), district medical officer in the Australian Public Health Service, together with the American virologist Daniel Carleton Gajdusek (1923–2008), worked to uncover the mystery of kuru. Initially they suspected that it was an inherited genetic disorder. They and others trekked across hundreds of miles of remote mountain and jungle regions, mapping and documenting the villages afflicted by kuru. They observed its symptoms – which included involuntary tremors, jerks, uncontrollable outbursts of laughter, loss of co-ordination, wasting and eventual death. They listened and talked to the Fore people, watching their eating patterns, their customs and rituals. They collected specimens of blood, cerebrospinal fluid and urine, and sent them off to research laboratories in Australia and the USA for examination. Women and children seemed to die from kuru far more often than men. But it was invariably a man who was accused of being the sorcerer responsible for the 'bewitched' victim's death, and who might subsequently be hacked to death by his fellow tribesmen in a ritual known as *tukabu*.

In Vincent Zigas' autobiography, *Laughing Death: The Untold Story of Kuru* (published posthumously in 1990), he described one of many tragic cases of kuru. Walking past a village hut he saw a Fore woman who held 'on her lap a limp figure, grossly emaciated to little more than skin and protruding bone, the shivering skeleton of a boy, looking up at me with blank crossed eyes.' The child died the next day. His father had already died in a *tukabu* killing. The combination of kuru and *tukabu* was beginning to destroy whole villages and break up the entire fabric of Fore society.

Deadly funeral feasts

Researchers, including Australians Robert Glasse, Shirley Lindenbaum and Michael Alpers, working in the Fore area in the 1960s, conducted further anthropological and epidemiological studies to try to understand the cause of this mysterious disease. Kuru, it was proposed, might possibly be related to the consumption of the brains of relatives who had died of the disease. From the late nineteenth century it had become a custom among the Fore people of Papua New Guinea to prepare their dead kinsfolk for burial by cooking and eating parts of their dismembered bodies at a funeral feast. Some Fore thought that the soul resides in the brain, so eating the brain of a dead relative was the way to give the deceased eternal life. It was the women, assisted by their children, who took the main role of cutting up the corpses, and scooping out and eating the brain tissue. It was suggested that it was in this way that kuru was passed from person to person, and the predominant role of women in this practice explained why they were far more commonly infected than men. It was also thought possible that an unknown 'infection' could have been acquired by handling the corpses, the infectious agent entering the body through skin lesions, sores or cuts, or via nose-picking or eye-rubbing.

The number of cases of kuru reached its peak in the late 1950s, but by the mid-1960s few if any children were contracting the disease. The decline of kuru was attributed to the end of ritualistic cannibalism in the mid- to late 1950s, which had come about as a result of government and missionary intervention.

The scrapie connection

On the other side of the world – in Britain, Iceland and the USA – a number of scientists who had been trying to elucidate the cause of a disease of sheep known as scrapie (or sheep distemper) were struck by its similarities with kuru.

Scrapie had been described in Europe since the early

eighteenth century, and is so called because the intense itching that accompanies the disease causes the sheep to rub themselves against walls, trees, rocks or fences. One of the first reports of scrapie among sheep was printed in the 1750s in the London *Journal of the House of Commons*. Its regional names included the 'shakings', 'goggles' and the 'rubbers'. Scrapie was, like kuru, also known as 'the trembles'. Sheep and goats affected by the condition were observed to lose control, staggering around and eventually dying from a slow wasting disorder. Thomas Comber described its symptoms in eighteenth-century Lincolnshire:

> The principal symptoms of the first stage of this distemper are a kind of high headedness. The affected sheep appear much wilder than usual . . . In the second stage the principal symptom of the sheep is his rubbing against trees, posts, etc. . . . with such fury as to pull off his wool and tear away his flesh . . . The third and last stage . . . the poor animal appears stupid . . . till death follows.

Over the following centuries, veterinarians and others tried to work out the cause of scrapie and to see whether it was an infectious or an hereditary disease. In 1954, an Icelandic scientist, Björn Sigurdsson (1913–59), suggested that a 'slow virus' might be the causative agent of scrapie. As chance would have it, a few years later an American veterinary scientist, William Hadlow (b.1921), who was also studying scrapie, visited an exhibition in London at the Wellcome Museum of Medical Science that told the story of kuru. Observing photographs of victims of the disease, it suddenly hit him: 'The kuru brains had holes . . . just like those in scrapie brains.' In 1959 he published a paper suggesting that scrapie and kuru had distinctly similar pathologies.

Carleton Gajdusek, inspired by such ideas, began to search for evidence of the 'slow virus' hypothesis for kuru. In collaboration with field workers in Papua New Guinea and with C. Joseph Gibbs (1924–2001) in the USA, Gajdusek and his colleagues were able to inject brain tissue from people who had dies of kuru into chimpanzees. Within two to three years the chimps developed very similar symptoms to those of kuru, suggesting that the agent causing kuru was infectious, like a virus, but that the disease had a long incubation period, with symptoms in humans taking many years to develop. Gajdusek, Gibbs and Alpers published their first findings based on these experiments in a paper in *Nature* in 1966. A decade later, in 1976, Gajdusek was awarded the Nobel Prize in Physiology or Medicine – which he shared with Baruch Blumberg (1925–2011), the latter receiving the prize for his work on the hepatitis B virus – 'for their discoveries concerning new mechanisms for the origin and dissemination of infectious diseases'.

CJD and the discovery of prions

'The story of prions is truly an odyssey that has taken us from heresy to orthodoxy.' Stanley Prusiner, Nobel banquet speech, Stockholm, 1997

This might have been the end of the story, but it proved to be only the beginning of one of the most intriguing medical discoveries of the late twentieth century. At the University of California, San Francisco, the physician and research scientist, Stanley Prusiner (b.1942), had been shocked by the symptoms of a patient who died of CJD (Creutzfeldt-Jakob disease) in 1972. CJD is named after two German doctors, Hans G. Creutzfeldt (1885–1964) and Alfons M. Jakob (1884–1931), who had first described a strange form of dementia in humans in the 1920s. (The term 'dementia' is derived from the Latin, *de-* 'out of' and *mens*, 'the mind'). The classical form of CJD is an extremely unusual sporadic neurological disease (with only one or two cases a year per million of the population), but for those afflicted it proves devastating. The patient begins to show early signs of dementia, which is followed by the destruction of the brain. Prusiner was told that the possible cause of CJD was a 'slow virus'. Intrigued, over the next decade Prusiner began exploring the possible links between CJD, scrapie and kuru.

He was especially struck by a 1967 publication by the radiation biologist Tikvah Alper (1909–95) and colleagues in London who had developed the theory that scrapie is caused by an infectious agent made solely of protein and lacking nucleic acid. The scrapie agent had also been found to have some strange properties, including being resistant to destruction by radiation or ultraviolet light. This 'unheard-of' idea of an 'infectious agent' that did not even contain RNA and DNA had provoked immediate scepticism, although Alper's theory had been taken up at the time by Cambridge scientist J.S. Griffith (1928–72) who proposed that under certain circumstances proteins might be able to self-replicate. In the late 1970s, however, Edinburgh-based researchers put forward the idea that a 'new' type of virus which they called a 'virino' could be the infectious agent for scrapie. Following up on these often confusing leads, Prusiner began to study the scrapie agent, and also visited Papua New Guinea to try to pull together some of the pieces of the story and to solve its mysteries.

In 1982 Prusiner published a paper in the prestigious journal *Science* that 'set off a firestorm'. By carrying out experiments with hamsters, he produced evidence to show that the cause of scrapie was not, as suspected, an 'unconventional slow virus' but in fact, a very different kind of infectious agent. It was an aberrant form of protein, or, as he called it, a prion (which he pronounced as 'pree-on' and was short for 'proteinaceous infectious particle'). Although able to self-replicate, prions – unlike other infectious agents such as bacteria, viruses, parasites and fungi – lacked nucleic acids, the conventional genetic agents of biology. In 1997 Prusiner was awarded the Nobel Prize in Physiology or Medicine for his discovery of prions – 'a new biological principle of infection'.

Mad cows and Englishmen

Between the time that Prusiner put forward his prion ('protein-only') hypothesis and the award of his Nobel Prize, another intriguing and alarming part of the puzzle unfolded – the outbreak of 'mad cow' disease in cattle, primarily in the UK.

In 1984 a farmer in Britain noticed that his cows were acting strangely: staggering around, and behaving aggressively. When one of the cows died, an autopsy revealed that the animal's brain had sponge-like holes in it. The symptoms and signs were curiously very much like scrapie and kuru. Across Britain, more and more cows began to show similar abnormal symptoms and eventually dying. Scientists quickly set to work to find out what was causing this 'mad cow' disease.

The disease was soon called by its scientific name, bovine spongiform encephalopathy (BSE). While its origins remained puzzling, it was suggested that one possible source of the infection was the consumption by cows of contaminated feed. Cows are herbivores, but by the 1970s intensively reared cattle were being fed all sorts of other substances, such as proteins derived from sheep and cattle offal, including brain and spinal cord. It was also suspected that changes in the rendering process, by which the proteins for animal feed were extracted from carcasses of cattle, might have resulted in less effective removal of the sources of the infection. Scrapie, the prion disease in sheep, had, it was speculated, jumped the species barrier to become BSE in cows. Once within the cattle population, the disease spread rapidly throughout herds in the UK. It was, according to some, reminiscent of kuru, but in this case the cannibalism involved was 'high tech'.

In 1988 the British government took action and banned the use of animal-derived feed supplements for cattle. All cattle that could possibly be affected by BSE were slaughtered, with major consequences for the farming and food industry, but by 1992/3 the number of infected cows had reached its peak. In spite of some politicians saying otherwise, however, there was a very real fear: if cattle could have been infected by consuming tissue from sheep with scrapie, could humans have been infected by eating 'mad cow' meat?

New variant CJD

In 1996 an article in the British medical journal *The Lancet* voiced the first serious concerns about the implications of BSE for human health. Over the previous years a CJD surveillance centre based in Edinburgh had monitored cases of patients dying of CJD. In a small number of cases they noticed significant differences from those with the rare classical or sporadic form of the disease. The patients were younger (with a median age of death of twenty-eight years, compared to sixty-eight years in the classical cases), the course of the disease was different – usually beginning with personality and behavioural changes before developing neurological signs and progressing to dementia – and the clinical course from the first symptoms to death was more protracted.

It was postulated that this new 'variant' form of human CJD (vCJD) had come from eating beef (possibly in the form of sausages and hamburgers) prior to the UK ban on using offal in cattle feed in the late 1980s. The official report cautiously stated the theory that vCJD 'is due to exposure to the BSE agent is perhaps the most plausible interpretation'. The press picked up the story as 'Mad Cow Disease Kills Humans'.

With the fear that an epidemic of vCJD was about to explode amongst people who had eaten contaminated beef products, more cattle were slaughtered. British beef was banned from export, and tighter regulations were imposed to prevent any infected meat ending up either within cattle feed or on supermarket shelves. By the early twenty-first century the British BSE epidemic had, however, come to an end and the ban on the export of British beef was lifted, but occasional cases of BSE have occurred in several parts of the world, including Canada and the USA, causing concern and prompting constant vigilance.

Initial predictions of a major human vCJD epidemic have not been borne out in practice, and this condition, thankfully, remains very rare. It has, however, been hugely traumatic for those afflicted by this progressive, degenerative and ultimately fatal 'prion' disease, and, of course, for their families and friends. Since the human disease was first reported in 1996, around 220 cases of vCJD have been identified, the majority in the UK, with small numbers in several other countries, including France and the USA.

Surveillance continues in order to diagnose and determine

whether or not cases of vCJD have peaked since BSE-infected cattle were removed from the human food chain – or whether, given its long incubation period, there is the possibility that new cases of vCJD are still to surface. Concern has also been raised as to whether 'silent carriers' could unknowingly pass on the infectious proteins or prions, for example, through donated blood – highlighting the need for screening every potential donor.

Scrapie (in sheep and goats), BSE (in cattle) and vCJD (in humans), as well as kuru, are also known as 'transmissible spongiform encephalopathies' (TSEs) because of their ability to be transmitted both by infectious prions and to cause the characteristic spongiform degeneration of the brain. What had begun as the mysterious disease, kuru, in Papua New Guinea and an esoteric discussion in scientific circles about the cause of a rare class of animal and human neurological disorders, has led to the revolutionary discovery of 'a new biological principle of infection.' But even that is not the end of the story . . .

Dementia and Alzheimer's disease

At the first ever G8 Dementia Summit held in London in December 2013, the British prime minister, David Cameron, spoke about the global challenge of dementia – a condition which has now been called the 'twenty-first century plague' – and described it in the following words: 'It doesn't matter whether you're in London or Los Angeles, in rural India or urban Japan – this disease [dementia] steals lives; it wrecks families; it breaks hearts.' In referring to 'dementia' the G8 Summit was addressing not the very rare transmissible spongiform encephalopathies (TSEs, i.e. the 'infectious' prion diseases), but the much more common non-transmissible sporadic neurodegenerative disorders which are also devastating diseases of the brain leading to dementia. Amongst these disorders the most common form, accounting for 70 per cent of all cases of dementia, is Alzheimer's disease, named after Alois Alzheimer (1864–1915), who, in a lecture in 1906, first described its symptoms and pathological character from observing a patient. Alzheimer's disease is now one of the most distressing and debilitating conditions of the modern age. It is estimated that some 40 million people worldwide suffer from this progressive neurodegenerative disease, with predictions that, unless effective treatments are found, there will be 140 million sufferers by 2050, including many in low- and middle-income countries, with incalculable personal, social and financial consequences. Alzheimer's disease is primarily a disease of the elderly – increasing age is the key risk factor in the vast majority of cases, and it is thought that over one-third of people who have reached the age of eighty-five have at least some symptoms of this condition. It has risen to prominence as life expectancy has increased in modern times. The financial cost, primarily of patient care, is huge – already approaching £30 billion per annum in the UK and over $200 billion in the USA – but it is impossible to quantify the fear and hopelessness that patients experience as the disease progresses, and the pain and anguish suffered by their relatives and friends.

The symptoms of Alzheimer's disease include memory loss, disorientation, and a decline in cognitive and intellectual functions. Understanding this particular set of currently incurable diseases is of enormous importance, given the effects of an ageing population on society and health care, and much progress has been made in the last two decades. Indeed, Alzheimer's disease is just one of a much larger group of at least fifty types of medical disorders that also includes Parkinson's disease (named after James Parkinson, 1755–1824) and Huntington's disease (after George Huntington, 1850–1916), and also rare conditions such as 'fatal familial insomnia'. This class of diseases is associated with a phenomenon in which proteins can 'misfold' and clump together to form toxic deposits in various different organs and tissues in the form of 'amyloid' fibrils or plaques. In the case of neurodegenerative conditions such as Alzheimer's disease, these damaging forms of proteins form in the brain, leading to cognitive impairment, although in some systemic conditions deposits can be found in many other locations in the body, including the liver, kidneys and heart. Remarkably, one of this group of 'protein misfolding' diseases is type 2 diabetes, in which the deposits form in the pancreas and affect insulin production and regulation. Interestingly, the major risk factor of this latter protein misfolding disease is not ageing, but another 'modern' phenomenon, namely obesity, resulting primarily from unhealthy diets and lack of exercise.

The underlying reasons for the aberrant deposition of misfolded proteins is currently being explored not just at the clinical level but also at the molecular level, the latter by interdisciplinary research groups including that led by Christopher Dobson (b.1949) in Cambridge. Some of these types of disease are 'familial', that is, they are associated with genetic mutations. In Huntington's disease, for example, all cases are familial, but in other disorders, such as Alzheimer's or Parkinson's diseases, only a small fraction of cases can be linked to specific mutations which usually give rise to early-onset forms of disease, while the vast majority are termed 'sporadic'. In these latter cases, the onset of disease occurs spontaneously, as the result of the 'clumping together' of misfolded forms of one specific type of protein in each of the diseases. Indeed, it is now evident that in general proteins have an inherent tendency to misfold, and hence to aggregate, but very efficient protective mechanisms have evolved within our bodies to detect and degrade such species before they can proliferate and cause damage. But such mechanisms become less effective as we get older, or in the case of type 2 diabetes if, we adopt unhealthy diets and take too little exercise, these protective mechanisms may, at some point, be overwhelmed, allowing the disease to develop.

In this context it is very interesting to note that although prion diseases such as vCJD differ fundamentally from disorders such as Alzheimer's and Parkinson's disease in terms of the transmissable nature of the former and the non-infectious nature of the latter, there are similarities in that both types of disorder are associated with the misfolding, aggregation and deposition of protein molecules. In the case of the prion diseases the condition is initiated by the ingestion of misfolded proteins, whereas in Alzheimer's disease, for example, it results from an increasing probability of the failure of our inherent protective mechanisms as we age. Moreover, there is increasing evidence that the mechanisms of the relentless progression of these diseases, once they have been initiated by the different means, could be similar, in the sense that the misfolding clumps of proteins in each case have the ability to 'spread' through tissue (in these examples the brain) from one cell to another.

At present – while scientists are unravelling the intriguing, detailed mechanisms by which the misfolding and aggregation processes are initiated and then spread in each type of neurodegenerative disease – it is frightening to realize that, as yet, there are no effective drugs or vaccines to prevent or cure these conditions (and even diagnosis cannot be generally confirmed in a definitive manner except at post-mortem by examining the brain). Nevertheless, there is increasing optimism that by understanding the molecular nature and inherent origins of these causes of dementia the international community will be able to devise rational diagnostic and therapeutic strategies that will enable the early detection, treatment and indeed prevention, of what has been called the 'twenty-first century plague'.

CANCER

Cancer is a generic term for a large group of over one hundred related disorders. Cancer can develop in any part of the body. It can cause diverse symptoms and result from many different causes, some known, others still unknown. Its unifying feature is a loss of control of normal cell division, which results in a proliferation of abnormal cells, often forming tumours. Cancer cells can also break away from their site or organ of origin to invade other parts of the body, a process known as metastasis. Cancer is not a new disease – it was known to the ancients. Over the centuries people have tried to remove, cure or control cancerous tumours, and scientists continue to search for ways to destroy rogue cells or 'switch off' the underlying mechanisms that lead to their proliferation. In the past century or so there have been some remarkable developments in diagnosing and understanding the disease, as well as the discovery of new therapies. The combination of surgery, radiotherapy and chemotherapy has been increasingly pivotal in helping cancer patients to survive. Campaigns to advertise the association of 'lifestyle' risk factors with cancer, such as smoking and unhealthy diets, are also important in preventing this tragic disease. But in spite of the successes of modern medicine, cancer remains a serious global disease in both advanced and, increasingly, in developing nations, accounting for around 8.2 million deaths worldwide every year and ranking as one of the leading global killers of the twenty-first century.

∽

In 1811 the English novelist Fanny Burney (1752–1840) was in France when she was 'cut', without anaesthetic, for cancer of the breast by the famous French military surgeon Dominique-Jean Larrey (1766–1842). She was lucky to survive, and later recalled her excruciating experience:

> when the dreadful steel was plunged into the breast – cutting through veins – arteries – flesh – nerves – I needed no injunctions not to restrain my cries. I began a scream that lasted unintermittingly during the whole time of the incision – & I almost marvel that it rings not in my Ears still! so excruciating was the agony. When the wound was made, & the instrument was withdrawn, the pain seemed undiminished, for the air that suddenly rushed into those delicate parts felt like a mass of minute but sharp & forked poniards, that were tearing the edges of the wound, – but when again I felt the instrument – describing a curve – cutting against the grain, if I may so say, while the flesh resisted in a manner so forcible as to oppose & tire the hand of the operator, who was forced to change from the right to the left – then, indeed, I thought I must have expired . . . I attempted no more to open my eyes . . . The instrument this second time withdrawn, I concluded the operation over – Oh no! presently the terrible cutting was renewed – & worse than ever, to separate the bottom, the foundation of this dreadful gland from the parts to which it adhered . . . yet again all was not over.

In the end the operation lasted a full twenty minutes – but it nevertheless saved her life. Even the surgeon, Larrey, was traumatized by the suffering he had inflicted on Fanny, as she had witnessed: 'I then saw my good Dr Larrey, pale nearly as myself, his face streaked with blood, its expression depicting grief, apprehension, & almost horror.'

In the early nineteenth century there were few effective therapies or treatments for cancer, and the cause and nature of the disease were baffling. And as Fanny Burney's case illustrates, it was only as a last resort, when the disease had spread and clearly manifested itself, that surgeons would attempt the removal of a tumour. Patients were offered little in the way of anaesthetics to help dull the pain of such a drastic operation. Fanny's experience is a chilling reminder of the agonies and suffering caused by cancer and its mutilating treatment.

The modern rise of cancer

While there are now far more effective ways of treating cancer than in Fanny Burney's day, the disease nevertheless continues to take a terrible toll on modern societies. Cancer has become increasingly 'visible' over the past century, touching many people's lives, whether as sufferers, carers or through bereavement. In the Western world, one in three or four of the population will develop cancer at some time. Cancer is today more common than it was in the past, for many reasons. Partly this has to do with the age-related spectrum of cancer. As life expectancies have risen in recent times in modern societies, so cancer has become one of the leading diseases of middle and older age groups (although a number of cancers affect young children). The process of ageing is also a fundamental factor in the development of many cancers – as people age their cellular repair-and-control mechanisms tend to be less effective. Modern lifestyles and environmental as well as genetic links have also been identified as 'risk factors', and infectious agents are now known to be associated with a number of cancers, contributing to an understanding of the rise in cancer in the developing world. Improvements in early detection, screening and diagnosis are also helping to increase awareness of this disease. Oncology – the scientific study of cancer (from the Greek *ónkos*- referring to a 'mass', 'bulk' or 'swelling') – is very much a product of modern medicine.

Cancer – a disease dating back to antiquity

Cancer is probably as old as the human race. Some of the first written accounts of human cancer were recorded in the Babylonian *Code of Hammurabi* (*c.*1750 BC), the ancient Egyptian Edwin Smith Surgical Papyrus (*c.*1600 BC), the Chinese Rites of the Zhou Dynasty (*c.*1100–400 BC) and the ancient Indian *Ramayana* manuscript (*c.*500 BC). A recently excavated skeleton of a young man buried in a painted wooden coffin in Sudan, dating back to around 1200 BC, shows evidence that cancer affected his bones.

The Greek physician, Hippocrates is thought to have been the first person to recognize the difference between malignant ('bad') and benign ('good') tumours. Indeed, the disease was named by the Greeks in the fifth century BC. The Latin word *cancer* means 'crab', and originally came from the Greek word for the same creature: *karkinos*. One possible reason for the name is that the pain of the disease was like being pinched by a crab. Or perhaps the allusion was to the way in which tumours grasp the tissues in which they grow. Another possibility is that the swollen blood vessels around a malignant tumour looked like the claws of a crab, as the Graeco-Roman physician Galen suggested: 'For just as in that animal the feet extend out from both sides of the body, so also in this disease the distended veins call to mind the picture of a crab.' Galen wrote a book on tumours, describing over sixty kinds, and the Roman encyclopaedist Aulus Cornelius Celsus (25 BC–AD 50), in his work, *De medicina*, clearly described superficial cancers of the face, mouth, throat, breast and penis, as well as cancers of the liver, spleen and colon.

Black bile and cutting-edge discoveries

The ancients sought explanations as to why cancer occurred, and why certain types of people were most at risk. Cancer was clearly very different from the epidemic plagues and pestilences that would arrive suddenly from time to time and rapidly strike many down with grisly symptoms and a quick death. Malignant tumours were relatively rare, less visible and slower to kill their victims than most 'murderous plagues'. In line with the humoral theory – in which health depended on the proper balance of four 'humours' within the body – Greek and Roman physicians held that cancer was the result of an excess of black bile (*melas*, 'black' and *khole*, 'bile'). People with a 'melancholic' disposition, accordingly, were seen as more susceptible to cancer.

A wide range of treatments was tried over the centuries for visible cancers, such as applying cabbage juice, or a mixture of honey, salt and egg white, or caustic creams and pastes. Paracelsus (*c.*1493–1541), the Swiss physician and alchemist, recommended that cancer should be treated with simple or compound chemicals, including mercury and arsenic (an early form of chemotherapy). Purging and bloodletting were also common practices for cancer, as well as for many other diseases. Some seemingly bizarre recipes made their way into ancient and medieval medical texts, including using frogs in oil and live toads to suck out the cancer poison. In cases of ulceration, rotten apples, frogspawn, pigs' ears, fresh veal or pigeon (cut up while still alive), or half a dog or cat placed on the tumour, were advised. One popular treatment – following the Doctrine of Signatures, the idea that nature would indicate the most appropriate treatment – was to lay a crab or crayfish on the tumour. But most people with deep-seated or 'occult' malignant growths were thought to be incurable. As the Hippocratic Corpus (c.fifth century BC) had suggested: 'It is better not to apply any treatment in cases of occult cancer; for, if treated, the patients die quickly; but if not treated they hold out for a long time.'

The tumours that were seen by the ancient and early medieval physicians were usually those that were apparent at the surface, especially breast cancers. The human body was deemed sacred in most ancient cultures in the West, and few physicians investigated internal human organs either of the living or the dead. Galen had based most of his anatomical investigations on animals, including pigs, goats, Barbary apes, and, on one famous occasion, the emperor's pet elephant. From the fourteenth century AD, however, anatomical dissections of human cadavers (mostly limited to a few executed criminals) began to be permitted in Europe as a teaching aid in medicine. One of the most influential anatomists was the Flemish physician Andreas Vesalius (1514–64). He dissected many human corpses – mostly of executed criminals or stolen from cemeteries – and in 1543 published a remarkable book called *De humani corporis fabrica libri septem*, with illustrations of the structure of the human body.

Anatomical studies – often in purpose-built anatomical theatres – increasingly led to an understanding of the make-up of the human body and how it functions, including the discovery by William Harvey (1578–1657) of the circulation of the blood. Cancer was still relatively rare in the early modern period. John Graunt (1620–74) compiled a 'Table of Casualties' in 1662 in which cancer was grouped among several miscellaneous causes of death (including gangrene and fistulas). Many puzzles about its pathology remained to be investigated, though in 1622 the Italian anatomist Gaspare Aselli (1581–1626) discovered the lymphatic system – challenging the old theory that black bile was the cause of cancer.

From the eighteenth and early nineteenth centuries, dissections were also increasingly conducted on those who had died in hospital (usually the poor), and the correlation of clinical and post-mortem examinations began to raise further questions about Galenic models of cancer, opening the doors to new understandings of the disease. Anatomists such as the Italian Giovanni Morgagni (1682–1771) highlighted connections between the symptoms of the sick person and the morbid changes in the organs found in their bodies after death, while the French anatomist Marie-François-Xavier Bichat (1771–1802) suggested that diseases were predominantly seated in tissues rather than whole organs. It is said that Bichat sometimes slept in the morgue of the Hôtel-Dieu hospital in Paris to maximize his dissecting opportunities!

'Omnis cellula e cellula'

The real breakthrough in our understanding of the pathology of cancer came with the ability to study human cells under the microscope (an invention of the late sixteenth century), whereby abnormalities could be seen not just in organs and tissues but at the cellular level. The term 'cell' had been first coined in the 1660s by Robert Hooke, the British natural philosopher. He had used this term to describe the minute structures in cork he has seen under the microscope. By the early nineteenth century more powerful microscopes, such as those designed by Joseph Jackson Lister (1786–1869) using achromatic lenses (which transmit light without separating it into its constituent colours), led to the beginnings of histology (study of tissues) – making it possible to differentiate cancer cells from normal cells. In 1832 Thomas Hodgkin (1798–1866), the English physicist and pathologist, described cancer of the lymph nodes, and in 1838 the German physician Johannes Müller (1801–58) analysed the microscopic features of benign and malignant tumours, attributing cancer to the formation of new cells inside a diseased organ, with a potential to spread to other parts of the body.

The German scientists Theodor Schwann (1801–82), Matthias Jakob Schleiden (1804–81) and Johannes Müller added further insight, and suggested that cells are the basic unit of life. This idea paved the way for the development of the cellular theory proposed by Rudolf Virchow (1821–1902), the German 'father of pathology'. Virchow placed slivers of flesh and smears of blood under the microscope and noticed that a mass of flesh that looked undifferentiated to the eye was, in fact, made up of millions of microscopic cells. He realized that cells were fundamental to life, and is best known for the theory he proposed in 1858: '*Omnis cellula e cellula*' – all cells come from cells. Virchow also recognized that the condition that he named leukaemia (from the Greek *leukos*, 'white', and *haima*, 'blood') was characterized by a proliferation of abnormal white blood cells. We now know that leukaemia is a cancer of the blood. Disease, Virchow argued, arose from abnormal changes within cells, and these could multiply out of control through division and spread to the rest of the body (a process in cancer known as 'metastasis'). This was the beginning of the modern science of oncology, and would eventually lead to the development of drugs to block the proliferation of tumour cells.

Tumours, surgery and the fire drill

Virchow published numerous studies on the cellular dimensions of cancer, urging his students 'to think microscopically'. But when presented with a case of cancer, the question always arising was: should the tumour be excised? Whether or not to wield the surgeon's knife is a quandary that goes back to antiquity.

Hippocrates and Galen, followed by the Persian physician Rhazes, and the French military surgeon Ambroise Paré (1510–90), were generally against excision of deep tumours. In their view the risk of death far outweighed the likelihood of cure, as incisions were likely to turn gangrenous and putrefy. In some desperate cases, however, cutting out a tumour does seem to have been tried, and attempts were made to cauterize the incision using a red-hot iron known as the 'fire drill'. The pain from both procedures, with no anaesthetics to put the patient to sleep apart from the soporific effects of alcohol or various narcotics such as opium, must have been horrific, as Fanny Burney's account attests.

Surgery (a word derived from the Greek *cheir*, 'a hand' and *ergon*, 'work' – i.e. 'handiwork') was always viewed with terror in the days before anaesthetics and antiseptics. With their knives, amputating saws and cauterizing irons, surgeons (the 'Mr Sawbones' of the early modern world) were satirically compared to butchers or torturers. The patient was often forcibly held or even chained down while the surgeon plied his knife into the diseased area and then used his red-hot cautery to staunch the flow of blood. Surgery was learned on the battlefield, on the kitchen table and below deck in the warship and, it has been said, it was a craft which required 'an eagle's eye, a lion's courage and a woman's hand' – and (perhaps most importantly for the patient) 'speed'. Though as one seventeenth-century cynic, Maximilianus Urentius, put it: 'wherein differs the surgeon from the doctor? In this way, that one kills with his drugs, the other with his knife. Both differ from the hangman only in doing slowly what he does quickly.'

However, by the late eighteenth and early nineteenth centuries, as the knowledge of human anatomy increased, surgeons were acquiring a newly elevated status, and more adventurous operations, including excising tumours, were being performed. Another stoic who underwent a bloody and traumatic operation for cancer without pain relief was Mrs Jane Todd Crawford. In 1809 Ephraim McDowell (1771–1830), a US country surgeon in Kentucky, performed the first successful operation to remove a diseased ovary (a procedure now known as an ovariectomy) from his patient using his kitchen table to operate on. The operation took twenty-five minutes, during which Mrs Crawford recited psalms and hymns – one can hardly imagine the agony as the surgeon cut through her abdomen to excise what proved to be a massive tumour (besides which, at one point, her 'intestines rushed out upon the table'). Mrs Crawford not only survived, but lived to the age of seventy-eight. When reports of this and several other daring operations reached London medical circles, they responded: 'A back-settlement of America – Kentucky – has beaten the mother country, nay, Europe itself, with all the boasted surgeons thereof in the fearful and formidable operation of gastrostomy, with the extraction of diseased ovaria.'

Back in London, Scottish surgeon Robert Liston (1794–1847) was famous for the speed of his operations, when, according to his admirers, 'the gleam of his knife was followed so instantaneously by the sounds of sawing as to make the two actions appear almost simultaneous.' With students packing the gallery of the University College Hospital operating theatre, pocket watches in hand, Liston would stride across the bloodstained floor, often in Wellington boots, and call, 'Time me, gentlemen, time me.' In 1823 he performed an operation that caused a sensation at the time. He removed a large scrotal tumour that measured 107 cm (42 inches) in circumference and weighed 20 kg (44.5 pounds). Blood loss was likened to a shower. The patient sank off the table, pulseless and flaccid, but with the help of a 'cordial' (a pint of good strong whisky) poured down his gullet, he began to show signs of recovery. Three weeks later, he walked out of the hospital.

Pain relief and sterile surgery –
anaesthesia, antisepsis and asepsis

The successful outcome of these operations for cancerous tumours, while widely publicized, was, nevertheless, very much the exception rather than the rule. As with many surgical operations and amputations, there was not only the horrendous trauma for the patient but also the huge risk of post-operative infections.

Surgery was, initially, transformed in the mid-nineteenth century by the introduction of anaesthesia which meant that not only was the patient oblivious to the painful cutting, but the surgeon, too, had more time to concentrate on where to put his knife and how best to remove, for example, a tumour. A Japanese physician, Hanaoka Seishū (1760–1835), had already achieved fame within Japan in the early nineteenth century by his method of rendering patients unconscious using a herbal concoction containing extracts of several different plants. This was based on an ancient Chinese remedy, which he called tsūsensan or mafutsu-san. In 1804, he excised a large cancerous breast tumour from a woman, and went on to perform many operations using tsūsensan and 150 operations for breast cancer. But the isolation of Japan prevented Hanaoka Seishū's achievements in anaesthesia from becoming known outside Japan until isolation ended in 1854.

In the Western world the first highly publicized demonstration of using the gas 'ether' as an anaesthetic in surgery was in the USA, at the Massachusetts General Hospital, Boston, in the now famous 'Ether Dome' on 16 October 1846. A young man, Gilbert Abbott, with a benign vascular tumour of the neck, was strapped down on the operating table, awaiting not just the surgeon's knife but the arrival of twenty-seven-year-old William Morton. This young dental surgeon had been experimenting with ether as a way to 'diminish the sensibility of pain' for patients.

As the clock ticked by, Morton arrived in the nick of time with an apparatus that he offered to the patient, allowing him to inhale its gaseous contents and, with luck, put him into a deep painless sleep. During the thirty-minute operation, carried out by the surgeon John Collins Warren (1778–1856), Abbott was heard to mutter, and said afterwards that he had felt some pain, but that it was only as if 'the skin had been scratched with a hoe'. Everyone in the audience watching this operation and its outcome was awestruck, and news of this amazing invention spread far and wide.

Chloroform was another gas used, shortly afterwards, as an anaesthetic in surgery. 'Conquering pain' was a radical step forward, but there remained the danger of what was often known as 'sepsis' following an operation. The pioneering discovery by the Scottish surgeon Joseph Lister of the use of carbolic acid to prevent wounds turning septic, first successfully tested in 1865 on a boy in Glasgow with a compound fracture, was another remarkable innovation. Lister quickly turned his attention to the general principle of 'antisepsis'. His aerosol spray of carbolic acid was used throughout operating theatres (literally spraying everybody and everything) and became an iconic piece of apparatus (known as the 'donkey engine') employed to minimize post-operative infections, though this was subsequently replaced by yet another practice, known as 'asepsis'.

As an understanding of 'germ theory' spread among a new generation of bacteriologists, the aim of asepsis was to exclude 'germs' in the first place, without the skin irritation of chemical antiseptics. Dramatic blood-encrusted frock-coats (once seen to be the most noteworthy attire of a successful surgeon) were gradually abandoned in favour of clean surgical gowns, caps, gloves and masks and the steam sterilization of surgical instruments and dressings. Following Lister, generations of brilliant surgeons pioneered new surgical techniques, becoming bolder and braver in their efforts. The newly sterile, well-equipped operating theatres of the late nineteenth century encouraged increasingly ambitious operations. For breast cancer patients, this included radical mastectomy in which the breast, all the lymph glands in the nearest armpit, and the muscles of the chest wall were removed. This procedure had been advocated by the British surgeon Astley Cooper (1768–1841) in the 1820s and was followed up by the American surgeon William Halsted (1852–1922) using aseptic techniques.

X-rays and radiotherapy – a ray of hope

By the end of the nineteenth century anaesthesia, antisepsis and asepsis had, undoubtedly, made some surgical operations for the removal of solid tumours less horrendous, but for the most part patients still preferred not to yield to the terrors of the surgeon's knife. The success of surgery was, moreover, limited, especially since it was usually only those patients with advanced stages of cancer who were seen by the physician and operated on by the surgeon. The early stages of cancer invariably went undetected. It was, however, becoming increasingly clear that cancer was on the rise in many countries, and was called by one surgeon, 'the emperor of all maladies, the king of terrors'.

In 1895 the chance discovery of X-rays by the German physicist Wilhelm Röntgen changed the outlook for cancer detection and treatment. X-rays were immediately used for non-invasive diagnostic purposes, and tumours could be detected long before the ominous signs and symptoms of cancer appeared. X-rays also proved to have a therapeutic function – it was noticed that they caused burns and could be used to treat minor skin problems such as moles, acne, ringworm and excessive hairiness. The potential for destroying cancerous cells was quickly picked up.

The discovery of X-rays was followed in 1898 by the discovery in France of the radioactive elements polonium and radium by the wife and husband team, Marie (1867–1934) and Pierre Curie (1859–1906). With various refinements in the technology of radiotherapy over the next few decades there was, at last, a way of treating cancer, albeit an expensive one. In the early days there was also a human cost, with some patients as well as radiographers dying as a consequence of excessive doses of radiation. Marie Curie, who received two Nobel Prizes (in Physics in 1903 and in Chemistry in 1911) for her outstanding contributions to science, died of leukaemia possibly caused by years of exposure to X-rays.

Radiotherapy did not replace surgery, but was initially often used to reduce inoperable tumours to operable size, and also to reduce pain and to help stop recurrence after the operation. Radiotherapy was sometimes advertised as 'surgery without the knife' to encourage people who feared surgery into becoming their own cancer sentinels – watching, waiting and seeking diagnosis and early treatment at the first possible signs of cancer. Geoffrey Keynes (1887–1982) at St Bartholomew's Hospital, London, in the 1920s and 1930s found that the simple removal of breast tumours (lumpectomy), rather than radical mastectomies, could be successfully followed up by radiation.

'Infallible cures', mustard gas and chemotherapy

Prior to the mid-twentieth century, surgery and radiotherapy were all that could be offered to cancer patients. There were no effective drugs, although over the centuries numerous 'cures' for cancer had been tried, including various chemicals. Mercury was often employed both externally and internally, while it was claimed that arsenic prevented cancers from ulcerating. Itinerant quacks sold supposedly 'infallible' remedies for any disease you cared to name – for example, in the late nineteenth century 'Hamlin's Wizard Oil' (containing camphor, ammonia, chloroform, turpentine and herbs) was said to cure everything from constipation to cancer. An advert in 1912 for 'Dr. Chamlee's Cancer Specific' offered a supposedly 'miraculous cure' simply by taking a teaspoonful in water before or after meals, claiming it: 'Purifies the Blood and Removes all Cancer Virus from the system. It will prevent the return of Cancer if taken freely for three months after the Cancer is removed . . . It is the only remedy that has ever been discovered to cure Cancer in the blood.' The label on the bottle did add the caveat: 'We will not be responsible if Cancer should come in another place, unless at least three bottles have been taken.'

By this time a range of alternatives to orthodox medicine – such as homeopathic remedies, water therapy, mesmerism and vegetable or electrical cures – had also been taken up by cancer sufferers. In the early decades of the twentieth century, many orthodox doctors and surgeons had become concerned that such 'treatments' were preventing people from seeking early diagnosis, radiotherapy and surgery.

It was not, however, until after the Second World War that chemotherapy became an added and vital component of cancer treatment. The term 'chemotherapy' was first used by the German bacteriologist Paul Ehrlich in the early twentieth century to describe a chemical agent that would target and kill a specific micro-organism in the body without unduly harming the host's healthy cells. His first so-called 'magic bullet' was Salvarsan, used to treat syphilis. Ehrlich went on to propose that cancerous cells could also be destroyed by chemicals without harm to the healthy host tissue.

The first step in cancer chemotherapy was the recognition that mustard gas, used as a deadly chemical weapon in the First World War, decreased the number of white blood cells in soldiers who had been exposed to it. Some reasoned that it might also be used therapeutically to destroy cancer cells. In the 1940s the Americans Louis Goodman (1906–2000) and Alfred Gilman (1908–84) tested a number of related nitrogen mustard agents. One was administered to a mouse with a lymphoma (a tumour of the lymph cells) and, amazingly, the tumour shrank. Several patients with advanced lymphomas were injected with the compound. Although successful in the short term, the effect proved only temporary. These experiments did, however, stimulate further research into new cytotoxic drugs – drugs capable of destroying rapidly proliferating cells in tumours.

One of the most fundamental advances in chemotherapy took place in 1948 at the Boston Children's Hospital in the USA and is described in fascinating detail by Siddhartha Mukherjee in his Pulitzer-prize winning book, *The Emperor of All Maladies: A Biography of Cancer* (2011). The US physician and paediatric pathologist Sidney Farber (1903–73) – now considered as the 'father of modern chemotherapy' – used folic acid antagonists (antifolates) for treating acute lymphoblastic leukaemia (ALL) in children – demonstrating that antifolates could interfere with and suppress the proliferation of malignant cell growth. Watching children coming into remission, albeit mostly only temporarily, following his initial trials was a remarkable first step.

One of Farber's patients was a twelve-year-old baseball fan known as 'Jimmy'. In 1948 his heroes from the Boston Braves baseball team visited Jimmy, and a national radio show was broadcast from Jimmy's hospital bedside. Americans were moved by his story and donations poured in for a 'Jimmy Fund', which continues to this day to help youngsters suffering from cancer. Jimmy (whose real name was Einar Gustafson) recovered from cancer and visited the charity on its fiftieth anniversary. He became an ambassador for the Jimmy Fund before his death from a stroke at age sixty-five in 2001.

The 'War on Cancer'

Farber's pioneering work was instrumental in showing that effective pharmacological treatment of cancer was possible, and initiated the modern postwar search for, and development of, a number of anti-cancer agents. In 1955 the Cancer Chemotherapy National Service Center in the USA was set up, and hundreds of thousands of compounds were screened and tested for anti-cancer activity under the slogan 'Nothing too stupid to test'. In the early 1960s the recognition that alkaloids of the Madagascar periwinkle (*Vinca rosea*) blocked proliferation of tumour cells led to the development of vincristine. With the introduction in the mid-1960s of combination therapy (using a number of drugs, each with a different action) there was optimism that further research would yield the answers to cancer. Farber together with the socialite and philanthropist, Mary Lasker (1900–94), campaigned for more funding and lobbied the US government to raise the profile of cancer. As Farber wrote in 1970: 'We are so close to a cure for cancer. We lack only the will and the kind of money and comprehensive planning that went into putting a man on the moon.' The following year, the US Congress passed the National Cancer Act of 1971, which committed an initial $500 million to wage a 'Crusade Against Cancer'. In signing the Act, President Richard Nixon announced that America would make a 'total national commitment' towards 'conquering this dread disease'. This was a major turning point in the history of cancer. Increasingly, more funds and resources were devoted to cancer research. In other countries, too, substantial resources were directed towards universities and research institutes, and a huge industry, involving pharmaceutical and biotech companies, grew up around what had become known as the 'war against the "Big C"'.

Paclitaxel (Taxol) from the bark of the Pacific Yew tree; tamoxifen (an antagonist of the oestrogen receptor in breast tissue); cisplatin and anti-cancer drugs based on platinum compounds, were some of the drugs to emerge following this huge input of resources for scientific and pharmaceutical research into chemotherapy. Three types of previously incurable cancer – childhood leukaemia, Hodgkin's disease (a cancer of the lymph nodes) and testicular cancer – were among the first to respond successfully to various newly discovered drugs. Anti-emetics (anti-nausea drugs) have also been developed to help overcome some of the unpleasant side effects of chemotherapy.

As more has been understood about cancer at the molecular level, one 'targeted' strategy has been to employ large biological molecules known as monoclonal antibodies or mAbs – proteins that can be created to bind to a chosen target with exquisite specificity. Herceptin, an mAb to combat breast cancer, was the first bioengineered drug to gain FDA approval in 1998. A complementary approach is to use small synthetic chemicals designed to target specific cancer-causing proteins caused by aberrant genes. Gleevec is one such molecule, and is used to treat chronic myeloid leukaemia (CML) and gastrointestinal stromal tumour (GIST).

With the increasing use of new diagnostic and computerized imaging techniques in the 1970s and 1980s, such as CT/CAT scans (computerized tomography), PET (positron emission tomography) and MRI (magnetic resonance imaging), as well as mass screening for some common cancers such as those of the breast and cervix, early diagnosis has helped to ensure a greater chance of survival. Many cancer patients can now be treated with a range of options. 'Adjuvant' and 'neo-adjuvant therapy' are terms applied when varying combinations and sequences of surgery, radiotherapy and chemotherapy are used.

There have been many significant recent advances in developing new drugs, innovative surgical and radiation techniques, and different approaches to treatment (with the further prospect that strategies such as immunotherapy, use of stem cells, gene therapy and personalized treatment can play a future role in the 'war on cancer'). However, for many cancers, especially those in advanced stages, there is, sadly, still a long way to go in terms of finding effective therapies.

Cancer hospitals, hospices and palliative care

Most cancer patients are treated in general hospitals, but in high-income countries there are also specialist cancer hospitals with state-of-the-art diagnostic and medical equipment. In fact, the earliest cancer hospitals were set up some centuries ago. The first hospital solely devoted to cancer patients was founded in 1740 under the will of Jean Godinet (1661–1739) in the city of Rheims, France. In Britain in the late nineteenth century, Samuel Whitbread (1720–96) – best remembered for his brewery – gave a substantial sum of money to the governors of the Middlesex Hospital in London for the establishment of a cancer charity for the hospital. The principle objects of the bequest were 'the relief of persons afflicted with cancer, and the investigation of a complaint which, though extremely common, is, both with regard to its natural history and cure, but imperfectly known.' The first cancer ward, with twelve beds, opened in 1792, and over the following decades as it expanded, careful clinical records were kept in the hope of understanding the 'nature of the disease'. Also in London, the Free Cancer Hospital (later the Royal Marsden Hospital) was founded by William Marsden (1796–1867) in the mid-nineteenth century. As a newly qualified surgeon, Marsden had already played a major role in helping the sick poor by setting up a hospital called the London General Institution for the Gratuitous Cure of Malignant Diseases (now known as the Royal Free Hospital), after finding a young girl one cold winter night in 1828 close to death on the steps of the church of St Andrew's, Holborn. She had been refused admission by three of the city's voluntary hospitals.

Marsden decided to open a hospital for those who had no letters of recommendation, which were then necessary for admission to Britain's voluntary hospitals, and in 1837 the hospital was granted a royal charter from Queen Victoria. The Royal Free remains a continuing centre of excellence. Following the tragic death of his first wife, Betsy Ann, aged thirty-six, from uterine cancer, Marsden, at a board meeting, expressed a wish: 'Now, gentlemen, I want to found a hospital for the treatment of cancer, and for the study of the disease, for at the present time we know absolutely nothing about it.' The Free Cancer Hospital was opened in 1851 and, now as the Royal Marsden (its royal charter was granted in 1910 by King George V), continues to be one of leading specialist hospitals for cancer in the world.

For many cancer patients, especially those in the terminal stages of the disease, palliative care is an essential component of a patient's treatment. The term 'palliative care' was coined in the 1970s and is derived from Latin, *palliare*, 'to cloak'. It embraces an approach that improves the quality of life for patients and their families facing problems associated with chronic and incurable life-threatening illness. Many organizations and hospices around the world now offer palliative care – some dating back to the early and mid-twentieth century. In 1911, the Society for the Prevention and Relief of Cancer was founded by Douglas Macmillan (1884–1969), following the painful death of his father from cancer. The Society became increasingly involved with cancer support, as indicated in its new name, Macmillan Cancer Support, and continues to play a vital role in fundraising and helping cancer patients and their families throughout all stages of the illness. Another charitable organization, the Marie Curie Memorial Foundation (now Marie Curie Cancer Care), was created in 1948 to support nursing and home care for the terminally ill, and remains dedicated to alleviating suffering from cancer.

A leading advocate of palliative or holistic care, as well as strong pain relief (using morphine – an alkaloid extracted from opium in the early nineteenth century) for the terminally ill, was Cicely Saunders (1918–2005). In 1967, she opened the world's first modern hospice – St Christopher's Hospice in south London. Her pioneering work has been instrumental in drawing attention to the end-of-life needs of cancer patients as her poignant message to patients reminds us: 'You matter to the last moment of your life. We will do all we can, not only to help you die peacefully, but also to live until you die.'

Environmental and lifestyle cancers

'To cease smoking is the easiest thing I have done. I ought to know because I have done it a thousand times.' Mark Twain (1835–1910)

While struggling to find cures and ways of caring for cancer patients over the past centuries, scientists and physicians have also tried to work out why cancers occur in the first place. The older Galenic idea that certain people with 'melancholic' temperaments were predisposed to cancer persisted for many centuries. Some physicians additionally suggested that cancer was hereditary, while others believed it was contagious. Medical and domestic health books advised people to avoid activities that might 'excite' the onset of cancer, such as the wrong diet, the wearing of corsets by women, incorrectly fitted dentures, or insufficient exercise.

Environmental associations were also considered. One of the

earliest studies to suggest a link between cancer and an external environmental agent dates back to the second half of the eighteenth century, when a British surgeon called Percivall Pott observed that men with cancer of the scrotum on his wards at St Bartholomew's Hospital in London had been chimney sweeps as boys, where they had been 'thrust up narrow, and sometimes hot chimnies where they are bruised, burned and almost suffocated; and when they get to puberty, become peculiarly liable to a most noisome, painful, and fatal disease'. Pott hypothesized that cancer of the scrotum was linked with the irritation caused by soot.

The English physician Alfred Haviland (1825–1902), using national mortality statistics for England and Wales in the second half of the nineteenth century, mapped the geography of cancer in an attempt to locate the areas with a high cancer rate and then look for the environmental determinants of the disease.

By the twentieth century, scientists began to examine some of these ideas and to speculate that external environmental as well as lifestyle factors – something in the air people breathed, the food they ate, the alcohol or tobacco they consumed, the conditions in which they worked – might be part of the cancer story. The list of possible carcinogenic (cancer-causing) agents that came under scrutiny was endless. Some of them were highly speculative, but others – such as tar on the roads, traffic fumes, industrial pollutants, smog, chemical dyes, viruses, radiation and pesticides – were more plausible.

With better statistics on the incidence and causes of death in the twentieth century, it became possible to examine long-term trends of cancer mortality and to map the distribution of various cancers with a view to finding environmental associations or behavioural risk factors. One of the most startling of all the findings came in the late 1940s as epidemiologists discovered that a dramatic increase in lung cancer had emerged over the course of the previous few decades: deaths from lung cancer in the USA had escalated from fewer than 400 recorded cases in 1900 to over 11,000 in the mid-1940s – and in Britain they had shot up by some six-fold between the 1920s and the 1940s. What was the cause of this alarming trend?

A number of studies were set up in the UK and the USA to find an answer, and by the early 1950s there emerged one key factor – smoking. Although both a German study in the early 1920s and an American publication in the late 1930s had suggested this link, their work had not received the attention it deserved. Indeed, the 'horrors' caused to the body by tobacco, shortly after it was introduced from the Americas to Europe, were publicized by King James I (r.1603–25) as long ago as the early seventeenth century. In 'A Counterblaste to Tobacco', he described smoking as 'a custom loathsome to the eye, hateful to the nose, harmful to the brain, dangerous to the lungs, and in the black stinking fume thereof, nearest resembling the horrible Stygian smoke of the pit that is bottomless'. King James organized the first public debate on the effects of tobacco at Oxford and, to make his point, he displayed black brains and black viscera, allegedly from the bodies of smokers. However, chewing or smoking tobacco (initially in pipes) remained widely popular, and, with the later mass production of cigarettes in the early twentieth century, smoking became a widespread, fashionable and, inevitably, addictive habit. Massive advertising campaigns promoted smoking, an activity also glamorized in Hollywood movies. Some advertisements even claimed that smoking had health benefits!

One of the most thorough investigations of the twentieth-century rise in lung cancer was the study initiated by the British epidemiologists Austin Bradford Hill (1897–1991) and Richard Doll (1912–2005) in the early 1950s. They wrote to all doctors in Britain to enquire about various aspects of their lives, including their smoking habits. Many doctors at that time smoked – often quite heavily – not perceiving any particular risk in the highly addictive habit. It was even quite commonplace in the 1950s for doctors to offer a cigarette to patients to calm them down. Over a number of years 40,000 male doctors were tracked, and it quickly became apparent that heavy smokers ran a significantly higher risk of lung cancer than non-smokers. Mortality fell if individuals stopped smoking (though still remaining higher than that of the group of lifetime non-smokers), thus high-lighting for the first time a possible way of preventing a major form of cancer.

Ironically, when this now classic study was begun in the 1950s, Richard Doll had not expected to come up with such a strong association between lung cancer and smoking. He later recalled: 'If I had to put money on anything at the time, I should have put it on motor exhausts or possibly the tarring of the roads ... but cigarette smoking was such a normal thing and had been for such a long time that it was difficult to think it could be associated with any disease.'

Further studies supported the smoking/lung cancer association, and from the 1970s, with increasing fears about passive as well as active smoking, anti-smoking lobby groups, supported by governments, began to take up the cause. 'Smoking kills' has become one of the biggest single health education messages of the late twentieth and early twenty-first centuries, with many countries introducing bans on advertising and smoking in enclosed public places, and imposing high taxes on tobacco and health warnings on cigarette packets.

Over the course of the twentieth century it is estimated that 100 million people died worldwide from smoking-associated diseases. Lung-cancer incidence and mortality has, however, now fallen for men in the USA and Europe, although the figures for women continued to rise through the 1990s, reflecting the more recent uptake of smoking amongst young women and the time lag between exposure and disease. In other parts of the world the message is only slowly having an impact. In China, annual cigarette consumption rose from 100 billion in the early 1950s to over 2,000 billion in the early twentieth century. It is predicted that over the coming years, smoking-related mortality (including fifteen other types of cancer besides lung cancer, as well as heart and chronic obstructive pulmonary disease) will rise in many parts of the world.

Cancer – a complex and varied disease

Smoking is one of the clearest lifestyle risk factors (accounting today for 70 per cent of global lung cancer deaths and 22 per cent of all cancer deaths), but cancer is a complex and varied disease with many causes – some known, others still to be identified. Indeed, in 1931, the American pathologist James Ewing (1866–1943) in his publication, *The Causation, Diagnosis and Treatment of Cancer*, stressed that cancer is not a single disease but has multiple forms and multiple causes.

Every day the media report on the latest scare story, or, if we are lucky, on the most recent optimistic scientific breakthroughs. More than one-third of cancer deaths could, it is thought, be prevented by modifying key 'risk factors', including diet. While some recommendations are clear (fresh fruit and vegetables, together with physical exercise, are good; high salt and sugar intake and too much alcohol are not so good), the issues are multi-faceted and the media often give us confusing and conflicting messages. The causes and consequences of obesity are anything but simple, though it seems that high body-mass index (BMI) might be linked to certain cancers as well as to other non-communicable diseases (NCDs).

Excessive exposure to the sun's ultraviolet light is a well-known key factor in the increase of skin cancer, and, like smoking, is avoidable (though even this has led to a dilemma, as there is concern that some children are now being so well-protected, for example with sun-screen lotions, that there is a rising incidence of rickets, associated with a lack of sunshine and Vitamin D). Additional cancer risk factors include air pollution, various occupational exposures, and many naturally occurring or industrial chemicals. Asbestos, for example, is one of a number of carcinogenic agents that has been identified since the 1980s, prompting its removal from many buildings where it had been used in the past prior to the knowledge of its dangers and risks.

Genetic factors add yet further complexities to the puzzle of how, why and who develops cancer. An insight into the role of genes in the development of tumours has increased profoundly since the remarkable discovery of the molecular structure of DNA (the famous double helix) by Francis Crick (1916–2004), James Watson (b.1928), Maurice Wilkins (1916–2004) and Rosalind Franklin (1920–58) in the early 1950s. Crick, Watson and Wilkins shared the Nobel Prize in Physiology or Medicine in 1962. Sadly, Rosalind Franklin, who made major contributions to their studies, had died from cancer by this time. In 1990 the Human Genome Project, an international collaborative effort, was set up to map the genetic make-up of the human species.

Numerous scientists have made tremendous contributions

to the rapidly expanding field of human genetics and DNA sequencing, including Fred Sanger (1918–2013) who won two Nobel Prizes in Chemistry (in 1958 and 1980), and over the last few decades there has been an explosion in an understanding of cancer at the molecular level. American cancer biologist, Robert Weinberg and colleagues in 1982 identified the first so-called 'oncogene' (a gene that causes normal cells to form tumours). Various genetic or hereditary links with certain forms of cancer have since been identified, including the mutations in the *BRCA1* and *BRCA2* genes. While 'internal' factors' (such as inherited oncogenes) predispose some individuals to cancer, exposure to 'external' or environmental carcinogens can also bring about genetic mutations leading to cancer. There are a number of studies, including the European Prospective Investigation into Cancer and Nutrition (EPIC, started in 1992), which are tracking volunteers to investigate contributory factors leading to cancer.

Cancer, like heart disease, is grouped into the category of 'non-communicable diseases' (NCDs) and has become increasingly 'visible' in an ageing population as a result of rising life expectancies and the shift over the past half century or so from deaths resulting predominantly from acute infectious diseases in the young to the chronic conditions emerging in older age groups. But, somewhat to the surprise of many, based on preliminary researches dating back to the early twentieth century, scientists have found that viruses, bacterial organisms and parasitic infections are also implicated in the development of some cancers, notably cervical cancer, liver cancer, Burkitt's lymphoma, Kaposi's sarcoma, stomach cancer and bladder cancer. In the developed world less than 10 per cent of malignant cancers are linked to infectious diseases, but in developing countries infectious diseases are now thought to cause as many as 20 to 25 per cent of all cancers.

Cervical cancer is the second most common cancer of women worldwide, with 85 per cent of deaths from this form of cancer occurring in the developing world where access to screening using Pap smears – to detect pre-cancerous changes in the cervix and named after Georgios Papanikolaou (1883–1962), the Greek pioneer in early cancer detection – is often limited or not available. Cervical cancer is known to be associated with certain types of the human papillomavirus (HPV), for the discovery of which German scientist Harald zur Hausen (b.1936) was awarded a Nobel Prize in Physiology or Medicine in 2008. Hepatitis B virus (HBV) can lead to liver cancer and American scientist Baruch Blumberg also received a Nobel Prize in 1976 for his pioneering work leading to this discovery. There are effective vaccines to prevent both these viruses and, while the HBV and HPV vaccines are increasingly being included in infant and adolescent immunization programmes, respectively, in high-income countries, there is still a desperate need to increase the distribution of these vaccines in the poorer countries of the world.

Two other Nobel laureates who identified an infectious agent are Australian scientists Barry Marshall (b. 1951) and Robin Warren (b. 1937) who shared the 2005 Nobel Prize 'for their discovery of the bacterium *Helicobacter pylori* and its role in gastritis and peptic ulcer disease.' *Helicobacter pylori* can also lead to stomach cancer. This new understanding was based on an extraordinary story of self-experimentation - in which Marshall drank some meat broth containing this bacterium. After several days, he became unwell and a pathologist reported that his stomach was swarming with bacteria and inflammation (gastritis) was present, so proving that *H. pylori* was the culprit. Fortunately, Marshall and Warren were then able to show that the infection could be treated with antibiotics which can cure most *H. pylori* infections and prevent the development of chronic conditions such as ulcers and stomach cancer.

These examples, highlight yet another aspect of the complex causes leading to cancers, though there is hope that vaccines and antimicrobial drugs to prevent and treat cancer-associated infections will become more widely available.

Given the bewildering diversity of cancer cell types, Weinberg and his colleague, Douglas Hanahan, in a seminal publication in 2000 in the journal *Cell*, suggested that the complexity of cancer can actually be reduced to a small number of underlying principles – known as the 'hallmarks' of cancer – which govern the transformation of normal cells to malignant or tumour cancer cells. It is also increasingly evident that the key 'hallmark' of malignant disease (as opposed to benign tumours) is the ability of cancer cells to metastasize and spread from the primary site to form secondary tumours elsewhere in the body. Metastasis is the main cause of death from cancer, and while scientists continue to unravel why and how this happens, it is a reminder that early detection, screening, diagnosis and treatment of cancer, prior to its spread, is imperative.

Cancer – is there a way forward?

With earlier detection, greater use of specialist surgery, screening programmes and advances in radiotherapy and chemotherapy, survival rates for some cancers have doubled in many advanced countries over the past thirty to forty years. The incidence of cancer, probably as a result of the reduction of risk factors, has also recently declined in some high-income countries. Nevertheless, cancer (or, strictly speaking, 'cancers', as there are hundreds of different types) still causes around 8.2 million deaths each year, and is the second leading cause of death after heart disease.

Many aspects of cancer continue to remain a mystery. 'Why me?' is a typical reaction to cancer, and one that it is often difficult to answer. The cost of cancer – whether in terms of lives lost, personal and family tragedies, lost earnings, research, health promotion campaigns, screening, funding for high-tech diagnostic tools, drugs and palliative care – is greater than it ever has been. Once considered a 'Western' disease, cancer is also now emerging as a major problem in developing countries, as the WHO states: 'Cancer is a global problem, and it's growing.' There are wide disparities in rates of mortality and morbidity between countries even in the Western world but it is also now estimated that more than 70 per cent of all cancer deaths currently occur in low- and middle-income countries where resources available for prevention, early diagnosis, treatment and palliative care are limited or virtually non-existent. Together with other NCDs, the burden of cancer in these countries has remained a neglected priority, overshadowed by the struggle against more acute threats like malaria and HIV/AIDS.

With increasing globalization and urbanization, lifestyles continue to change in poorer countries, leading to the adoption of 'unhealthy' Western diets, tobacco consumption and sedentary lifestyles. Accordingly, cancers, cardiovascular disease, type 2 diabetes and chronic respiratory diseases are predicted to rise in those countries in the coming decades, especially in parts of Asia and sub-Saharan Africa, if prevention measures and global policy initiatives are not quickly adopted. The double burden of cancers associated with both lifestyles and infections is another area that requires attention. Integrating prevention and control strategies for cancer with other ongoing disease programmes, such as HIV/AIDS and tuberculosis, is an important aim. Researchers also point towards the 'causes of the cause' which need to be addressed, including the role of poverty; indeed, in most countries throughout the world the highest rates of cancer are in the lowest socio-economic groups.

In 2011 the UN General Assembly held its first high-level meeting on NCDs, and in 2013 the WHO Global Action Plan for the Prevention and Control of Non-communicable Diseases 2013–2020 was launched with the aim to reduce premature mortality from NCDs by 25 per cent by 2025 (the 25 by 25 goal). Some are optimistic that these goals will be reached and the time will come when cancer is no longer feared, or, as US President Bill Clinton said at the announcement of the completed working draft of the human genome sequence in 2000: 'It is now conceivable that our children's children will know the term cancer only as a constellation of stars.'

Whether we will, eventually, succeed in the 'Crusade against Cancer' – the 'emperor of all maladies' – remains to be seen, but there are certainly many people across the world – in laboratories, hospitals and homes – who are working hard to help tackle the pain and suffering from this tragic disease.

HEART DISEASE

Heart disease is a term used to describe a diverse range of problems affecting the heart and its related blood vessels. Coronary heart disease, congenital heart disease, rheumatic heart disease, aortic aneurysm, angina, deep vein thrombosis and pulmonary embolism, peripheral arterial disease and arrhythmia are among the main conditions – each of which may have different underlying causes, symptoms, prognoses and outcomes. Heart disease may well have afflicted the ancients and, indeed, blockages found in the arteries of over a hundred mummies (a sign of atherosclerosis) reveal that heart disease is not just a modern problem. In the 1930s it was noted that heart disease was increasing to such an extent that it became known as an epidemic. There have been some remarkable recent innovations to diagnose and treat heart disease, as well as surgical procedures, such as heart transplants, to prolong the life of those suffering from potentially fatal conditions. Preventive measures (associated with 'risk factors') have also played a key role in reducing heart disease in recent decades in high-income countries. However, cardiovascular disease or CVD (heart disease, together with stroke) currently accounts for 17.5 million deaths each year. CVD is the leading cause of death globally and is an increasingly serious problem in developing countries. The coexistence of persisting infectious diseases, poverty- and nutritional-related disorders, and the rapidly rising incidence of 'non-communicable' diseases, such as heart disease, cancer and diabetes, represents one of the major challenges to global development.

∽

The beating of the heart is a fundamental sign of life. An embryo's heart starts to beat in the uterus usually a month after conception. Normally, the heart beats at least once a second for our entire lives, without taking a single rest. During an average lifetime, it will beat over 2.5 billion times. When the heartbeat stops, unless reversed within a very few minutes, life comes to an end.

The heart has played a key role in shaping our understanding of the vital physiological forces of the human body, and has also, metaphorically, been a central concept in an understanding of our emotions. Indeed, prior to the twentieth century, more emphasis was given to the cultural, philosophical and scientific ideas concerning the role of the heart than to the incidence of heart disease itself. It is only in the last century or so that death or disease associated with a malfunctioning heart has become a critical issue, and it is only in the very recent past that major advances have been made to prevent and repair this vital organ when it goes wrong.

The heart of the matter

'All motions of sensation, including those produced by what is pleasant and painful, begin and end in the heart.' Aristotle (c.384–322 BC)

In ancient times, the heart, brain and liver were ascribed varying degrees of importance, which differed from culture to culture. The Babylonians considered the liver to be the seat and mirror of the soul. The livers of sacrificial animals were carefully inspected for signs of damage before being offered to the gods. Prayers at ceremonies were inscribed on tablets shaped like livers.

The ancient Egyptians, by contrast, treated the heart with reverence – to the Egyptians the heart held the mind and soul of the body. It was the source of wisdom, as well as emotions, memory and personality. When Egyptian embalmers mummified their dead, major internal organs – the liver, the intestines, lungs and stomach – were removed, dried, wrapped in linen and placed in canopic jars to be buried alongside the mummified corpse. The brain was considered unimportant – its only function was to pass mucus to the nose. It was removed from the skull through the nose using long hooked tools, and probably thrown away. The heart was given special significance. It was generally left in the body and would, in the afterlife, be weighed against the feather of truth in the hall of the goddess, Ma'at, during the divine judgment of the deceased. An unburdened heart would balance with the feather and enjoy eternal life. To help the heart on its voyage to the afterlife, a heart scarab or amulet, with an inscription from *The Book of the Dead*, would be placed on the chest of the mummy.

The classical Greeks and Romans generally prohibited mutilation of the dead, so their ideas about human anatomy and physiology were largely speculative, or based on animal dissection. Like the ancient Egyptians, the majority, including the philosopher Aristotle, believed that the brain had no psychological significance, while it was the heart that was the primary source of intelligence, emotions and sensations. Expressions that are still with us today – 'heartbroken', 'disheartened', 'sweet-heart', 'heart-to-heart', 'heartfelt', 'hard-hearted' and 'from the bottom of my heart' – all reflect the close link that was assumed to exist between emotions and the heart. We also often talk about learning something 'off by heart' when memorizing texts and poems.

The Greek philosopher Plato (c.427–348 BC) challenged the 'cardio-centric' view. He favoured a tripartite explanation of the soul and the body in which parts of the soul – mind, spirit and desire – were located respectively in the brain, heart and liver. The Graeco-Roman physician Galen reinforced Plato's view that the heart had no cognitive significance and that it was the brain that was the centre of sensation, speech, intellect and conscious-ness. Galen also explained how to take the pulse, how to classify its rhythm and differentiate between abnormalities – whether it was languid, racing, regular or erratic. In other parts of the ancient Western and Eastern world, physicians would feel the pulse with the finger and often remark on the regularity or abnormality of the pulse in a sick patient. Taking the pulse still remains a hallmark of the medical profession. It was, however, many centuries before it was fully understood that the arterial pulse was the product of the impulse of the heart, and it is diffi-cult to gauge to what extent heart disease or heart failure affected the populations of the ancient world.

Blood and guts

While the ancient writers debated whether the brain or the heart was the fundamental core of the individual, most acknowledged that blood was the 'liquid' or, indeed, the 'very essence' of life, nourishing the body in health or causing disease when disordered, in excess, or 'bad'. Galen, furthermore, proposed an influential theory on the movement of the blood through the body. Based primarily on dissections and vivisections of animals, he held that the veins, which carried the 'venous blood', originated in the liver. Dark blood was 'cooked' or 'concocted' in the liver and supplied with nutrients from the intestines; it then flowed through the veins carrying nourishment and was 'consumed' (used up) in various parts of the body. Venous blood also reached the lungs and the right ventricle of the heart, where it was imbued with 'vital spirits'. 'Arterial' or red blood stemmed from the left ventricle of the heart, flowing through the arteries to give 'life and motion', but did not return to the heart. It was the arteries, and not the heart, which, according to Galen, propelled the blood around the body.

There was, though, a missing piece in this theory: how did the blood flow from the right to the left ventricle of the heart – from the veins to the arteries? Galenic theory suggested that there were 'invisible' pores that allowed the blood to seep across the septum (wall) of the heart (in fact it is quite solid). Galen's ideas about the heart and the circulation of the blood persisted for nearly a millennium and a half in the Western world.

The heart – a living pump

There was a brief period in Hellenic Alexandria, Egypt, in the fourth to third centuries BC, when human dissections were permitted in the ancient world. But in Christian Europe it was not until the fourteenth century that dissection (on a few executed criminals) was permitted, leading to the questioning of old Galenic theories. Andreas Vesalius, the great Flemish anatomist, believed that the heart and not the liver was the centre of circulation, and in 1543 published his *On the Fabric of the Human Body* with elegant anatomical illustrations of the human body. He also described a condition now known as 'aortic aneurysm', explaining the symptoms he had observed in his living patient by reference to the pathological alterations revealed post-mortem. He openly criticized Galen's anatomical knowledge and corrected some of his errors. He was not, however, able to see Galen's so-called 'pores' in the septum of the heart and expressed his wonder of God at producing invisible passages for the blood to move across the heart! The famous artist and polymath, Leonardo da Vinci (1452–1519), observed that the 'vessels in the elderly through the thickening of the tunics, restrict the transit of the blood' – an early description of what we would now call atherosclerosis. He produced beautiful and remarkably accurate drawings of the heart, based on post-mortem dissections of animal and human cadavers.

It was not, however, until the discoveries of the Cambridge-educated London physician, William Harvey (1578–1657), that some of the old Galenic theories were eventually overturned. Harvey, following up leads from a number of European anatomists after studying at Padua University in Italy and using a combination of observational and experimental scientific methods, proved conclusively that the blood continuously circulates through the body. He conducted anatomical dissections in front of audiences of barbers and surgeons in the anatomy theatre of the College of Physicians to examine the structure of the heart as well as carrying out countless vivisections on a wide range of creatures in the house in London to demonstrate that the blood, rather than simply flowing outward from the heart and liver to the extremities to be consumed and then somehow 'regenerated', actually remained constant in volume. It circulated through the veins and arteries, continuously returning to the heart. Dark venous blood flowed towards the right ventricle of the heart and bright red arterial blood flowed away from the left ventricle of the heart. Harvey also explored the mystery of how the blood moved from one side of the heart to the other. He proposed that the blood passed through the lungs (rather than 'invisible pores' in the septum as Galen had speculated) in its passage between the right and left ventricle of the heart – an idea of pulmonary transit that had been posited by the Italian anatomist Realdo Colombo (c.1516–59). The heart, moreover, Harvey recognized, acted as a living pump – vital to keep the blood flowing and circulating. It was, he said, the 'foundation of life, and author of all.'

In 1628 he published his monumental work: *Exercitatio anatomica de motu cordis et sanguinis in animalibus* ('Anatomical Exercises Concerning the Motion of the Heart and Blood in Living Creatures'), dedicated to King Charles 1, outlining his new theory:

> All things do depend upon the motional pulsation of the heart: so the heart is the beginning of life, the Sun of the Microcosm, as proportionably the Sun deserves to be call'd the heart of the world, by whose virtue, and pulsation, the blood is mov'd, perfected, made vegetable, and is defended from corruption, and mattering; and this familiar household-god doth his duty to the whole body, by nourishing, cherishing, and vegetating, being the foundation of life, and author of all. (From the 1653 translation)

Although there is evidence that similar ideas had been proposed by the ancient Chinese as well as by medieval Arabic physicians (notably Ibn al-Nafis, AD c.1210/13–88), it was Harvey's views on the circulation of the blood that gained wide acceptance – at least by the 1660s. There were, of course, critics and sceptics who, especially initially, found it hard to dismiss the old Galenic ideas and Harvey's account of the movement of the heart as a 'living pump' remained controversial until well into the nineteenth century. Thomas Wright in his book, *Circulation: William Harvey's Revolutionary Idea* (2013), charts the remarkable rise of Harvey from yeoman's son to the physician who made a major contribution to science and demolished beliefs held by doctors since ancient times.

Other scientists in the mid-seventeenth century added further insights to Harvey's theory of the circulation of the blood. Using experiments in 'warm-blooded' animals such as the snake and frog, they also solved the mystery of how the blood moved from one side of the heart to the other. They showed that the blood passed through the lungs (rather than 'invisible pores' in the septum as Galen had speculated) in its passage between the right and left ventricle of the heart. In 1661 Marcello Malpighi of Bologna (1628–94) discovered the microscopic capillaries which connect the arteries and the veins, and in 1669, the English scientist Richard Lower (1631–91) suggested (correctly) in his *Tractatus de corde* ('Treatise on the Heart') that the change causing the difference in colour and consistency between the dark colour of the venous blood and the bright red of arterial blood took place not in the left ventricle of the heart but in the lungs (later shown to be where it was oxygenated).

Bloodletting and blood transfusions

If anybody comes to I,
I physics, bleeds, and sweats 'em;
If, after that, they like to die,
Why, what care I, I lets 'em.
'On Dr Lettsom', Anonymous

As exciting and revolutionary as these ideas were – and initiating the beginnings of modern scientific medicine – they apparently made little impact on the diagnosis or treatment of human heart disease. The discovery of the circulation of the blood, did, however, increase the popularity of bloodletting! This ancient practice was used on the sick (to get rid of 'bad' blood) as well as on the healthy (mostly as an annual 'spring-cleaning' venture). Various methods were adopted: venesection or phlebotomy (opening a vein with a lancet); leeching (leeches were ideally selected for their cleanliness and fitness for the task – usually three or four were recommended at a time, but some physicians advised fifty or more leeches to gorge on the blood!); and cupping (for example, cutting the skin's surface with a scarificator and then using an animal's horn or glass to draw out the blood). Bloodletting was also offered by barber-surgeons; the red-and-white striped poles still seen outside many barbers' shops are a reminder of the service they provided. Often patients were bled until they fainted – one wonders how many might have suffered a heart attack under such circumstances.

While doctors and barber surgeons were taking blood out of their patients, supposedly to cure them, in the 1660s, scientists looked at ways of putting blood back into people (blood

535

transfusions). Richard Lower began these experiments by transfusing blood between dogs. At a meeting of the Royal Society of London in 1667 (witnessed by Samuel Pepys) he also transfused blood from a sheep into a 'poor and debauched man . . . cracked a little in the head' that it might 'have a good effect upon him as a frantic man by cooling his blood'. The recipient, Arthur Coga, survived, but further experiments in France to carry out blood transfusions from animals to humans led to the death of one subject, halting blood transfusion for another 150 years.

Dying of a broken heart

On 18 January 1796 a young servant girl in south-east England dropped dead while reading a letter. She had apparently discovered that the love of her life – who had formerly been her fellow servant – had married another. Her story was reported in the *Gentleman's Magazine*. The poor young woman had tragically 'died of a broken heart'.

Descriptions of diseases and causes of death in the seventeenth, eighteenth and nineteenth centuries – whether in journals, mortality records, doctors' case books or diaries and letters – contain many 'diagnoses' that might suggest a heart problem. Some, like the servant girl, were said to have died 'heartbroken' or from a 'broken heart'. Others were said to have died 'sad', 'weak', 'infirm', or suffering from an 'oppression of the spirits', a 'pining sickness', or an 'iliac passion'. Some died 'suddenly' or 'untimely', while others were 'planet-struck', inflicted by the 'visitation of God' or 'the work of the Devil'. Some died simply because they were 'worn out', 'frenzied', 'distracted' and 'short of breath', or declined through 'exhaustion', 'grief' or 'old age'. 'Decay' or being 'bedridden' were typically given as causes of death for the elderly. An 'apoplectic fit' may have been what we would now call 'a stroke' (caused by an interruption of blood supply to the brain either due to a blood clot in an artery or a burst blood vessel in the brain) but how many either sudden or slow deaths were related to heart disease and stroke is impossible to tell.

Recognizing and treating symptoms of the heart

Some physicians in the eighteenth century did, however, begin to identify clinical signs and underlying symptoms associated with heart disease. For example, in the 1720s Friedrich Hoffmann (1660–1742) of Halle, Germany, speculated that the reduced passage of blood within the coronary arteries could lead to disease and death.

One of the first clear descriptions that we can now recognize as a heart-related condition was by the English physician, William Heberden (1710–1801). In 1768, he coined the term 'angina pectoris' and differentiated it from other pains in the chest:

> They who are afflicted with it, are seized while they are walking, (more especially if it be uphill, and soon after eating) with a most disagreeable sensation in the breast, which seems as if it would extinguish life, if it were to increase or continue; but the moment they stand still, all the uneasiness vanishes . . . In all other respects, patients are, at the beginning of the disorder, perfectly well . . . Males are most liable to this disease, especially such as have passed their fiftieth year.

A medical term, much used in the past but now obsolete, is 'dropsy'. The word literally means an excess of fluid, and was applied to a number of diseases in which an abnormal accumulation of fluid in the liver, kidneys or heart could lead to death. One remarkable cure for 'dropsy of the heart' (which may relate to those suffering from congestive heart disease) was discovered and promoted in the eighteenth century. William Withering (1741–99), a doctor practising in Birmingham, England, was given a recipe for treating dropsy by an old lady. The recipe contained a concoction of different plants, but Withering worked out that the vital ingredient was the purple foxglove (*Digitalis purpurea*), which, if used carefully and in small doses (for it is extremely toxic), can act as a powerful stimulant on the heart, as well as increasing urine flow and reducing oedema (pathological accumulation of fluid in the tissues).

In 1785 he published 'An Account of the Foxglove and Some of its Medical Uses etc; with Practical Remarks on Dropsy and Other Diseases', recommending foxglove or 'digitalis' for 'dropsy of the heart'. When Withering died in 1799, his friends carved a bunch of foxgloves on his memorial. The discovery of digitalis as a remedy for 'dropsy of the heart' in the eighteenth century provided one of the first drugs of value for treating heart conditions. Digitoxin and digoxin – the active substances, respectively, of the purple foxglove and the woolly Balkan foxglove (*Digitalis lanata*) – are still used today to improve the speed and force of cardiac contractions.

By the early nineteenth century, several other forms of heart disease were identified as medical entities. 'Syncope' (fainting) was a condition associated with an extremely slow pulse. It became known as 'heart block' or Adams-Stokes syndrome in the nineteenth century after the two physicians who described it (and is now the condition we would call bradycardia, treated with pace-makers). 'Rheumatism of the heart' was probably the result of rheumatic fever, an infectious disease (shown later to be caused by a streptococcal bacterium) which affects the valves of the heart.

Listening to the heart

Doctors in the past mostly had to rely on their five senses – touch, sight, smell, taste and hearing – to detect and diagnose the outward signs of disease in the 'living' patient. Checking for unusual signs or symptoms relied on practices such as feeling the pulse or touching the body to check for lumps and bumps. These were, and still are, classic ways of spotting abnormalities. Looking at the colour of a patient's urine was a common practice known as uroscopy or 'urine-gazing'. In medieval times, doctors were sometimes known as 'pisse-prophets' and uroscopy per-sisted to the mid-nineteenth century. Doctors have always needed a keen eye to spot and diagnose peculiarities – from rashes, blotches, pimples, pustules, running sores, ulcers and fleshy growths, to tell-tale signs of infection on the tongue, in the throat, eyes, ears, nose, or discharges from orifices of the body. 'You look ill' remains a common phrase.

Sniffing urine, stools, pus, perspiration or breath was another way to diagnose disease. Bad odours, foetid breath, pus-filled gangrenous sores, stinky stools and other nauseous evacuations were key indicators that all was not well, and doctors' case notes usually contained detailed descriptions of their patients' sick-ening smells. Tasting urine was not as common as gazing at or sniffing it, but in 1776 Matthew Dobson (1735–84) demon-strated that the sweetness of the urine in patients with diabetes was due to sugar.

Listening (literally) to the patient's story to find out where 'it hurts' (whether in body or mind) was also an important part of the doctor-patient encounter in both Western and Eastern medicine, and remains today a vital aspect of diagnosing disease. Doctors in the past could also use their sense of hearing to listen to the gurgles, coughing, creaking and croaking of the body. Auscultation – or the act of listening to sounds generated within the body – dates back to ancient times. Hippocratic writings describe 'succussion' – shaking a patient to hear splashing noises within the chest. Percussion – tapping the chest wall with a finger and listening with the ear for reverberations – was an idea suggested in the mid-eighteenth century by the Austrian physician Josef Leopold Auenbrugger (1722–1809). In 1761 he published his book: *A New Discovery that Enables the Physician from the Percussion of the Human Thorax to Detect the Diseases Hidden Within the Chest*, in which he gave the first definite information as to pathological changes in the heart.

In 1806 Jean-Nicolas Corvisart (1755–1821), the French physician, published his *Essay on the Diseases and the Organic Lesions of the Heart and Large Vessels*, based on years of correlating sounds emanating from the chest of living patients with findings at autopsy. His work provided a new standard for the diagnosis, treatment and pathological anatomy of heart conditions, stimulating widespread interest in the technique of percussion. But too much touching was often considered indelicate, and feeling beneath the clothes seemed undignified for a genteel physician. The invention of the stethoscope in 1816 by René Laënnec to investigate sounds and murmurs in the heart and lungs transformed the way 'bedside' physicians could 'hear' and detect heart abnormalities and valvular disorders while keeping a safe distance from the patient. The stethoscope – still an iconic symbol of the medical profession today – was also especially useful for diagnosing pulmonary tuberculosis at this time. The nineteenth century saw the development of the first sphygmomanometers (*sphugmo-* is from the Greek 'the beating of the heart or the pulse') to measure blood pressure – and with further refinements (such as the inflatable 'cuff') these machines remain some of the most basic diagnostic tools in modern medicine.

Prevention is better than cure

'The doctors all say we eat too much . . . My experience is that they do too.' Edward Cook, English journalist (1857–1919)

Along with a number of specific recognizable clinical descriptions of heart disease and 'new' ways of listening to the heart, physicians also offered a plethora of ideas about possible 'predisposing' causes of disease and death which, today, might be known as 'risk factors'. It was frequently noted that 'gross' individuals of 'corpulent living, ruddy complexion, hard drinking and overindulgence' ran a high risk of disease and death, as did those who had 'a want of fresh fruit and greens and the disadvantages of a low diet'.

In the London Bills of Mortality for August 1665 (during the Great Plague of London), seventy-four deaths were recorded from 'surfeit' – a polite term for overeating. The famous seventeenth-century London doctor Thomas Sydenham acknowledged: 'corpulency may be ranked amongst diseases arising from original imperfections in the functions of some of the organs, yet it must be admitted also, to be most intimately connected with our habits of life.' George Cheyne (1671–1743), one of the foremost British physicians of his day, spent much of his time eating and drinking with his patients – at one point he weighed 32 stone (448 pounds or 203 kg) and feeling 'excessively fat, short-breath'd, lethargic and listless', required a servant to walk behind him carrying a stool on which to recover every few paces. He eventually converted to vegetarianism and took to exercise and fresh air, vigorously exercising on a 'chamber horse' (a type of rocking chair) when bad weather prevented outdoor exercise. In 1763 James Boswell (1740–95), the biographer of Samuel Johnson, was advised by his physician to take two or three brisk capers around the room upon waking. Boswell said this had the 'most agreeable effects' and 'expelled the phlegm from my heart'.

Indeed, prescriptions for exercise, diet and lifestyle changes can be found in every Western and Eastern medical tradition. Advice manuals on preventing disease and maintaining a healthy constitution, based on ideas dating back to ancient times, became increasingly popular in the medieval and early modern periods. The Latin poem *Regimen sanitatis Salernitanum* ('The Salernitan Rule of Health'), believed to have been written in the twelfth or thirteenth century, was hugely popular and contained a wide range of advice which would be appealing and amusing to modern readers (and, while too long to quote here, is well worth reading on the internet). Thomas Elyot (*c.*1490–1546) in 1536 published his *Castel of Helth*, one of the earliest 'preventive health' manuals written in English. Recommendations by writers included a good diet, plenty of physical exercise, sound sleep, a joyful mind, moderate alcoholic consumption, regular bowel movements, and, overall, a balanced lifestyle.

In 1863 one of the first commercially available works on dieting, *A Letter on Corpulence Addressed to the Public*, was published by William Banting, while Gustav Ernst in the early 1860s produced a book recommending ideas for setting up a portable gymnasium for the discerning Victorian, along with a comprehensive series of exercises. And the Olympic Games (which had originally been held in Olympia, Greece, from the eighth century BC to the fourth century AD) were revived in the mid-to-late nineteenth century and these ongoing events should inspire us to take exercise!

'Stress' is another so-called 'risk factor' which we tend to associate with heart disease today and – whether emotional, physical or occupational – may in the past have been labelled as one of the 'exciting causes' of disease. Galenic theory held that anger was the result of a rush of choler, or bile, to the heart. Centuries later, the famous Scottish surgeon, John Hunter (1728–93), who described disease of the coronary arteries, declared, after performing an autopsy on a person who had died 'in a sudden and violent transport of anger': 'My life is in the hands of any rascal who chooses to annoy me.' His words proved true. In 1793, soon after a violent argument with a hospital colleague, he suddenly collapsed and died. An autopsy identified the cause of death as a 'diseased heart' and he may well have had a heart attack, having suffered from angina pectoris for some years. Hunter's fatal attack was a reminder to his contemporaries that the heart remained an organ of emotion as well as a structural organ of the body that could become diseased.

The hazard of tobacco smoking was a debated issue following its introduction to Europe in the sixteenth century shortly after the discovery of the New World but, prior to the twentieth century, did not receive the emphasis as a 'predisposing' cause of heart disease (or even lung cancer) as it does now.

Heart attacks and abnormal heartbeats

People doubtless died of heart problems in the past. Indeed, evidence of atherosclerosis – calcified plaques in the walls of arteries – has been found in ancient mummies in Egypt and Peru and in a number of hunter-gatherer societies spanning 4,000 years, raising all sorts of intriguing questions about the role of diet, genes, infections and ageing in contributing to heart disease in 'pre-modern' societies. But it is difficult to estimate the overall historical significance and impact of deaths from heart disease.

The first formal use of the term 'heart attack', which accounts for a high proportion of all deaths from coronary heart disease, was not until the early twentieth century. A heart attack (myocardial infarction) normally occurs when blood is prevented from flowing to the heart muscle by a blood clot (thrombosis). This can typically arise from arteriosclerosis – the narrowing of the arteries by deposits of fatty substances such as cholesterol. The risk of dying from a heart attack became increasingly apparent during the first half of the twentieth century. In 1892, William Osler (1849–1919), Canadian physician and later Regius Professor of medicine at Oxford, had described coronary heart disease as 'relatively rare'. By the 1920s, however, one in eight deaths in the Western world was attributed to heart disorders. As statistics began to highlight the increasing prevalence of heart disease and its associated risk of death, so physicians began to explore ways to monitor, intercept and prevent heart disease.

In the early twentieth century the electrocardiograph

544

machine (a 'string galvanometer') was developed by Willem Einthoven (1860–1927) of the Netherlands for diagnosing abnormal cardiac rhythms. He was awarded the Nobel Prize in Physiology or Medicine in 1924 for his invention. British physician Thomas Lewis (1881–1945) and American physician James Herrick (1861–1954) were some of the first to master the use of this machine as a diagnostic tool for heart disease. It was, initially, an unwieldy and expensive contraption – needing five technicians to operate it! The patient had to place both hands and feet in buckets of water but the machine was able to measure the electrical signals generated by the heart's beat, which were then reproduced visually in the form of an electrocardiogram (which became known as ECG, or EKG in the USA). Scottish physician James Mackenzie (1853–1925), following up on the earlier development of machines to record the pulse, devised a 'polygraph' that allowed him to make simultaneous records of the arterial and venous pulses and their relationship to cardiovascular disease. These technologies transformed diagnosis, and so began the scientific field of 'cardiology'.

A change of heart: from cardiac surgery to heart transplants

'Surgery of the heart has probably reached the limits set by Nature to all surgery; no new method, and no new discovery, can overcome the natural difficulties that attend a wound of the heart.' British surgeon Sir Stephen Paget (1855–1926), writing in 1896

There had been huge improvements in surgery over the second half of the nineteenth century, following the introduction of anaesthetics, antiseptics and asepsis, but the heart had remained a 'no-go' area. Any attempt to tinker with the heart – the vital organ which kept the body ticking – was deemed just too risky (although one or two brave surgeons did try to correct some cardiac defects). While tumours or certain parts of the human body could, if diseased, be removed, there was no way that the heart could be excised.

During the early twentieth century, a number of surgeons including Nobel laureate Alexis Carrel (1873–1944) were making strides in the field of vascular surgery, and during the First World War heart surgery was carried out in an attempt to save the lives of soldiers wounded by bullets. In the Second World War, American surgeon Dwight Harken (1901–93) found a way to take out shrapnel safely from the heart, and went on to develop the concept of intensive care. By the early 1940s, cardiac surgeons in civilian hospitals also began to attempt bolder surgery of the heart. In 1944 the first surgical intervention for 'blue babies' (those born with congenital heart disease) took place at the Johns Hopkins Hospital, Baltimore, carried out by Alfred Blalock (1899–1964), Vivien Thomas (1910–85) and Helen Taussig (1898–1986) – a milestone in cardiac surgery. Fast procedures, surgeons showed, could be performed on a beating heart, but more complicated procedures required the heart to be stopped. A key innovation of the early 1950s was the heart-lung machine. The first open-heart procedure on a human utilizing the heart-lung machine was performed by American surgeon John Gibbon (1903–73) in 1953 at Thomas Jefferson University Hospital in Philadelphia. This technology, along with body-cooling techniques (hypothermia), enabled surgeons to 'bypass' the heart, maintaining circulation and respiration artificially while surgery was conducted on the stopped organ. Meanwhile, leading surgeons, for example René Favalora

(1923–2000), Walton Lillehie (1918–99), Norman Shumway (1923–2006), Richard Lower (1929–2008) and Adrian Kantrowitz (1918–2008), in the 1950s and 1960s began to envisage the opportunities not just of open-heart surgery but also the possibilities of heart transplants.

The greatest publicity coup for cardiac surgery came in 1967 when Christiaan Barnard (1922–2001) at the Groote Schuur Hospital in Cape Town performed the first human heart transplant. Barnard sewed the heart of a young woman, who had died in a car crash, into a recipient, Louis Washkansky. As Barnard described the diseased heart of this first recipient of a human heart transplant: 'Louis Washkansky's heart came into full view – rolling in a rhythm of its own like a separate and angry sea, yellow from the storms of half a century, yet streaked with blue currents flowing from its depths – blue veins drifting across the heaving waste and ruin of a ravaged heart.' Washkansky, sadly, died of pneumonia eighteen days later, and the operation caused both sensation and controversy.

Prior to this momentous event, Bernard had worked alongside and been inspired by Norman Shumway (often called the 'father of heart transplantation') and colleagues in the US who (while 'pipped to the post' to be the 'first' to conduct a heart transplant) nevertheless continued these revolutionary trials in heart transplantation. But one of the main problems of transplants was that the recipient's immune system could 'reject' the donor tissue – an area of investigation for which Australian immunologist Frank Macfarlane Burnet (1899–1985) and British immunologist Peter Medawar (1915–87) had shared a Nobel Prize in 1960. Few patients were surviving for long, and the number of heart transplants dropped from 100 in 1968, to just 18 in 1970. With the development of effective immunosuppressive drugs (following the discovery of cyclo-sporine derived from soil fungus) to prevent transplant rejection, heart transplants became routine. By the mid-1980s hundreds of heart transplants were being conducted, with many of the recip-ients surviving for over five years.

In the UK, Papworth Hospital, Cambridgeshire (formerly a tuberculosis sanatorium) was at the forefront of surgical innova-tions for heart disease. Building on the pioneering endeavours of Benjamin Milstein (1918–2013), who in 1958 performed the first open-heart surgery at Papworth, Terence English (b.1932) carried out the first successful heart transplant in Britain in 1979, and in 1986 Roy Calne (b.1930) and John Wallwork (b.1946), performed the world's first triple transplant operation – heart, lungs and liver. Harefield Hospital in London also became one of the leading heart transplant centres in the UK and, under the leadership of Magdi Yacoub (b.1935), who per-formed the UK's first heart and lung transplant in 1983, had by the end of the 1980s carried out around a thousand of these procedures.

Heart transplantation has led to a fundamental change in the legal definition of death in various countries, from cessation of heartbeat to the absence of brain function, enabling surgeons to remove a donor heart before it stops beating. Today around 5,000 heart transplants are performed worldwide each year, and survival rates have increased radically since the early days, though, as with other organ transplants, finding sufficient suit-able donors continues to be a problem. Advances are being made to overcome the shortage of organ donors. Artificial hearts powered by pumps can now keep a patient alive while awaiting a donor, and trials of artificial heart implants for longer-term use are in progress.

Mending broken hearts

Over the course of the past fifty or so years, a wide range of other techniques has also been introduced, enabling surgeons to intervene and restore or repair faulty hearts before a transplant becomes necessary. These techniques include the insertion of artificial pacemakers and defibrillators (electrical devices that maintain or restore regular heartbeat), balloon angioplasty (where a small balloon-like device is threaded through an artery to open the blockage), coronary bypasses, valve repair and replacement, and patch repair for congenital holes in the heart. New and non-invasive imaging methods – from ultrasound to CT, PET and MRI scans – have also transformed the early diagnosis of heart disease and, in many advanced countries, special coronary care units have been set up to treat and care for patients.

Paget and others of his time would be amazed to see the sophisticated (and extremely expensive) state of the art equipment that now makes it possible to overcome 'the limits set by nature'. A damaged or failing heart is no longer the death sentence it once was.

Taking advice to heart

'A man is as old as his arteries.' Attributed to Thomas Sydenham

While surgical techniques have advanced dramatically in recent decades, there has also been a growing interest in understanding the underlying causes and possible ways of preventing

549

cardiovascular disease. By the 1930s heart disease was the leading killer in the USA, raising many questions as to why it had reached such epidemic proportions. The perceived rise may have been due to improved diagnosis and a better understanding of the symptomatology and pathology of heart disease but there was also a need to discover why so many people were dying from this disease. An important epidemiological study was set up in the late 1940s in Framingham, Massachusetts – partly in response to concerns over the rise in this condition in the USA and also triggered by the awareness that President Franklin D. Roosevelt (who had survived polio) died from a stroke in 1945, shortly before the end of the Second World War, after suffering from uncontrolled high blood pressure. Epidemiologists in 1948 began to trace the lives of an initial cohort of 5,209 healthy adult residents and examine them every two years. The Framingham Heart Study (now in its third generation of participants), as well as a number of other ongoing similar longitudinal studies, has highlighted significant risk factors (a term first used in 1961 by Framingham researchers) for heart disease and stroke. These include physiological markers such as high blood pressure (hypertension) and raised blood cholesterol levels as well as behavioural risk factors – notably, smoking; lack of physical exercise; diets rich in saturated fat, sugar and salt; and heavy alcohol consumption. Some studies have suggested that up to 80 per cent of all premature deaths from cardiovascular disease can be attributed to these key lifestyle risk factors. Indeed, the four main groups of non-communicable diseases (NCDs) – cardiovascular disease, chronic obstructive pulmonary disease (COPD), type 2 diabetes and cancers – all share common risk factors highlighting that the majority of deaths from these conditions (which, together account for two-thirds of all deaths globally) are essentially preventable.

The media and health education campaigns now constantly remind us of the importance of adopting a healthy lifestyle, though sometimes current guidelines can be confusing. As the American author and humorist Mark Twain (1835–1910) once quipped: 'The only way to keep your health is to eat what you don't want, drink what you don't like, and do what you'd rather not.' But there is no doubt that smoking is particularly dangerous while unhealthy diets and lack of exercise are contributing to the rising global 'epidemic' of obesity and the associated risks of developing one or more of the NCDs. Genetic susceptibility to heart disease (for example, familial hypertension) may also play a role, and scientists are now hunting for the 'heart attack' gene or, more likely, genes which might be linked to an increased risk of heart disease.

One fascinating historical and geographical study by British epidemiologist David Barker (1938–2013) was begun in the 1970s and showed a strong correlation with low birth and infant weight and the likelihood of developing heart disease in later life. The 'Barker Hypothesis' has now become the field of Developmental Origins of Health and Disease (DOHaD), suggesting that while we might concentrate on 'obesity' in adult life as a predisposing cause of chronic diseases, attention should also be given to lifelong adverse effects of 'under-nutrition' of pregnant women and infants. Further insight into the lifestyle and diets of ancient and pre-modern societies with evidence of atherosclerosis may also throw more light on the complex pathways that can lead to heart disease.

Detecting the signs and a range of drugs

A range of old and new drugs is available for those identified to be at risk, and early detection of warning symptoms (such as high blood pressure, high cholesterol levels, shortness of breath and chest pains) is imperative. Amongst the many drugs that are prescribed, under medical supervision, are thrombolytic or 'clot-busting' drugs; beta blockers; ACE inhibitors (angiotensin-converting-enzyme inhibitors) and a number of antihypertensive drugs; diuretics; and statins. Penicillin can be given to treat rheumatic fever – a bacterial infection caused by streptococcus A, which if left untreated can lead to heart disease and is currently a serious problem for children in developing countries.

Statins, which, like penicillin, were originally derived from a mould, are one of the best-selling and most widely prescribed pharmaceuticals in history. They are taken to reduce cholesterol levels in the blood and prevent arteriosclerosis – lowering the risk of a heart attack or stroke and the need for heart surgery. Aspirin is another drug derived from a natural product that may be prescribed in low doses for preventing blood clots. The active ingredient in aspirin, acetylsalicylic acid, is a synthetic derivative of a compound, salicin, which occurs naturally in plants, notably in the bark of the willow tree and the plant meadowsweet. Aspirin was first launched in 1899 by the German pharmaceutical company Bayer – and originally packaged with heroin! Bayer also advertised aspirin's safety by saying that the drug 'does not affect the heart.' A century later, the benefit of low doses of aspirin for certain people at risk of cardiovascular disease was recognized by the medical profession. New drugs are also being explored by pharmaceutical and biotech companies and 'polypills', which combine different drugs, are a promising development.

Heart disease – a global pandemic

'Coronary heart disease is now the leading cause of death worldwide. It is on the rise and has become a true pandemic that respects no borders.' *The Atlas of Heart Disease and Stroke*, WHO, 2004

Whatever the complex and overlapping pathways are that lead to chronic heart conditions or acute events such as heart attacks and strokes, there is no doubt that CVD, as the number one global killer leading to 17.5 million deaths a year, is still a frightening disease (or, indeed, group of diseases). Once thought of as a disease of 'civilization' and 'ageing' populations, CVD is increasingly becoming a serious contribution to premature mortality in low- and middle-income countries. Indeed, while rates of mortality from CVD have declined substantially in some high-income countries (though there are still wide variations between and within countries) over the past few decades – in part as a result of medical therapies and advances in life-saving interventions and in part as a result of reductions in major risk factors and taking advice on heart disease prevention – it is now estimated that 80 per cent of deaths from CVD occur in the developing world.

The rapidly rising incidence of CVD and other NCDs in low- and middle-income countries has been attributed to a range of factors, including – on what we might think of as the 'positive' side – the reduction of infant, child and maternal mortality, a decline in infectious diseases and increases in life expectancy (thereby shifting the balance from acute infections to longer-term chronic diseases) – and, on the 'negative' side, the adoption of unhealthy, sedentary and stressful lifestyles more typically associated with advanced countries. Paradoxically, as antiretro-viral drugs for HIV/AIDS are helping people to manage and survive this viral infection, it follows that many are living longer but at increased risk of developing one or more of the NCDs. This is predicted to pose a huge problem for some countries, for example in sub-Saharan Africa, which are not yet ready to shift from dealing with 'acute' infections to 'chronic' diseases. Epidemiologists also emphasize the significance of the under-lying social and economic determinants of heart disease and other NCDs – or what they call 'the causes of the causes' – including rapid urbanization and poverty. The continuing toll of infections which can lead to heart disease, such as rheumatic fever and Chagas' disease, is also a reminder that heart disease is not always just a 'non-communicable' disease.

Advances and ways forward

With advances in the fields of genetics, molecular medicine, xeno-transplantation, nanotechnology, keyhole and robotic-as-sisted surgery, telemedicine, personalized medicine, gene therapy, stem cell research and regenerative medicine, scientists are optimistic that further insights into the mechanisms that lead to heart disease will be discovered and new ways of detec-tion, prevention and treatment will be forthcoming in future years.

Moreover, it is hoped that these advances will benefit not just those in high-income countries but also those who now desperately need help in the poorest societies of the world where high-tech life-saving equipment is often beyond reach, and prevention and screening strategies are poorly established. There are a number of outstanding and inspirational examples where charities and philanthropic ventures are helping to combat heart disease for the poor. The world-renowned heart specialist and transplant surgeon Magdi Yacoub set up a British component to the French 'Chain of Hope' charity in 1995 which sends medical teams to the developing world to treat children suffering from heart disease free of charge. In India, cardiac surgeon Devi Shetty (b.1953) at the huge Narayana Hrudaylaya Health Centre in Bangalore ensures that no one is turned away for lack of funds. Nigel Crisp (b.1952), former Chief Executive of the NHS in the UK, in his book, *Turning the World Upside Down: The Search for Global Health in the 21 Century* (2010), also reminds us that while advanced nations can make significant contributions to supporting health improvements in developing countries, so lessons can be learned from those who are doing pioneering work in resource-limited settings.

While we await novel scientific and technological breakthroughs and further inputs to saving lives in the developing world, the 'take home' message from the WHO and many health campaigns is that the key to future reduction in heart disease lies in minimizing risk factors. 'Prevention is better than cure' is an old saying, but for heart disease it is a strikingly significant global message.

Glossary

acute refers to symptoms or illnesses which are severe and intense for short lengths of time.

anaemia ('without blood') the medical condition anaemia can be caused by a diet low in iron, or may be triggered by parasites.

antibiotic a general term for a range of drugs, including penicillin, that are effective in treating bacterial infections.

antibody a protein produced by the immune system for the detection, and ultimately destruction, of foreign pathogens such as bacteria and viruses.

antigen a foreign substance introduced into a body which stimulates the production of antibodies and provokes an immune response. Antigens include bacteria, viruses and toxins.

anti-contagionist a term used in the nineteenth century to describe a scientist or physician who did not believe that diseases were caused by contagious particles spread from person to person.

bacillus (pl. bacilli) a rod-shaped bacterium.

bacterium (pl. bacteria) a group of single-celled microscopic organisms found everywhere in the environment and in the human body. Bacteria can live harmlessly in the human body and while some are beneficial, others may cause serious infections, including plague, cholera and tuberculosis.

bubo a visible swollen lymph node in the armpit or groin which is a hallmark of bubonic plague.

CDC (Centers for Disease Control and Prevention) the national public health institute of the United States with its headquarters in Atlanta, Georgia. First founded in 1946 as the Communicable Disease Center, its main goal is to protect public health and safety through the control and prevention of disease, injury, and disability.

chronic often used to refer to diseases or symptoms that are protracted, persistent or recurring over time.

contagious a contagious disease is one that might be transmitted by close touch or contact with an infected person.

disease (literally 'dis-ease' or absence of 'ease') the opposite of good health. In practice, the term is applied to any sickness, ailment or departure from sound health.

DNA (deoxyribonucleic acid) a type of molecule that encodes the genetic instructions used in the development and functioning of all known living organisms; found in the nucleus of human cells most famously as a 'double helical' structure.

endemic a disease that is not necessarily widely prevalent but typically found and always present among people in a particular place.

epidemic a disease that affects a large number of people at a given time.

epidemiology the statistical study of the incidence and distribution of diseases, and of the factors that cause and might prevent and control them.

epizootic an unusually widespread disease present in an animal population.

FDA (Food and Drug Administration) a branch of the United States Department of Health and Human Services. The FDA is responsible for protecting and promoting public health through the regulation of a wide variety of products given to humans and animals, notably prescription pharmaceuticals and vaccines. These have to go through rigorous clinical trials before they are approved.

febrile with fever; an increase in body temperature.

genome the whole genetic sequence of an individual, including the coding and non-coding portions of DNA.

germ theory a term often used to describe the theory developed in the mid- to late nineteenth century that diseases are caused by specific micro-organisms.

gram-positive/gram-negative bacteria two major classes of bacteria which can be distinguished under the microscope by a method known as the Gram stain (developed by the Danish bacteriologist, Hans Christian Gram (1853-1938)), which produces a purple (positive) or pink (negative) colour depending on the composition of the bacterial cell wall.

haemophilia an inherited bleeding disorder caused by a deficiency of a particular blood protein, especially Factor VIII, which is essential to the process of blood clotting.

haemorrhage (adj. haemorrhagic) bleeding or blood loss. Haemorrhagic fevers typically cause bleeding internally (where blood leaks from blood vessels inside the body) and externally (from the mouth and other orifices).

immunology the study of the immune system, which plays a vital role in the outcome of disease in an individual.

inoculation a term used initially for the practice of inserting matter from dried smallpox scabs into a person's body in the hope of providing long-term protection against the disease; later superseded by smallpox vaccination. The terms inoculation and vaccination are often both used today to describe a procedure for immunizing a person against a specific disease.

in vitro the technique of performing an experiment in a controlled environment outside the living organism (e.g., in a test tube or other laboratory glassware).

in vivo in a living system.

latent (n. latency) describes a period between initial infection and the time when the symptoms of a disease become fully manifest.

malignant a term most commonly used to refer to cancerous tumours that are likely to spread and recur.

miasmatist a nineteenth-century term referring to a scientist who believed that diseases were caused by 'miasmas' or noxious vapours.

palaeopathology the scientific study of the signs of ancient diseases, most often from skeletal remains.

pandemic used to describe a disease that is global, or that affects a significantly high proportion of people across the world.

parasite an organism that requires the resources of another organism (its host) to live and reproduce; parasites are generally harmful to their hosts, although the damage they do ranges widely from minor inconvenience to debilitating or fatal parasitic diseases such as malaria.

pasteurization a process of destroying germs in liquids by heating, named after the French chemist Louis Pasteur (1822–95).

pathogen any biological agent, such as a bacterium, virus or parasite, that causes a disease.

pestilence an epidemic of a serious disease, typically infectious.

prion (short for proteinaceous infectious particle) a particle of protein molecules that acts as an infectious agent causing such diseases as CJD (Creutzfeldt-Jakob disease). Unlike other disease-causing agents, prions lack genetic material (DNA and RNA).

psychotic a psychotic episode usually refers to a profound mental aberration marked by loss of a sense of reality.

quarantine a term (meaning 'forty days') first used by Italians to describe the period of isolation required of individuals who had been exposed to an infectious disease, with the aim of preventing its further spread.

retrovirus a virus that contains single-stranded RNA as its genetic material; these viruses also contain proteins that enable the RNA to be copied as DNA and then to be incorporated into the genome of the host cell.

RNA (ribonucleic acid) a type of molecule that is present in all living cells, and plays a variety of essential roles, including the synthesis of proteins and the transmission of genetic information transcribed from DNA.

sanatorium (or in the US sanitorium) an institution or place of refuge for the care of people suffering from chronic diseases such as tuberculosis.

The Lancet an international medical journal, founded by English surgeon Thomas Wakley (1795-1862) in 1823.

tracheotomy a surgical procedure performed on the neck to open a direct airway through an incision in the trachea (windpipe).

tubercles various small anatomic lumps, including those which develop in the lungs as a result of infection by the tuberculosis bacterium.

vaccination in the nineteenth century, the term vaccination was limited to the inoculation of a preparation derived from cowpox that protected people from smallpox. It was later extended more widely to describe similar measures taken to protect (i.e. to immunize) people against other diseases.

vector an intermediate 'vehicle', such as an animal, that is the carrier of an infectious disease or an insect capable of transferring an infectious agent from one host to another.

virus a small infectious agent, containing DNA or RNA, which replicates only within cells of living hosts; viruses cause many diseases, including the common cold, influenza and HIV/AIDS.

WHO (World Health Organization) established in 1948 with its headquarters in Geneva, Switzerland, the World Health Organization (the WHO) is a specialized agency of the United Nations (UN), acting as the directing and co-ordinating authority on international health.

zoonosis an animal disease that can be transmitted to humans.

Further Reading

Over the years, I have accumulated an ever-increasing personal library of books on the history of disease and medicine, as well as on current medical topics, along with an archive of thousands of articles from scientific and historical journals, all of which I have enjoyed reading as part of my research. Some of my favourite reads are still the great classics on the subject such as Daniel Defoe's semi-fictional *A Journal of the Plague Year* (1722), Paul de Kruif's best-selling book *Microbe Hunters* (1926) and Hans Zinsser's popular study *Rats, Lice and History* (1935).

Inevitably, in condensing each of the rich and varied histories of thirty diseases encompassed in *Murderous Contagion: A Human History of Disease* into short chapters, I have had to generalize, simplify and touch only briefly on some of the continuing historical and academic debates. For those who want to explore the history of disease further there are many excellent sources in libraries and archives around the world, as well as on the internet. As a starting point I would recommend any of the following reference works.

The Cambridge World History of Human Disease, edited by Kenneth Kiple (Cambridge University Press, 1993) is some 1,000 pages in length and contains detailed descriptions of all the major human diseases. The two-volume *Encyclopedia of Pestilence, Pandemics, and Plagues* (edited by Joseph Byrne,

Greenwood Press, 2008) also has in-depth entries from many of the world's most distinguished historians of medicine. A number of books by Andrew Cliff, Peter Haggett and Matthew Smallman-Raynor, including their *World Atlas of Epidemic Diseases* (Arnold, 2004), as well as the *Oxford Textbook of Infectious Disease Control: A Geographical Analysis from Medieval Quarantine to Global Eradication* (Oxford University Press, 2013) by Andrew Cliff and Matthew Smallman-Raynor, are mines of information and are illustrated with some excellent maps of the geographical distribution and spatial impact of epidemic diseases. *The Wellcome Trust Illustrated History of Tropical Diseases*, edited by F. E. G. Cox (Wellcome Trust, 1996) and *Forgotten People, Forgotten Diseases* by Peter Hotez (ASM Press, 2008) are valuable sources for the history and current toll of many of the Neglected Tropical Diseases.

A short selection of general and accessible books which cover the field in diverse ways include: John Aberth, *Plagues in World History* (Rowman & Littlefield, 2011); Ron Barrett and George J. Armelagos, *An Unnatural History of Emerging Infections* (Oxford University Press, 2013); Frederick F. Cartwright and Michael Biddiss, *Disease and History* (3rd edition, Thistle Publishing, 2014); Dorothy H. Crawford, *Deadly Companions: How Microbes Shaped Our History* (Oxford University Press, 2007); Nigel Crisp, *Turning the World Upside Down: The Search for Global Health in the 21st Century* (Royal Society of Medicine Press, 2010); Laurie Garrett, *The Coming Plague – Newly Emerging Diseases in a World Out of Balance* (Penguin Books, 1995); David I. Grove, *Tapeworms, Lice, and Prions: A Compendium of Unpleasant Infections* (Oxford University Press, 2014); Anne Hardy, *The Epidemic Streets* (Oxford University Press, 1993); Mark Harrison, *Disease and the Modern World* (Polity, 2004);

Tom Koch, *Disease Maps: Epidemics on the Ground* (University of Chicago Press, 2011); Michael B.A. Oldstone, *Viruses, Plagues, & History* (Oxford University Press, 2010); Peter Piot, *No Time To Lose: A Life in Pursuit of Deadly Viruses* (W.W. Norton, 2012); David Quammen, *Spillover: Animal Infections and the Next Human Pandemic* (The Bodley Head, 2012); Irwin W. Sherman, *The Power of Plagues* (ASM Press, 2006); Nancy Leys Stepan, *Eradication: Ridding the World of Diseases Forever?* (Reaktion Books, 2011); Nathan Wolfe, *The Viral Storm: The Dawn of a New Pandemic Age* (Allen Lane, 2011); and Carl Zimmer, *A Planet of Viruses* (University of Chicago Press, 2011). I have also learned much from many books on specialist topics and specific diseases and have included quotes and references to a few of these in the text.

There are also excellent books covering some of the broader aspects of the history of medicine such as *The Cambridge Illustrated History of Medicine*, edited by Roy Porter (Cambridge University Press, 1996); *Western Medicine: An Illustrated History*, edited by Irvine Loudon (Oxford University Press, 1997); and *Great Discoveries in Medicine*, edited by William Bynum and Helen Bynum (Thames & Hudson, 2011). The five-volume *Dictionary of Medical Biography*, edited by William Bynum and Helen Bynum (Greenwood Press, 2007) is a good source of reference for discovering more about the world's greatest doctors and scientists. In addition, any of the stimulating books by the late Roy Porter including *The Greatest Benefit to Mankind: A Medical History from Antiquity to the Present* (Harper Collins, 1997) and *Blood and Guts: A Short History of Medicine* (Penguin Books, 2003) are well worth reading. My illustrated book, *The Story of Medicine: From Bloodletting to Biotechnology* (Quercus, 2013) – a companion volume to *Disease: The Extraordinary*

Stories Behind History's Deadliest Killers (Quercus, 2007; Metro Books, 2013) – contains further references on the history of medicine. And for informative entertainment on this subject, the BBC Radio 4 programme *The Making of Modern Medicine* (available as BBC Audiobooks, 2007), written and narrated by Andrew Cunningham, is an enthralling six-hour listen.

There are many other fascinating books and articles which are too numerous to cite here but which are well worth discovering and reading. I have also benefited from visiting numerous medical museums, archaeological and historical sites around the world. My husband, Christopher, in our overseas travels, has patiently accompanied me to 'unusual' and sometimes rather 'morbid' places – from hospitals, anatomy theatres, sanatoria, and laboratories to plague pits, cemeteries, sewers and quarantine stations – often wondering what will be next round the corner and hoping it might be a coffee shop! Highlights include the *Bimaristan Al-nuri*, a twelfth-century hospital in Damascus, where early ideas about the circulation of the blood were suggested; the Lazaretto Nuovo, a late fifteenth-century plague quarantine island in the Venetian Lagoon; Ronald Ross's laboratory in Secunderabad, India, where in 1897 he discovered the role of mosquitoes in transmitting malaria; and the Old Bacteriological Institute, now part of the Hong Kong Museum of Medical Sciences, the first purpose-built medical laboratory in Hong Kong which was established at the turn of the twentieth century near to the site of a major plague outbreak. Such visits really help to make the history of disease and medicine come alive, and I would encourage anyone with an interest in the subject to take the opportunity to go to places of medical interest at home and abroad. A compendium entitled *Medical London: City of Diseases, City of Cures* by Richard Barnett and Mike Jay

(Wellcome Collection and Strange Attractor Press, 2008) is a marvellous guide, which includes maps, for visitors to London wanting to trace the history of disease and medicine over the centuries in the evolving capital city of the United Kingdom.

Medicine, today, moves at an ever-increasing pace. The international medical journals, *The Lancet* and *Nature Medicine* are excellent sources for keeping abreast of the latest developments, while the World Health Organization (www.who.int) provides up-to-date information on the incidence, prevalence and out-breaks of major diseases. I have used these sources for estimates of the current global toll of each of the diseases at the time of writing the chapters over the spring and summer of 2014. The international health community, however, recognizes that it is not always possible to get accurate mortality and morbidity esti-mates and is working hard to try to improve reporting, especially in some of the poorer areas of the world. It would be good to think that by the time *Murderous Contagion* reaches the book-shops some of the figures I cite here will have changed – in a downward direction – and in the coming years we will see not just more accurate reporting but a significant reduction in the toll of human diseases.

Author acknowledgements

I am indebted to my family, friends and many colleagues, students and scholars across the globe for sharing with me their ideas, knowledge and expertise over many years. I would particularly like to thank all those who so meticulously read and commented on individual sections and chapters of an earlier version of this book, *Disease: the Extraordinary Stories Behind History's Deadliest Killers* (Quercus, 2007), as well as those who have read recent revisions for this current edition of *Murderous Contagion: a Human History of Disease*. Amongst the many colleagues who have helped me with my research and writing are: John Aberth, Michael Alpers, Warwick Anderson, Virginia Berridge, Greg Bock, Linda Bryder, Bill Bynum, Helen Bynum, David Cantor, Frank Cooper, Frank Cox, Ian Crofton, Mary Crawford, Marguerite Dupree, Jacalyn Duffin, Peter Elwood, Myron Echenberg, Tony Gould, Ian Glynn, Jenifer Glynn, Peter Haggett, Steven Hajdu, Jonathan Heeney, John Henderson, Josephine Hill, Mark Honigsbaum, Rosemary Horrox, Margaret Humphreys, Kiheung Kim, Simone Kropf, Efraim Lev, John Iliffe, David Lomas, Judith Lomas, Irvine Loudon, John Manton, Richard Milbank, Malcolm Nicolson, Philip Oakes, Randall Packard, Steven Palmer, Janet Pickering, Carol Rawcliffe, Carole Reeves, Guenter Risse, Charlotte Roberts, Colin Robins,

John Skehel, Matthew Smallman-Raynor, Susan Smith, Oliver Thomas, Patrick Wallis, Andrew Wear, Robin Weiss and Michael Worboys. Andrew Cliff and Roger Snowden kindly read the near final drafts of the entire book and I have really appreciated the trouble they have taken to send me their perceptive comments and suggestions. I am, also, exceptionally grateful to Bill Tyrrell who has devoted many hours to helping me with my research and has done a superb job in checking the final manuscript. Thank you all for your generous input and your rapid responses which have been invaluable. If I have not been able to incorporate all your suggestions and changes – my apologies. And, of course, all remaining mistakes are mine alone.

St John's College, Cambridge, has provided me with a stimulating intellectual environment while I have been working on this book. I am most grateful to the Author's Foundation of the Society of Authors which gave me a grant to enable me to conduct a number of aspects of the research for the original 2007 publication of this book. I would also very much like to thank the team at Quercus who have worked with me to bring this current book to fruition, including Joshua Ireland and Charlotte Fry, as well as copy editor Seán Costello and proofreader Louisa Sladen.

My sincerest gratitude goes to Anne Hardy and Maureen Malowany who, as friends and colleagues, have played a major role in this book. Our exchanges have been many, as well as both fun and fascinating, and their expertise, ideas and knowledge have been hugely helpful in writing *Murderous Contagion*.

A very special tribute goes to my husband Christopher, whose scientific knowledge, curiosity and insight are incredible and who, despite the many demands on his time, has given me so much valuable advice on all stages of researching and writing this book. Our sons Richard and William have also been a fantastic support and encouragement to me throughout my career.

Christopher, Richard and William – you have contributed to this book in more ways than I could mention. I dedicate this book to my family – with my love and thanks.

Mary Dobson

Index

Diseases and page numbers in bold type refer to main entries